WITHDRAWN

A CABINET OF CHARACTERS

THE LIVELY PORTRAICTURE OF SIR THOMAS OVERBURY.

Ætatis suæ
32.

A CABINET OF CHARACTERS

CHOSEN AND EDITED BY

GWENDOLEN MURPHY

1925

LONDON : HUMPHREY MILFORD

OXFORD UNIVERSITY PRESS

HUMPHREY MILFORD

OXFORD UNIVERSITY PRESS

London   Edinburgh   Glasgow   Copenhagen
New York   Toronto   Melbourne   Cape Town
Bombay   Calcutta   Madras   Shanghai

PRINTED IN GREAT BRITAIN BY ROBERT MACLEHOSE AND CO. LTD.
THE UNIVERSITY PRESS, GLASGOW.

INTRODUCTION

DEVELOPMENT OF THE CHARACTER

THE character is one of the most prolific of the literary kinds which flourished in the seventeenth century. Its contemporary popularity is shown not only by the large number of separate works that were issued, but by the numerous editions of these which an eager audience called for. To-day the greater number of these little books have an historical rather than a purely literary interest; but the interest that they have is strong enough to justify their being always accessible to those who would overhear the quaint gossipings or the satiric wit in which the manners and customs of that time are represented; a few—and the existence of these depends on all those others—will always be treasured for themselves.

We may sometimes consider the literature of a given period not solely for the sake of its outstanding works, but rather as a continuity of literary effort, the manifestation of a special tradition and temper determined by special circumstances. From this point of view the very absence of intrinsic excellence may allow us to perceive more clearly this continuous historical background of literature, the contrasts and relations of which in the greater works are already merged into the singularity of artistic perfection. The historian

v

of literature, so far as his history is more than
an uncritical record of literary events in their
sequence, must turn often towards this matter of
background, and therefore often towards those
lesser spirits whose work depends more evidently
on an accepted tradition. In the tapestry of literature, the general tone and colouring give a special
significance to the single figures which alone are
noticed at first sight by the spectator.

The Character Defined

In the seventeenth century, one of these minor
literary kinds which belongs peculiarly to the
general background of literature is the character-
sketch. Its interest for the literary historian lies
in the number of ways in which it reflects the
spirit of the time, not only within its own limits,
but through the media of five other literary forms
—satire, epigram, essay, sermon, and drama.
Before these relations are examined the nature
and scope of the character can be best indicated by the testimony of its writers. The
earliest account is that of Bishop Hall in
1608, who, following his master Theophrastus,
stresses the didactic purpose, a feature to be recalled
by many subsequent protestations. Small sign of
it, however, is to be seen in the characters of
Ben Jonson and Overbury, which were to be the
leading type in the seventeenth century. These
are described in the ninth edition of Overbury's
Characters (1616): 'Character is also taken for an
Egyptian hieroglyphic, for an impress or short
emblem: in little comprehending much. To square
out a character by our English level, it is a picture

(real or personal) quaintly drawn in various colours, all of them heightened by one shadowing. It is a quick and soft touch of many strings, all shutting up in one musical close: it is wit's descant on any plain song.' But the 'wit' that Overbury commends was too often abused, and in 1631 Richard Brathwaite condemns its excess, and pleads for 'the pith before the rinde.' As if he had had this racy disclaimer before him, Wye Saltonstall in the same year boldly declares, 'It is not the nature of a character to be as smooth as a bullrush, but to have some fast and loose knots, which the ingenious Reader may easily untye.' The most interesting of these discussions are those of Richard Flecknoe, who in four of his works, which contain characters, epigrams, and portraits amongst them, compares these three forms. He contrasts the English and French methods in his *Heroick Portraits* (1660): '*The Portrait* has this advantage of the *Character*, that it gives you the Bodies resemblance together with the disposition of the Mind; and the *Writer* of the *Painter*, that he both paints the Minde, and Body too. This manner of writing is altogether in fashion in *France*, and I should be glad to bring it into *England*.' Except here, Flecknoe does little to practise this theory. The character is compared first with the epigram in his *Epigrams and Characters* . . . of 1673, where he writes, 'Epigrams, which I aptly couple with the Characters, since these are onely Epigrams in Prose, as the others are onely Characters in Verse.' It is then in a single sentence admirably contrasted with the essay, '[*Characters*] differ from *Pourtracts*, in that they are onely *Pictures of Mind*, abstracting from the *Body*, and from *Essays*, in that they discourse not, but give you onely the heads of things in general.' In his first collection of characters he works out his charming comparison of the character to 'a journey where you may see the end from the beginning.'

From these accounts, and from the characters themselves, the following definition may be constructed. The character-sketch is a short, concise, objective account of the properties of a typical person, place, or object which are combined together to make a small whole. The most effective examples illustrate the properties of a person by describing actions, with a minimum of 'theory' or comment. The motive is most often satirical, or didactic, and the style generally aims at wit. In one of the most usual forms the beginning is a definition, frequently conceited, the middle is an accumulation of characteristic traits, each phrase usually beginning with 'he,' the effect being that of a string of adjectives rather than of a reasoned narrative, and the progress is thus not logical but grammatical; the ending tends to be an epigrammatic summary expressed either simply or in a sounding conceit. In this attempt to localize the character in the literature of the seventeenth century, the term character has been taken to mean 'literary form,' as just defined. Content alone does not constitute a character unless a definite form is followed.

Before the Seventeenth Century

Characters are to be found in very various types of literature belonging to countries and times far apart, and it is thus probable that

wherever they occur they are expressions of an
impulse that is universal. Men still, whether
writers or not, will give a brief objective description of a type for purposes of information or
amusement. A prominent instance of such thinking can be seen in a certain kind of character-
satire. The various types in ordinary life have a
flavour of 'shoppiness' about them, and a member of any type hopes that his individuality is
strong enough to escape the 'taint.' Thus an
effective way of laughing at one's opponent or foe
is to relegate him to a type, and so to assert in
him the presence of the qualities by which his
likeness to others is proclaimed, instead of the
differences by which he fain would be distinguished. But though the chief, this is not the only
way in which types have been pointedly sketched.
Examples of many kinds are to be found in the
classics[1] and in the Bible, in mediæval and Elizabethan literature, and this study will show that the
practice has continued to the present day.

[1] E. C. Baldwin has collected references to characters in
the following writers, Homer, *Iliad*, xiii. 278; Aristophanes,
Wasps, ll. 87-134; Horace, *Satires*, i. ix.; Juvenal, *Satires*, 8
and 9; Martial iii. 63, *Cotilus*; Rutilius Lupus, *De Figuris
Sententiarum et Elocutionis*, ii. 67; *Auctor Rhetoricorum ad Herennium*,
Lib. iv. cap. 50; Synesius, *Epistle* civ. [Mod. Lang. Association America Publications, vol. 19, p. 77, 1904].

To these could be added: Lucian, in *Timon*, Thrasycles a
toady, and in *Bion Prasis* [Philosophies for sale], a cynic (Loeb
ed. ii. pp. 386-8, 468). Seneca, *Ad Lucilium Epistulae Morales*
contains several brief characters, e.g. 'The happy man,' Ep. 45,
i. p. 297, and 'The grateful wise man,' Ep. 81, ii. pp. 235-6
(Loeb ed.); *L. Annaei Senecae Opera* . . . Lipsiae, 1905, i. 1;
De Ira, ii. 35, and cf. Thomas Lodge's translation in 1614,
The Workes . . . London, Of *Anger*, ii. 35, p. 549, 'The description of wrath, both in bodie and mind.'

The account given in *Proverbs* of the 'properties of a good wife' took its place among other characters of that type in the seventeenth century, and was recognized as their prototype by Hall, and one Lawrence Price. The method in Overbury's sketch of a 'Good Woman' is akin to that in the earlier picture: 'She perceiveth that her merchandise is good: her candle goeth not out by night. She layeth her hands to the spindle and her hands hold the distaff. She stretcheth out her hand to the poor: yea, she reacheth forth her hands to the needy.' Such type-descriptions can be readily found in the *Ancren Riwle* or in *Piers the Plowman*, and a century after Chaucer in the *Shyp of Folys*. Chaucer's alone are noteworthy, and some of the sketches in his *Prologue* are amongst the vivid portraits of our literature. But they may also be considered as amongst the best of the characters, for they delineate types with a conciseness and a witty satire akin to Earle's or Fuller's, while the power in some few of suggesting an individuality as well is more notable than that displayed in any but the rarest achievements of the character-writers; look at the word that makes the repulsive Somnour real for ever, 'Of his visage children were aferd.'

Another Chaucer could have made the central idea of the *Shyp of Folys* extremely entertaining, for Sebastian Brant's plan was to collect and export all the fools in the country. He marshalled them into groups, and his descriptions of these, helped out by dramatic woodcuts, made the notion of type-classification familiar among the large audience to whom the book appealed. When even a list of type-names, as in the *Dance of Death*, becomes familiar, it is not a long step, though it is an important one, to define or describe such names.

The motives for which the descriptions are given are various. They are at first mainly didactic, as in the *Shyp of Folys*, and in the many different settings in which the Seven Deadly Sins appear. They are inspired by purposes of social protection, as in Thomas Harman's descriptions of rogues in his *Caveat or Warening For Commen Cursetors commonly called Vagabones*. Little thumbnail sketches of human types are used to illustrate abstract topics and discussions, as in Wilson's *Art of Rhetorique* (1553), in Guevara's *Golden Epistles* (1575), or in the *Mirror of Mans Lyfe* (1576); the first contains a single 'Descriptio,' which is a completely Theophrastian sketch, 'A Covetous Man' being thus illustrated: 'There is no such pinch peney on live as this good fellowe is. He will not lose the paring of his nailes. His haire is never rounded for sparing of money, one paire of shone serveth him a twelve moneth, he is shod with nailes like a Horse. He hath bene knowne by his coate this thirtie Winter. He spente once a groate at good ale, being forced through companie, and taken short at his worde, whereupon he hath taken such conceipt since that time, that it hath almost cost him his life.'[1] At least four brief 'descriptions' or accounts of the 'properties' of a type amplify the ethical discourse of the *Golden Epistles*. The *Mirror of Mans Lyfe* is the translation of a mediæval work of edi-

[1] Quoted from G. H. Mair's reprint of the edition of 1567, p. 187, Oxford, 1909.

fication, and contains about ten sketches close to
the style of Theophrastus. The use of the character
in both these books is probably in a fairly direct
descent from its original relation with rhetoric and
ethics, for Theophrastus's academic connexion with
moral philosophy formed at least the background
for his characters, although Jebb seems right in
suggesting that their direct motive was 'his own
amusement.' John Grange's *The Golden Aphro-
ditis* (1577) contains a single type-sketch, in verse,
'The paynting of a Curtizan,' which occurs in a
manner unusual at that date, as one of a number
of detached pieces, in prose and verse, contained
in the section of the book called *Granges Garden*.
Finally, towards the end of the Elizabethan period,
these descriptions are attractively presented as concrete verbal pictures of types to illustrate the social
commentaries of Nashe or Greene or Lodge.

This tendency to deal directly with human
types, without an allegorical medium, was one
of the ways in which the Elizabethan age made
progress towards the modern method. Though
the writers on social themes still frequently used
a mediæval form, yet it was in such a way that the
form was separable in thought from its context, and
the reader for instance of Nashe's lively pamphlets
at once located his devils in Cheapside and not in
their traditional habitat. For it is contemporary
life that is vividly reflected in his *Pierce Penilesse*,
and the character-historian is interested in the silhouettes scattered throughout the book, which
have a form fairly similar to that of the character.

Satire and Epigram and the Character

There seems to be a relation closer than the time-relation between the following works : Casaubon's Latin translation[1] of Theophrastus' characters in 1592, the satirical work of Sir John Davies in his *Epigrams*, c. 1590-4, of Edward Guilpin in his *Skialetheia*, 1598, in John Marston's *Scourge of Villanie* in the same year, and in two of Ben Jonson's comedies, *Every Man Out of His Humour*, 1599, and *Cynthia's Revels* in 1601. Ben Jonson's work will be discussed later, but is mentioned here because of the likeness of its character-sketches to those found in the early satirists.

It is probable that the similarity in these works is due primarily to influences from the spirit of the time that affected them all in common. The reaction from the first outburst of creative activity in the Elizabethan period to a cooler analytic attitude was already beginning. This was reinforced by the interest taken in the medical doctrine of humours then current throughout Europe which caused the terms 'disposition' and 'temperament' to be much discussed. There was plenty of material for these new modes of thinking to work upon. And they found scope in the lighter forms of literature for describing the manners and habits of certain typical figures that were newly prominent and in whom the public were greatly interested. There were, particularly, the various

---

[1] This was the first complete Latin translation of the characters. The first 15 characters had been translated into Latin in 1527 at Nuremburg.

classes connected with the court or the city which the Elizabethan period had produced by the end of the sixteenth century, and which it then, with its new love of introspection, began to take pleasure in analysing. The characters of Theophrastus supplied an opportune model of a short convenient method for such descriptions.

It is possible to suppose that we come close to Theophrastus for the first time in these satirists. Yet the characters in the extant satires, though perhaps numerous enough to support this suggestion, are comparatively few. And the number is not so much greater in Ben Jonson's plays. For this reason, and for the more important one that the character-sketch was not yet written for its own sake alone, it does not seem worth while disturbing the title usually given to Hall of being the first 'character-writer' in England. He certainly wrote the first character-book that was published.

Flecknoe's statement that epigrams and characters are closely connected has been already quoted; the relation holds when the subject of both is a type. Such a statement is equally true of the early satires. For it was while epigram and satire were comparatively immature that their forms could not be readily distinguished either from each other or from the character. Developed satire is essentially subjective, but immature satire had not attained personality, and it was its objective style which made it temporarily akin to the character. Sir John Davies's epigram, *In Afrum*, is a good example of a piece which might be classified almost equally well as epigram, or satire, or character. He is here more Theophrastian in style than else-where :

> ' The smellfeast *Afer*, travailes to the burse
> Twice every day the newest newes to heare
> Which when he hath no money in his purse,
> To rich mens tables he doth often beare :
> He tells how *Groningen* is taken in,
> By the brave conduct of illustrious *Vere* :
> And how the *Spanish* forces *Brest* would win,
> But that they do victorious *Norris* feare.
> No sooner is a ship at sea surpris'd,
> But straight he learnes the newes and doth disclose it.
> No sooner hath the Turk a plot devis'd
> To conquer Christendom, but streight he knows it :
> Faire written in a scrowle he hath names,
> Of all the widowes which the plague hath made,
> And persons, times, and places, still he frames,
> To every tale, the better to persuade :
> We call him Fame, for that the wide-mouth slave,
> Will eate as fast as he wil utter lies,
> For Fame is said an hundreth mouthes to have,
> And he eates more than would five score suffice.'

Essay and Sermon

The terms 'essay' and 'character' were in frequent association during the whole period from Bacon to Addison, that is, during the childhood of the essay. The two forms have sometimes a certain similarity, but any resemblance in spirit is less frequently seen. In essence, the essay is different from the character. The essay proper is the essay as it was written pre-eminently by Charles Lamb : as it was foreshadowed in the seventeenth century by Sir Thomas Browne, for though he can hardly be said to have used the essay-form, he possessed, in a remarkable degree, the true essay-spirit.

Judged by this standard, the so-called essays of the early seventeenth century have only a doubtful claim to their title. This is true even of Bacon's essays, for, in spite of their dignity, they present accounts of the various qualities belonging to the 'Complete Statesman,' with an impersonal air that made contemporaries recognize their kinship with the character. Nicholas Breton dedicated his *Characters upon Essaies* to Bacon as a humble tribute to their inventor. But the abstract subjects, such as 'Wisdom,' or 'Valour,' were not for him; though his study of Bacon's style probably helped him to write concisely, and thus to be one of the earliest of the band of character-writers whose power to use a concise pointed style was to be their valuable contribution to the formation of English prose. The treatment in his next volume, *The Good and the Badde*, continued to be somewhat vague and theoretical, in spite of the change of subject. A typically indefinite description is that of 'A Worthy Prince '—'He is the morning-star that hath light from the sun, and the blessed fruit of the tree of earths paradise '—which suggests a memory haunted by the Apocrypha rather than an observer with his eye on his object. It would be easy to quote such vivid passages as that on 'Death,' 'He is seen but in a picture, heard but in a tale, feared but in a passion, and felt but in a pinch,' but they are not yet sufficiently numerous to warrant the wholehearted praise that cannot be withheld from the charming *Fantastickes*, his last published work.

John Stephens sometimes falls into the essay style in writing a character, but Geffray Mynshul distinguishes the two fairly consistently in his *Certaine Essayes and Characters of Prison and Prisoners*, and this though the book has an unusual unity, due to its being the record of the strenuous emotional experience suffered by Mynshul as a prisoner for debt in the King's Bench. The essays express his general meditations on his life in prison, but he uses characters when he wants to impress definite facts. He sets these facts in a slight but suggestive context of theory and comment. Theoretical statements in a character as a rule make it dull and vague. But in Mynshul's work, though they help to increase the prolixity of his style, the effect is not so unhappy as usual, for his conception of his subject is in itself dramatic. It is as action and the effect of action that the whole appeals to him. He also uses similes and metaphors not as a rule for the mere words' sake, but to make his notion clearer; the Prisoner, for instance, is like 'Tantalus, who hath freedom running by his door yet cannot enjoy the least benefit thereof.' The impression given by the whole is more that of an essay than a character, but still more of an autobiography-in-little than either.

Thomas Fuller should be called the 'well-beloved,' for he belongs to the company of Browne and Lamb. He was born to be an essayist, but the form of the essay was born only about the same time as himself, and was not fully matured till he had been dead many years. He helped to develop it by an original use of existing forms. For in addition to expressing his personality freely in his various meditations and biographies, he took the character-sketch and used it as the framework for a kind of essay. Fuller's style is as wise as it is witty, and its pre-eminent quality is its charm. He writes directly and clearly, and his conceits are remarkable for their wit rather than their ingenuity.

The Sermon did not ignore one of the most popular forms of light expression at the time. Many preachers brightened their discourses with type-sketches, like Donne[1] with his 'rich man whose riches perish in his travail': 'Such is an overfull and spungy covetous person: he must pour out, as well as he hath suck't in: if the least weight of disgrace, or danger lye upon him, he bleeds out his money: . . . If he be stirr'd from one place to another, if he be suffered to settle where he is, and would be, still these two incommodities lye upon him; that he is loathest to part with his money, of any thing, and yet he can do nothing without it. He labours for riches and still he is but a bagg, for other men.'

Mr. J. E. Spingarn has emphasized the close connexion of the seventeenth century sermon with the metaphysical fashion of the age. One of the most prominent marks of this style was an excessive use of metaphor. Sometimes the metaphors occurred in groups, to elucidate it might be, or more often, to surprise. Such writing is to be found in the

---

[1] *XXVI. Sermons* ... London ... 1661, p. 146. Compare, too, Jeremy Taylor, *A Course of Sermons*, 1668, p. 45, 'Prayer is an Action and a state of entercourse and desire, exactly contrary to this Character of Anger.' This is a link sentence between two brief characters of Anger and of Prayer. Taylor sometimes varies his pictorial narrative style by such sketches.

sermon as elsewhere. But when these metaphors are arranged like a string of beads, each introduced in the same way, and that way the succession of phrases each beginning with ' it,' then the influence of the character may be suspected. Henry King,[1] for instance, thus describes prayer: ' It is our scaling Ladder, . . . our Engine of Battery, by which Heaven is besieged . . . 'Tis our weapon with which we wound our enemies . . . even God himselfe . . . 'Tis the Rudder which keepes our soules steady . . . 'Tis the Compasse . . . Lastly, 'tis our Key which opens the gates of Heaven, be they lockt never so fast.'

About twenty characters of a delightful kind are buried in the large folio of the collected sermons of Thomas Adams. Most of these serve as descriptions of persons afflicted with the different spiritual diseases grouped together in a formidable discourse called ' The Souls Sicknesse.' They are not mere unrelated ingenuity, the trap into which the character-writer who merely followed the fashion only too regularly fell, but they are, for the most part, as thoughtfully built as those of Earle himself. They are written with a wit that attracts by its sincerity; and, most individual trait of all, there are touches of picturesque fancy giving a hint of horizons beyond which seem at once to lend the piece a new perspective.

Comedy and the Character

Three of Ben Jonson's plays show such decided character influence that the reader might imagine

---

[1] *An Exposition upon the Lord's Prayer* . . . London, . . . 1628, p. 13.

the possibility of a direct connexion between comedy and the character, were it not that almost in proportion to the extent of the character-influence the plays are undramatic.

We can say that *Love's Labour's Lost* gives us a character-study of a pedant; but it would be inaccurate to call the portrait of Holofernes a character in the formal sense, for there is no continuous passage in the play which describes him in the manner in which, for instance, Ben Jonson's character of Amorphous is described. Shakespeare's aim here is akin to Ben Jonson's, but the difference is that Shakespeare presents his points dramatically, Ben Jonson his in a set piece.

Out of 1100 plays published before 1700, only about forty comedies have a fairly definite relation with the character. Of these Ben Jonson's *Every Man Out of His Humour*, *Cynthia's Revels*, and *The Magnetic Lady* alone have a close connexion. The *Return from Parnassus* is the most notable of the twenty or so seventeenth century plays which have short passages resembling the character-sketch. About a dozen plays of earlier dates contain rudimentary type-descriptions which act as dramatic labels.

Apart from the characters which could be collected from the forty plays, the connexion between comedy and character seems to have been of a general nature, and to have resulted in stimulating the development of the proper tendency of either form; comedy was stimulated by the character to seize type-peculiarities more keenly, but it would express these in its own way, by means of action; while the character had its attention drawn by the drama to certain fresh types, or to unnoticed details of familiar ones, and then it would express these, also in its own way, in its thumbnail sketches. For there is a great difference between the 'type' which is the subject of the character-sketch even when it has touches of individuality, and the creation of individual character, which is the greatest achievement of the drama. The character-writer is concerned with the common features which unite a man with others of his type rather than with the peculiar qualities which make up his individuality, for the primary business of the character-sketch is not to 'draw character.' Its scale is too small, and its methods too limited. As in life itself, we require time to become acquainted with a strange personality. The drama and the novel can give the illusion of time, and show their personages in relation to people and circumstances. It is often by 'trifles' when their contexts are suitable, though it may need genius to perceive them, that personality is revealed. Irene, in the *Forsyte Saga*, is an extreme instance, presented to us, as her creator says, through the impressions she makes on the other people in the story. The delicacy of this method is not possible for the character-writer; in life, his 'Wise Man' is not only wise nor is his 'Traveller' only boastful, but his scheme must insist on wisdom and on boasts, and he may select different expressions of the same trait from many individuals, ignoring most of the other factors of the personality until his sketch becomes that of a typical quality, but is a caricature if attached to a single individual. The character has been so often criticized for failing to 'draw character,' or praised unwisely for doing so, that it seems worth while to suggest that this function is outside its province.

The Seventeenth Century. The Character proper

The collection of characters usually known as Overbury's was followed in three particulars by succeeding writers. Their general objectivity of outlook, in which they were closer to Theophrastus than had been Bishop Hall, his professed imitator, was to be the predominant feature of the character-writers. Then, their subjects were the customs and occupations of the typical figures, and even of the institutions, that most interested contemporary readers; these social topics were shared with comedy, which in the early seventeenth century largely devoted itself to representing the manners of the middle classes: both comedy and character were fond of portraying such groups as courtiers and would-be courtiers, and such dependents or associates of these classes as the host and ostler, the French cook or the waterman, the actor, the lawyer, and the unpleasantly familiar creditor or 'Jailer'; the ethical qualities which Theophrastus had so vividly embodied, though they were always in a sense[1] maintained in

[1] It was only in a 'sense,' for the great difference between the ethical characters of Theophrastus and such characters of ethical types as were written in English is that in Theophrastus was implied the man of nicely balanced behaviour, whereas in some of the English characters, of Earle and others, was implied man at his best. Behind Theophrastus was evident the Aristotelian philosophy of the mean, behind the English writers the ethics of Christianity, and the idealism which has always characterized our literature.

the English tradition, were yet as constantly over-shadowed by the more immediate appeal of current interests. Their third, and dangerous, gift to their successors, was their generally 'conceited' style. To make this arresting was the main object of the Overburian writers in their weaker sketches. If such a phrase as that which describes an Apparitor as ' a chick of the egg abuse hatched by the warmth of authority ' would ever pass current it was in the first half of the seventeenth century. Too many startling phrases defeated their object, and a less vivid picture emerged than would have been produced by a more moderate use of the trick. When they wrote simply their brevity formed an attractive contrast to the unwieldiness of much of the contemporary prose. The seventeen editions through which the collection passed reflect the interest aroused by Sir Thomas Overbury's fate, but are also a marked tribute to the topical brilliancy of the characters.

The student of the character-sketch is not denied the pleasure of reading characters for their own sake. For there are five sets of characters that remain fresh in the memory, when all the others are allowed to fade, after they have once played their part in giving certain historical impressions to the modern reader. Mynshul's *Essays and Characters*, Earle's *Microcosmographie*, Brathwaite's *Whimzies*, Fuller's *Holy and Profane State*, and Steele's and Addison's *Tatler* remain green, because, in spite of that part of them that is no longer living, namely their representation, with a wit now nearly pointless, of persons in aspects already forgotten, and of small problems

settled long ago, these five are human; and they
are human in a way that is properly outside the
province of a character. Mynshul's little book
casts a keen light into the darkness of the seventeenth century prison, and upon the mind of a
sensitive spirit who suffered there; Earle attracts
us with his sympathy and wit; Brathwaite is genial
and whimsical, and the figure of 'Dandy Dick'
with his red coat, who charms us again and again
in his *Spiritual Spicerie*, makes an excuse unnecessary for the undoubted imperfections of his
Whimzies; Fuller stands with Sir Thomas Browne
and Charles Lamb; Steele gives us his own portrait in his *Character of a Gentleman*, and, though
the form had become well-nigh exhausted, makes
it live for a time by putting into it his own life.

The character-book of John Earle is distinguished by its thoughtfulness from the work of
the other character-writers. Of all such it is Earle
who for weight can best be likened to Theophrastus,
though a close comparison is not possible. The conventional way of writing a character was to describe
what a typical subject did; Earle's way was to
explain not alone what he did, but why he did it.
He is conscious of this, and indicates the difference
of his method in 'A Weake Man,' where he begins
by accounting for him, to the text, 'The rest of
him is grown to be a man, only his brain stays
behind'; and then he proceeds to give what most
characters give alone, the marks by which his subject is to be identified: 'Some tokens of him
are,—he loves men better upon relation than
experience, for he is exceedingly enamoured of

strangers, and none quicklier aweary of his friend . . .'

Earle's characters have been praised for combining the typical with the individual. This must not be taken to mean that Earle has achieved something outside the range of the character. It means he has made the type real. In life the individual often makes the type credible. Earle has given his characters a touch of this reality by including in his types elements of individual portrayal.

His characters seem to fall into groups according to the nature of his interest in them. Seven can be grouped together as an illustration of what the 'spirit of man' meant to him. These are 'A Grave Divine,' 'A Down-Right Scholar,' 'A Contemplative Man,' 'A Staid Man,' 'A Modest Man,' 'A Good Old Man,' and 'A High-Spirited Man,' and the gentle portrait of 'A Child' may be included with these others because like them it has been illuminated by an enthusiastic sympathy which shows how near these subjects were to his heart. In 'A Down-Right Scholar,' a list is given of the ways in which his scholar may be ridiculous, but Earle cannot give such details without the characteristic comment, 'But practise him a little in men . . . and he shall outbalance those glisterers as . . . gold, gold-lace.'

A second group contains seven sketches of types that fail where the first group were eminent; they are 'A Weake Man,' 'The World's Wise Man,' 'A Sceptic,' 'A Pretender to Learning,' 'A Plodding Student,' 'A Profane Man,' and 'A Vulgar-spirited Man,' the last, perhaps, the most foreign to Earle's own nature. The remaining groups are those of the University types of which Earle would naturally see much; then some moral types, a small group of characters of places, and a number of figures selected from the usual stock subjects, or observed by himself in daily life.

Earle's style was like himself, direct and simple. It has very few of the conventional conceits which were to lead the character astray. And at its best, its finest quality is that it is human and gracious.

Richard Brathwaite took part in most of the literary activities stirring during his long life. His best work in the character-fashion is *Whimzies*, 1631. He promises in his preface to prefer 'the pith before the rinde.' It would have been better if he had given more attention to the 'rinde,' for his style suffers from prosiness in its trailing sentences, and the characters are often much too lengthy. But the wordiness is relieved by a wit which is unforced, and which has small dependence on conceits. Its Elizabethan atmosphere is notable in its keen interest in contemporary life, especially that of the 'knave' class which Nashe or even Harman would have delighted in. Brathwaite makes his 'characters' seem so many parts of a picturesque narrative rather than a series of generic types. The characters are sketches of occupations, and the writer is interested in manners, not in mental processes. There is mild satire, much pure fun, and a certain amount of didacticism. The quality of the pieces varies a great deal; some are dull, but others, in spite of their long-windedness, are vivid and entertaining.

The Pamphlet-Characters

Before indicating what happened to the character during the Civil War, we may pause to survey its achievement, and to glance briefly at the course of its subsequent history.

The English character had reached the height of its development with Earle. It cannot be quite fairly said that it had developed from Theophrastus, for in his direction it did not go beyond him, but from the stimulus he supplied it evolved in its own way, and became a somewhat different thing in English. It arose in England from many unconscious and some perhaps partly conscious beginnings which had prepared the ground by the time the fresh Greek seed fell upon it in 1592, and its possibilities had been shown by 1628. These, it must be remembered, were not many, because at its best the character was of only limited range; it has been happily compared to a gem, a small thing, which can be taken in at a glance, and in which it is possible, though not easy, to achieve a certain kind of perfection that cannot belong to a larger work. Selection, a clear-cut shaping and polish were to be desired for it. Comment and illustration are in the nature of a setting, and the setting must properly be subordinate. Earle's achievement was that he gave his gems a setting which brought out their quality. But some of his successors over-emphasized the setting. To enlarge the scope of the character further than its nature permitted was to weaken it and bring about its decline. This is what finally happened.

But the decline was not extinction, for it contained elements akin to other kinds of literature. Very soon the biographer and the historian, the traveller and the social critic adopted the form.

To resume, we need do little but mention the important non-literary political use which developed rapidly about 1642, when the warring parties in the State quickly produced numbers of so-called characters of their opponents, and, with rare exceptions, both purposes and methods were controversial. These, as may be expected, had been heralded, and there had been at the end of Elizabeth's reign hostile portraits of Jesuits and Puritans. These controversial characters, the expression of fleeting political and religious passions, have a decided historical interest, but their literary significance is small.

As these sketches were lengthy and were generally issued singly it is convenient to call them 'pamphlets.' One group followed the character-form in nearly every particular except conciseness: in another group the form was all but lost in the abundant illustration; a third group were characters in nothing but name.

After the Restoration the controversial type continued, concerned with the Popish Plot, with the 'neuters' or 'trimmers,' and the 'informers,' who were the natural and hated results of the controversial methods of the time. Occasionally good writers took part in this strife of writing, and their contributions have little in common with the mass. One or two examples of their work are given in the text. A single sketch may be referred to here which though extravagant is typical. *The Character of a Fanatick in General* was printed in

1675, but its method of wild abuse could be amply paralleled at any period of the controversial character. The language and style overwhelm the reader with a confusion of words and details from many sources. 'His Principles are like the Chaos, a confused Lump of every thing, and nothing; or a Gallimaufry of Negatives; nor this, nor that nor t'other, but what he is, no man knows, no not the Angels in Heaven, nor himself to boot; this only excepted, that he is more party-coloured than *Joseph's* coat, and patcht together of more pieces, then a Taylor's Cushion [as for] his Preachment; which what other is it, then a wild career over Hill and Dale, till the afternoon chimes stop him; Thump upon Thump, Yelp upon Yelp . . .' Eleven more similar phrases leave us longing for restraint and quiet.

The character as a whole, especially when of the controversial type, probably exerted some influence on the growth of the 'historical character.' The origin and development of this was distinct, but its early stages coincided with the decline of the character-sketch, and particularly at this time examples can be found which are related to both forms of literature. The character-sketch depicted a type, the 'historical character' an individual. When once hostile sketches of Puritans, for example, were given a particular as well as a general reference, very speedily so-called 'characters' were issued that were intended primarily to refer to a definite person. Francis Wortley's *Characters and Elegies*, 1646, are on the border between the two kinds of character, and most of the hostile or adulatory 'Characters' of Charles I, for instance, belong properly to the 'historical character.'

The traveller and the exile soon wrote 'Characters' of the places they visited. This was no innovation, but their adherence to the form was nominal. Even a book like Feltham's *Character of the Low Countries* (100 pp. 12mo), which sets out to be a character and follows the conventional form as closely as its length permits, is, by that length, defeated in its technical object. In 1659 and 1660 was produced the main set of these pamphlets, describing England, France, Spain and Italy. John Evelyn's satirical *Character of England* (66 pp. 12mo) is a continuous narrative letter. It is not a character, but it is hard to resist a brief quotation : 'London' he defines as 'a City consisting of a wooden, northern, and inartificial congestion of Houses; . . . The Religion of England is Preaching, and sitting stil on Sundaies . . . and such a cloud of sea-coal, as if there be a resemblance of Hell upon Earth, it is in this Vulcano in a foggy day.'

After the Seventeenth Century

The 'character' lingered here and there in the eighteenth century, but in the nineteenth, whenever it was written, it was of more set purpose, for it was no longer the mode, but the choice of the writer who, perhaps, like Thackeray or Blanchard, had an affinity for its style, or, like Lamb, loved its flavour of former times. It occurred in the eighteenth century, chiefly in the periodical essay, for elsewhere it was to be found only in a few belated separately-issued characters, generally reprints, of no particular interest, or as 'concrete illustrations,' as in some of William Law's works.

It was under the 'character'-inspiration that Mr. Bickerstaff personified in the *Tatler* the faults of the time. Steele confides his aims to his readers at once; he has undertaken to 'distinguish Merit, and expose false Pretences to it; to this end he will introduce what he thinks fit from France,' and from La Bruyère. He turns round, again and again, in his arm-chair, to address a wider audience than that immediately listening to him; and, in a manner that Fielding may have noted, explains the meanings latent in his words and acts. He was fond of doing this so far as his aims were fully conscious; but the relation, rich in meaning, that existed between his invention of the name *Tatler* [1] in honour of the 'Fair Sex,' and his later account of the close connexion of the work with Comedy, was to wait till Meredith [2] for its full enunciation. Steele was too near Congreve, and too much a part of the movement that was gradually to replace Comedy by the Novel, or rather to give

[1] (a) 'It would have been a jest, sometime since, for a Man to have asserted, that any thing Witty could be said in praise of a Marry'd State, or that Devotion and Virtue were any way necessary to the Character of a fine Gentleman. *Bickerstaff* ventur'd to tell the Town, that they were a parcel of Fops, Fools, and vain Cocquets ; but in such a manner as even pleased them, and made them more than half enclin'd to believe that he spoke Truth.' John Gay, *The Present State of Wit*, 1711, p. 12.

(b) The Tatler and Comedy, cf. *Tatler*, No. 64.

[2] *Essay on Comedy*, 1897, p. 60. 'But there never will be civilisation where Comedy is not possible ; and that comes of some degree of social equality of the sexes.'

the Comic Spirit a new habitation, to view these incipient changes as if they had been completed. But we honour him no less as we watch him continuing his pioneer work, and recognize that the amiable manner of its presentation was the most effective possible. On the first birthday of the paper Addison summarizes what was by then beginning to be the joint achievement of himself and Steele. Writing as Mr. Bickerstaff he compares the work, in No. 162, with the Roman censorship. He has classified the types of 'this great country,' the 'Dappers and the Smarts,' 'the Pedants and the Men of Fire'; . . . he has degraded one species of Men into Bombs, Squibs and Crackers, and another into Drums. . . . It is especially under such type-names that we find character-sketches in plenty in the *Tatler*. About one-sixth of the papers can fairly be called 'character-papers,' for though their framework is in the essay-style, their object is to give a description of types in the old way, and, in these papers, set-descriptions could be detached entire from these contexts, and could then be called 'characters.'

'Character'-influence is less evident in the *Spectator*, for though a fairly long list of 'characters' could be collected, they are briefer and they hold a subordinate place in its scheme. The different atmosphere of the two papers is clearly indicated by Addison's editorial announcement in No. 249. 'When I make choice of a Subject that has not been treated of by others, I throw together my Reflections on it without any Order or Method, so that they may appear rather in the Looseness and Freedom of an Essay, than in the Regularity of a Set Discourse.' Thus in No. 598 mankind is divided into the merry and the serious, but we are not given the portrait of the merry man and the serious man as almost certainly we should have been given them in the *Tatler*. It is commonly said that the account of Sir Roger is a character-sketch, but it happens that his portrait is one of those presented to us gradually as the story of the Club is told, and we do not find more than three or four lines of consecutive description that could be extracted for a 'character-sketch.'

If La Bruyère's influence was evident in the *Tatler*, it is paramount in the *Spectator*. Steele and Addison must have found the particularly varied forms which La Bruyère's essays assumed full of suggestion. His truly 'dispersed' meditations on the 'manners of the time' are intrinsically as interesting, for their general observations and epigrammatic thought, as are the famous 'characters' which form the illustrations. As these were portraits drawn from life, only thinly veiled under their classical names, they attracted at first additional attention on that account, but the traits selected are such that the portraits have a generic and so a permanent value. The number of portraits of the French kind make the *Spectator* noteworthy from the 'character' point of view, not as illustrating the 'character,' but as illustrating the replacement of the objective 'character' by the subjective 'essay'; and it does this at a stage which is specially interesting to the historian, for the transformation is incomplete, and on that account its process is more clearly visible.

The history of the character-sketch as a form is

over, for the fashion that embodied the original impulse has been superseded. But we need no other evidence to show that the impulse is not dead than that our contemporaries are expressing it with freshness and point.

This anthology has been long in preparation, for it has grown from research on the 'Character' begun in 1917, but has been delayed by the lengthy and fascinating work required for my *Bibliography of English Character-Books, 1608-1700* (Bibliographical Society, 1925), which it seemed desirable to produce first. The index there shows the number of characters to be large, 1430 being contained in 308 editions of character-books of various classes issued in the seventeenth century alone; not all, unfortunately, prove as attractive as their titles. Not many characters could be added before 1600, and after 1700, though such a list would be fairly long, it would be so rambling and indeterminate that its main interest would lie not in the number but in the location of its names.

I have found it difficult and exciting to try to give a faithful reprint—with certain exceptions noted later—of texts of a time before spelling and punctuation were regularised. Recourse to the invaluable *Oxford English Dictionary* whenever a spelling seemed unusual most often showed an interesting and dignified history. Not only Miss Daisy Ashford but Lamb and Dickens used 'visiters,' a form that goes back to Wyclif. Occasionally, spellings like 'extravigance' (see pp. 320, 335), though not recorded, prove their right to remain by their repetition in more than one book. Nor is the punctuation as haphazard as it might seem. The diction and punctuation of the seventeenth century can in a real sense be said to have formed a means of expression more delicately adjustable to shades of meaning than the rigid monotony—desirable as this is on other grounds—of our practice to-day. This is well known in regard to Shakespeare and Milton, but it is also to be observed in this lighter prose of that time. On page 320, for instance, in the description of the 'Town-wit' is the following good example of a rhetorical pause, the semicolon after 'vulgar' suggesting a satirical antithesis which without it might be missed: 'By means of some small *scraps of learning* matcht with a far greater stock of Confidence, a voluble Tongue, and bold delivery, he has the ill-luck to be celebrated by the vulgar; for a man of *Parts*, which opinion gains credit to his Insolences, . . .'

The semicolon and capitals are used, too, to build up a periodic sentence or paragraph which is sometimes so clearly and rhythmically designed that we cannot consider the modern tendency to use short sentences as entirely a gain. The central paragraph on page 328 is a fair example.

Obvious misprints, and one or two words likely to distract the modern reader, have been silently altered, but a list of these changes is given at the end of the index.

It is a pleasure to offer my most sincere thanks for much valuable help to Miss Ethel Seaton, and to Mr. A. I. Ellis, to whom I am specially indebted for his reading of the book in manuscript and proof; to Mr. John Galsworthy for his very kind permission to use a long extract from *A Commentary*; and to Mr. John Murray for leave, courteously granted, to quote from the late Mr. G. W. E. Russell's *Social Silhouettes*, which he now publishes.

G. M.

CONTENTS

CONTENTS

LIST OF ILLUSTRATIONS

THEOPHRASTUS (B.C. *c.* 373–287)

Theophrasti Characteres Ethicae. Theophrastus His
Morall Characters : Or Description of Maners.
[Translated by] Jo. Healey. London, . . . 1616,
12mo. Reprinted in the Temple Classics edition of
Earle's Micro-cosmographie, 1899. [pp. 7, 32]

The Characters of Theophrastus. An English Translation by R. C. Jebb, 1870. A new edition edited by
J. E. Sandys, 1909.

30 characters.

The characters consist of thirty sketches of moral
qualities embodied in representative Athenian figures early
in the third century B.C. Only ' vices ' have reached us,
and we do not know if they were originally accompanied
by a set of ' virtues.' The vices are superficial, or
apparently so, for the deep faults of human nature could
hardly be suggested on the small canvasses employed. The
method is simple ; it consists in giving a list of the typical
acts that such a generalized individual as ' The Stupid
Man ' or ' The Mean Man ' might be expected to perform.
There is no comment to weaken the brilliant impression
produced by the few strokes of the artist-philosopher's
brush. His humour, and his subtle and yet clear observation enabled him to seize upon the significant acts by
which his subjects give themselves away ; and through the
admirable terseness of his style there resulted a picture
which is still successful, not only in rendering the ethical
quality it symbolizes, but in bringing an individual
before us.

Of Flatterie

FLATTERIE may be sayd to be a foule deformed
custom in common life, making for the advantage
of the Flatterer. A Flatterer is such a one, as if

hee walke or converse with you, will thus say unto you : Do you observe, how all mens eyes are upon you? I have not noted any in this Towne, to be so much beheld. Yesterday in the Gallerie you had reason to be proud of your reputation. For there being at that time assembled more then 30 persons, and question being made which should be the worthiest Citizen; the company being very impatient it should be disputed, concluded all upon you. These and such like he putteth upon him. If there be the least moat upon his clothes, or if there be none, hee maketh a shew to take it off : or if any small straw or feather bee gotten into his locks, the Flatterer taketh it away; and smiling saith, you are growne gray within these few dayes for want of my companie, and yet y.our haire is naturally as black as any man of your yeares. If he reply, the Flatterer proclaimeth silence, praiseth him palpably and profusely to his face. When hee hath spoken, he breaketh out into an exclamation, with an *O well spoken!* And if hee breake a jest upon any, the Flatterer laughes as if he were tickled; muffling himself in his cloake, as if hee could not possibly forbeare. As he meeteth any, he plaieth the Gentleman-usher, praying them to give way; as if his Patron were a very great Person. Hee buyes peares and apples, & beares them home to his children, and gives them (for the most part) in his presence : and kissing them, crieth out, *O the worthie Fathers lively picture!* If he buy a shoo, if he be present, hee sweares his foot is far handsomer, and that the shoo mis-shapes it. If at any time he repaire to visit a friend, the Flatterer plaies the Herbinger; runs before, & advertiseth

them of his comming: and speedily returning
backe againe, telleth him that he hath given them
notice thereof. Whatsoever belongeth to the
womens Academie, as paintings, preservings,
needle-workes, and such like; he discourseth of
them like my Ladies woman. Of all the ghests,
he first commends the wine, and alwaies sitting
by his Ingle, courts him; asking him how sparingly
he feeds, and how he bridles it: and taking some
speciall dish from the Table, taketh occasion to
commend it. Hee is busie and full of questions;
whether this man be not cold; why hee goes so
thinne; and why hee will not go better cloth'd?
Then hee whispers in his Patrons eare: and, while
others speak, his eye is still upon him. At the
Theater, taking the cushions from the boy, he
setteth them up himselfe: hee commendeth the
situation and building of the house; the well till-
ing and husbanding of the ground. In conclusion,
you shall alwayes note a flatterer to speak and doe,
what he presumeth will be most pleasing and
agreeable.

Of News-forging, or Rumor-spreading

FAME-SPREADING, is a devising of deeds and
words at the fancy or pleasure of the Inventer. A
Newes-monger is he, who meeting with his
acquaintance, changing his countenance and smiling, asketh whence come you now? How go the
rules now? Is there any newes stirring? and still
spurring him with questions, tels him there are
excellent and happy occurrents abroad. Then,
before he answereth, by way of prevention asketh,
have you nothing in store? why then I will feast

you with my choicest intelligence. Then hath hee at hand some cast Captaine, or cassierd Souldier, or some Fifes boy lately come from war, of whom hee hath heard some very strange stuffe, I warrant you: alwaies producing such authors as no man can controle. He will tell him, hee heard that *Polyspherchon* and the King discomfited and over-threw his enemies, and that *Cassander* was taken prisoner. But if any man say unto him, Doe you beleeve this? Yes marry doe I beleeve it, replyeth he: for it is bruited all the Towne over by a generall voice. The rumor spreadeth, all generally agree in this report of the warre; and that there was an exceeding great overthrow. And this hee gathereth by the very countenance and cariage of these great men which sit at the sterne. Then he proceedeth and tels you further, That hee heard by one which came lately out of *Macedonia*, who was present at all which passed, that now these five days hee hath bin kept close by them. Then he falleth to terms of commiseration. Alas, good, but unfortunate *Cassander*! O carefull desolate man! This can misfortune doe. *Cassander* was a very powerfull man in his time, and of a very great commaund: but I would entreat you to keep this to your self; and yet he runneth to every one to tell them of it. I do much wonder what pleasure men shuld take in devising and dispersing those rumours. The which things, that I mention not the basnesse and deformity of a lye, turne them to many inconveniences.

For, it fals out oftentimes, that while these, *Mountebanklike*, draw much company about them, in the Baths and such like places, some good

Rogues steale away their clothes: others, sitting in a porch or gallery, while they overcome in a sea, or a land-fight, are fined for not appearance. Others, while with their words they valiantly take Cities, loose their suppers. These men lead a very miserable & wretched life. For what Gallery is there, what shop, wherein they waste not whole dayes, with the penance of those, whose eares they set on the Pillorie with their tedious unjointed tales?

POPE INNOCENT III (d. 1216)

[Liber De Contemptu Mundi. Sive De Miseria Conditionis Humanae. A Domino Innocentio Papa Tertio Compositus. Lipsiae. M.D. xxxiiii.]

The Mirror of Mans lyfe. Plainely describing, what weake moulde we are made of : what miseries we are subject unto : howe uncertaine this life is : and what shal be our ende. Englished. by H. K. [Woodcut, with the inscription, 'O Wormes Meate : O Froath : O Vanitie : Why Art Thou so Insolent : ']. . . . London, . . . 1576. 8vo. [C7ᵛ, G3ᵛ]

This little book was written by Pope Innocent during a compulsorily quiet interval of his brilliant career. He became Cardinal Lothair under the pontificate of his uncle Clement III, at the almost unprecedentedly early age of twenty-nine and went into retirement when his uncle was succeeded by Celestine III, a representative of a family hostile to Lothair's.

The monastic theme of 'the misery of human life' appealed strongly to the disillusioned young recluse. The book has no hint of the enlargement of vision to come to the writer eight years later when he himself became Pope.

The title page of Henry Kerton's translation is hardly more dismal than the text. The most cheerful pages are those in which the moralist gives a brief description of some typical figure to illustrate his theme. About twelve such sketches occur, some in the course of a chapter, others in a chapter by themselves.

A Shrewde Wife

OFTEN times she sayeth unto hir husbande, such a mans wife goeth gorgeously and finely apparelled, and is estemed and much made of by every one : but I poore wretche, all alone, am nothyng regarded amongst my neighbours :

I am contemned and despised of every one. She only will bee loved and praysed : she thynketh the good countenance showed unto an other, to procure hatred unto hir : and shee surmiseth the commendation of an other, to be for hir disgrace. All that she loveth, must be lyked of, and all that she hateth must be disliked : she will be mistresse, and cannot be maister : she may not abide to serve as a subject, but she must rule as a governour : shee will seeme experte in all things, and will shewe hir selfe ignorant in nothing.

A Proude Man

[He] contemneth the companye of his olde friendes, and disdayneth the sight of hys former famyliars, and turneth hys face from his wonted acquayntaunce : his countenance is proude, his gate is glorious, his mouthe is filled with haughtye termes, his mynde is fixte uppon waightie matters. Hee is impatient of subjection, and desirous to beare rule : hee is a clogge unto the cleargye, a great burthen unto his subjectes, and a heavye yoke unto his neighbour. Hee can not patiently beare any greevous thing that shall touche hym selfe, nor delaye that which hee hath conceyved in his mynde : but he is rashe, bold, boasting, arrogant, soone moved, and verye importunate.

GEOFFREY CHAUCER (*c.* 1340–1400)

The Complete Works. Edited . . . by the Rev. Walter
    W. Skeat . . . Oxford : . . . 1906.

(*a*) The Prologue ; (*b*) The Miller's Tale, ll. 3190 ff.

What charming complementary pictures are presented
by the Clerk, and the povre scoler, of Oxenford! This
contrast of the ' Melancholy ' and the ' Merry ' Man was
a favourite in the seventeenth century.

The Clerk of Oxenford

A Clerk ther was of Oxenford also,
That un-to logyk hadde longe y-go.
As lene was his hors as is a rake,
And he nas nat right fat, I undertake;
But looked holwe, and ther-to sobrely.
Ful thredbar was his overest courtepy[1];
For he had geten him yet no benefyce,
Ne was so worldly for to have offyce.
For him was lever have at his beddes heed
Twenty bokes, clad in blak or reed,
Of Aristotle and his philosophye,
Than robes riche, or fithele, or gay sautrye[2]:
But al be that he was a philosophre,
Yet hadde he but litel gold in cofre;
But al that he myghte of his freendes hente,
On bokes and on lerninge he it spente,
And bisily gan for the soules preye
Of hem that yaf hym wher-with to scoleye.
Of studie took he most cure and most hede,
Noght o word spak he more than was nede,
And that was seyd in forme and reverence,
And short and quik and ful of hy senténce.

[1] short coat.   [2] harp.

8

Souninge[3] in moral vertu was his speche,
And gladly wolde he lerne, and gladly teche.

The Povre Scoler of Oxenford

With him ther was dwellinge a povre scoler,
Had lerned art, but al his fantasye
Was turned for to lerne astrologye. . . .
A chambre hadde he in that hostelrye
Allone, with-outen any companye,
Ful fetisly[4] y-dight with herbes swote; . . .
His Almageste and bokes grete and smale,
His astrelabie, longinge for his art,
His augrim[5]-stones layen faire a-part
On shelves couched at his beddes heed :
His presse y-covered with a falding[6] reed.
And al above ther lay a gay sautrye,
On which he made a nightes melodye
So swetely, that al the chambre rong;
And *Angelus ad Virginem* he song;
And after that he song the kinges note;
Ful often blessed was his mery throte.
And thus this swete clerk his tyme spente
After[7] his freendes finding[8] and his rente.

[3] tending to. [4] daintily. [5] numeration-counters.
[6] a coarse cloth. [7] according to. [8] provision.

SEBASTIAN BRANT (1457–1521)

The Shyp of folys of the worlde . . . translated . . . by
    Alexander Barclay Preste : . . . 1509. fol. [fol.
    xiii b]

Reprinted 1874, ed. T. H. Jamieson.

[The German original. Das Narren Schyff. 1494.]

The Boke-Fole is one of the first of the numerous
English sketches of the ' pedant mind ' as Addison terms
the type. One of his illustrations is his Tom Folio, who
is certainly the Boke-Fole's descendant.

There are, of course, many examples of the Boke-Fole
and the pedant outside English literature. Lucian's
diatribe against *The Ignorant Book-Collector* has rich
material for a character-sketch though hardly the form.
One remark offers an interesting parallel to Brant's Fole :
καὶ σὺ τοίνυν βιβλίον μὲν ἔχεις ἐν τῇ χειρὶ καὶ ἀναγιγνώ-
σκεις ἀεί, τῶν δὲ ἀναγιγνωσκομένων οἶσθα οὐδέν, ἀλλ᾽ ὄνος
λύρας ἀκούεις κινῶν τὰ ὦτα. ' You have always a book in
your hand, you are always reading ; but what it is all
about, you have not an idea ; you do but prick up asinine
ears at the lyre's sound.' [1]

The illustration depicts the essentials of the type
sufficiently to prove an apt commentary on its many
subsequent embodiments whether these were created by
Overbury, Earle, Butler, 'A Lady,' or Addison himself.
The woodcut is the second of that remarkable series which
made the *Shyp of Folys* famous all over Europe far more,
it is to be suspected, than the somewhat pedestrian text.
This, however, had the recognised merit of substituting
concrete types for the abstractions of medieval allegory.

The Boke-Fole

STYLL am I besy bokes assemblynge
For to have plenty it is a pleasaunt thynge

[1] Lucian, trans. by H. W. and F. G. Fowler, iii. p. 267.
Oxford Library of Translations, 1905.

THE BOKE-FOLE

In my conceyt and to have them ay in honde
But what they mene do I nat understonde
But yet I have them in great reverence
And honoure savynge them from fylth and ordure
By often brusshynge, and moche dylygence
Full goodly bounde in pleasaunt coverture
Of domas,[1] satyn, or els of velvet pure
I kepe them sure ferynge lyst they sholde be lost
For in them is the connynge wherin I me bost

But if it fortune that any lernyd men
Within my house fall to disputacion
I drawe the curtyns to shewe my bokes then
That they of my cunnynge sholde make probacion
I kepe not[2] to fall in altercacion
And whyle they comon[3] my bokes I turne and
    wynde
For all is in them, and no thynge in my mynde

    .   .   .   .   .

Lo in lyke wyse of bokes I have store
But fewe I rede, and fewer understande
I folowe nat theyr doctryne nor theyr lore
It is ynoughe to bere a boke in hande
It were too moche to be it suche a bande[4]
For to be bounde to loke within the boke
I am content on the fayre coverynge to loke.

[1] damask.   [2] care not.   [3] discuss. Cp. *O.E.D.*   [4] bond.

ANTONIO GUEVARA (1490–1545)

Golden Epistles, Contayning varietie of discourse both
    Morall, Philosophicall, and Divine : gathered as
    well out of the remaynder of Guevaraes workes, as
    other Authors, Latine, French, and Italian. By
    Geffray Fenton. Mon heur viendra.... London
    ... 1575. 4to.

Several brief characters occur in this book. The
most attractive is this charming sketch from the letter
on p. 129*b*. 'The author [? Guevara] writeth to
his sister serving in the Court : partly hee instructeth her
how to live in Court, and partly satisfieth her request
under a short discription of love.'

Properties in a true lover

HE offereth no excuse, but is ready to execute:
he is not required to be liberall, but findes out
wherin he may be acceptable : he suspectes not his
mistres, but takes all to the best, he beleeves no
report, since he is assured of her vertue : he is not
importunate, but makes his hope his felicitie : if
she but begin to like, he puts wings to his affection,
yea he makes her the image of his thoughts, & lives
wholy dedicated to her devotion. And therefore
if he love dearly, he lives in thought to please, in
care to offende, in desire to suffer, & in feare to
disclose, and loving much he gives much, thinking
it no liberalitie if he refuse any thing, since if he
have once given his wil and consent, it is nothing
to give withal his abilitie and wealth : and being
possest by another, he must think he hath nothing
of his owne : In like sort the true lover studies to
be circumspect in behaviour, esteeming it a sweet
felicity to have his thoughts & delytes private : he

is modest in countenance the better to bleare the
eyes of spies, & please the minde of his mistres.
And he is patient to suffer, esteeming him not
worthy of reward unlesse he endure to the ende.
And where true love is, there wronges must be
borne, and no wordes delivered to the dyshonour
of his Lady: By whom if any occasion be given,
yet he must alwayes have this lesson, that patience
is a vertue, and secret scilence doth best solicite,
since the true Trumpet of love, is not the Tongue
that speaketh, but the harte that sigheth.

SIR JOHN DAVIES (1569–1626)

Epigrammes and Elegies. By I. D. and C. M. At
Middleborough. 8vo. [No date. B.M. catalogue
queries ? 1590.]

Complete Poems. Ed. A. B. Grosart. 2 vols. 1876.

All Ovids Elegies; 3 Bookes. By C. M. Epigrams
by I. D. . . . Etchells & Macdonald . . . London,
Sept. 1925.

Sir John Davies's forty-eight epigrams are concerned
with the various affectations and follies displayed by
aspirants to position at Court. Three of his pieces,
the Gull, Tobacco, and 'Fame,' can be described as
characters, and are among the earliest of the many subsequent sketches of these subjects.

Of a Gull

OFT in my laughing rimes, I name a gull,
But this new terme will many questions breede,
Therefore at first I will expresse at full,
Who is a true and perfect gull indeede.

A gull is he, who feares a velvet gowne,
and when a wench is brave, dares not speake to her:
A gull is he which traverseth the towne,
and is for marriage knowne a common wooer.

A gull is he, which while he prowdlie weares,
a silver hilted Rapier by his side,
Indures the lyes, and Knockes about the eares,
Whilst in his sheath, his sleeping sword doth bide.

A gull is he which weares good hansome cloathes,
And standes in presence stroaking vp his hayre:
and filles vp his unperfect speech with othes,

but speakes not one wise word throughout the
    yeere
  But to define a gull in termes precise,
  A gull is he which semes, and is not wise.

EDWARD GUILPIN (fl. 1598)

Skialetheia. Or, A shadowe of Truth, in certaine Epigrams and Satyres.   At London, ... 1598.   8vo.   [B4]

In his satires Guilpin refers lightly to various types ; in satire 1, for example, he gives a general account of what he saw in the streets, and as he walks, he points out various illustrations of what he is denouncing. ' Yonder comes Clodius,' he says, ' an oylie slave,' and soon he sees the traveller, and then the cowardly Gallant.

The Cowardly Gallant

SEE you him yonder, who sits o're the stage,
With the Tobacco-pipe now at his mouth?
It is *Cornelius* that brave gallant youth,
Who is new printed to this fangled age :
He weares a Jerkin cudgeld with gold lace,
A profound slop, a hat scarce pipkin high,
For boots, a paire of dagge[1] cases; his face,
Furr'd with *Cads*[2]-beard : his poynard on his thigh.
He wallows in his walk his slop to grace,
Sweares *by the Lord*, daines no salutation
But to some jade that's sick of his owne fashion,
As *farewell sweet Captaine*, or *(boy) come apace:*
   Yet this Sir *Bevis*, or the fayery Knight,
   Put up the lie because he durst not fight.

[1] pistol.   [2] Cadiz-beard.

JOHN MARSTON (? 1575–1634)

The Scourge of Villanie.... At London, ... 1598. 8vo.
  [H4, H7]

In the tenth (and last) satire, called 'Humours,' the
satirist abandons his 'snarling rage' for 'sporting merriment' and laughs lightly at the typical figures he hails
in turn, such as 'capering Curio,' Drusus an actor, or
the 'Fashion-mounger.' The invocation was, no doubt,
known to Milton, cf. L'Allegro, for this is Marston's

> 'Sleep grim *Reproofe*, my jocund Muse dooth sing
> In other keyes, to nimbler fingering.
> Dull sprighted *Melancholy*, leave my braine
> To hell *Cimmerian* night, in lively vaine
> I strive to paint, then hence all darke intent
> And sullen frownes, come sporting meriment,
> Cheeke dimpling laughter, crowne my very soule
> With jouisance.'

An Ardent Playgoer

Luscus what's playd to day? faith now I know
I set thy lips abroach, from whence doth flow
Naught but pure *Juliat* and *Romio*.
Say, who acts best? *Drusus*, or *Roscio?*
Now I have him, that nere of ought did speake
But when of playes or Plaiers he did treate.
H'ath made a common-place booke out of plaies,
And speakes in print, at least what ere he sayes
Is warranted by Curtaine *plaudeties*,
If ere you heard him courting *Lesbias* eyes;
Say (Curteous Sir) speakes he not movingly
From out some new pathetique Tragedie?
He writes, he railes, he jests, he courts, what not,
And all from out his huge long scraped stock
Of well penn'd playes.

The Fashion-Mounger

'O SPRUCE! How now *Piso*, *Aurelius* Ape,
What strange disguise, what new deformed shape
Doth hold thy thoughts in contemplation?
Faith say, what fashion art thou thinking on?
A stitch'd Taffata cloake, a payre of slops
Of Spanish leather? O who heard his chops
Ere chew of ought, but of some strange disguise.
This fashion-mounger, each morne fore he rise
Contemplates sute shapes, & once from out his bed,
He hath them straight full lively portraied.
And then he chukes,[1] and is as proude of this,
As *Taphus* when he got his neighbours blisse.
All fashions since the first yeere of this Queene,
May in his studdie fairely drawne be seene,
And all that shall be to his day of doome,
You may peruse within that little roome.
For not a fashion once dare show his face,
But from neate *Pyso* first must take his grace.
The long fooles coat, the huge slop, the lugg'd
    boot
From mimick *Piso*, all doe claime their roote.
O that the boundlesse power of the soule
Should be coop'd vp in fashioning some roule!'

[1] chuckles.

SAMUEL ROWLANDS (?1570–?1630)

Looke to it : For, Ile Stabbe ye. . . . London . . . 1604.
    8vo. [Copy used, Bodl. Malone 599.]
    Out of 34 pieces, about 16 are characters.
Complete Works of S. Rowlands. Hunterian Club.
    1880.

Rowlands's 'characters' are homely relations of those
written by Sir John Davies and Ben Jonson. He
was keenly interested in contemporary manners, which
he describes in an easy and good-natured style with
frequent dramatic touches.
    Looke to it : For, Ile Stabbe ye is spoken by Death, who
issues a general challenge. The work is a rendering of
the medieval conception of the ' Dance of Death,' in
which personages representing all ranks of life were
variously grouped, and shown, one and all, to be attended
by Death.

Curious Divines

Divines, that are together by the eares,
Puft up, high-minded, seedes-men of dissention,
Striving untill *Christe*s seame-lesse garments teares,
Making the Scriptures follow your invention,
Neglecting that, whereon the soule should feede :
Imployde in that, whereof soules have no neede.

Curious in thinges you neede not stir about,
Such as concerne not matter of salvation :
Giving offence to them that are without :
Upon whose weaknes you should have compassion,
Causing the good to grieve, the bad rejoyce ;
Yet you with *Martha*, make the worser choyce.
                                    Ile Stabbe yee.

Sooth-sayer, or Figure-flinger

You Cunning man, or rather co'sning Knave,
That will tell good-man *Ninney* of his Mare:
Cysley, how many Husbandes she shall have,
Tom Carter, when the weather will be faire:
My neighbour *Powling*, who hath found his Purse,
And *Jone* his wife, who did her Chickens curse.

Whether a man shall have a happy life,
Whether a Lover shall his Love enjoy:
Who shall die first, the husband or the wife?
Whether the childe unborne, be girle or boy?
You that can fetch home Servantes runne away,
And finde out any Cattle gone astray.
                              Ile Stabbe yee.

HENRY FITZGEFFREY (fl. 1617)

Satyres : And Satyricall Epigram's : With Certaine
 Observations at Black-Fryers. By H : F : . . .
 London . . . 1617. 8vo. [F4ᵛ]

While H. F. is at the theatre with a friend, waiting
for the performance, they discuss the typical figures they
see entering, in a lively satirical narrative.

The descriptions most like characters are those of
Captain Martio (the Swaggerer), Sir Iland Hunt, a
Travailer, a plumed Dandebrat, the Spruse Coxcombe,
and crabbed Websterio the critic.

The Coxcombe

W'ANT it for Women we shu'd all be men.
I cannot present better instance, then
In yon Spruse *Coxcombe*, yon Affecting *Asse*,
That never walkes without his *Looking-glasse*,
In a *Tobacco* box, or *Diall* set,
That he may privatly conferre with it.
How his *Band* jumpeth with his *Peccadilly*,[1]
Whether his Band strings ballance equally :
Which way his *Feather* wagg's : And (to say truth)
What wordes in utterance best become his mouth.
Oh! Hadst thou yesterday beheld the *Valour*
I saw him exercising on his *Taylour*,
How, *out of measure*, hee the Rascall beat,
Not fitting to his *minde* his Doublet.
Lord! how I laught to see the witlesse Noddy,
Durst not reply, he meant it to his *Body*.
See Villain, Rogue! (And in he shrinks his brest)
Oh Heauens! Too wide a handfull at the least,
Straight it is Cut! And then proves (being try'd)
As much too little on the other side.

[1] broad collar.

22

But what skil't!   Hee'l have an attractive *Lace*,
And *whalebone-bodyes*, for the better grace,
Admit spare *dyet*, on no sustnance feed,
But *Oatmeale*, *Milke*, and crums of *Barly-bread*.
Use Exercise untill at last hee fit :
(With much adoe) his Body vnto it.
Hee'l not approach a *Taverne*, no nor drinke ye
To save his life *Hot-water*, (wherefore thinke ye,)
For heating's *Liver!* which some may suppose
Scalding hote, by the *Bubbles* on his *Nose*.
Hee'l put up any *publique* foule disgrace,
Rather then hazzard cutting of his *Face*.
If in his element you'd have the *(Foole!)*
Aske him when he came from the *Dauncing-schoole*.
Whereas much *Leather* he doth dayly waste
In the French *Cringe*, which *Ieremy* brought last.
And more, then *Coriat*,[2] (I dare maintaine)
In going to the *Alpes* and backe againe.
Whereof, that all the world may notice take,
See! every step an *Honor* hee doth make
That Ladyes, may *denote* him with their *Fan*,
As he goes by, with a *Lo: Hee's the man*.

[2] Thomas Coryate (d. 1617), the traveller.

THOMAS NASHE (1567–1601)

Pierce Penilesse his Supplication to the Divell. . . .
    London, . . . 1592, 4to. [C4^v, G4^v]
The Works of Thomas Nashe. Edited . . . by R. B.
McKerrow. 1904.

Pierce Penilesse is an exuberant commentary on contemporary abuses, and is arranged loosely in 7 sections, each being called a ' Complaint ' of one of the Seven Deadly Sins. The ' Complaint of Pride,' for instance, contains pictorial accounts of the various typical personages referred to, such as an upstart, a counterfeit politician, merchants' wives, the Spaniard and the Dane.

Mistris Minx

Mistris Minx, a Marchants wife, that will eate no Cherries forsooth, but when they are at twentie shillings a pound, that lookes as simperingly as if she were besmeard, & jets it as gingerly as if she were dancing the Canaries : she is so finicall in her speach, as though she spake nothing but what shee had first sewd over before in her Samplers, and the puling accent of her voyce is like a fained treble, or ones voyce that interprets to the puppets. What should I tell how squeamish she is in her dyet, what toyle she puts her poore servants unto, to make her looking glasses in the pavement ? How she will not goe into the fields, to cowre on the greene grasse, but shee must have a Coatch for her convoy : and spends halfe a day in pranking her selfe if she be invited to anie strange place ? Is not this the excesse of pride signior Sathan ?

24

Sloth, a Stationer

IF I were to paint Sloth, .. by Saint *John* the Evangelist I sweare, I would diaw it like a Stationer that I knowe, with his thumb under his girdle; who if a man come to his stall to aske him for a Booke, never stirres his head, or looks upon him, but stands stone still, and speakes not a word: only with his little finger poynts backwards to his boy, who must be his interpreter, & so all the day gaping like a dumbe image he sits without motion; except at such times as hee goes to dinner or supper: for then he is as quicke as other three, eating sixe times everie day.

THOMAS DEKKER (1570–? 1641)

The Seven deadly Sinnes of London. . . .   At London . . .
 1606.   4to.   [B2ᵛ]

Worke for Armorours : Or, The Peace is Broken.
 Open warres likely to happin this yeare 1609. . . .
 London, . . . 1909.   4to.   [D4ᵛ]

A Strange Horse-Race, . . . London, . . . 1613. 4to. [C3]

In the course of Dekker's fanciful but brilliant treatments of contemporary London life, he gives now and again sketches of some of the passing figures in the crowded scenes.   The part selected here from his picture of the ' Politick Bankrupt ' is an early example of the ' Turncoat,' a type very familiar later in the century.

[*The Religious Turncoat*]

THE Politick Bankrupt is a *Harpy* that lookes smoothly, a *Hyena* that enchants subtilly, a Mermaid that sings sweetly, and a *Cameleon*, that can put himselfe into all colours. Sometimes hee's a Puritane, he sweares by nothing but Indeede, or rather does not sweare at all and wrapping his crafty Serpents body in the cloake of Religion, he does those acts that would become none but a Divell. Sometimes hee's a Protestant, and deales justly with all men, till he see his time, but in the end he turnes Turke.

Parsimonie

Parsimonie, . . . to save a pennie, hee will damne halfe his soule, hee weares cloathes long, and will sooner alter his religion ten times, then his doublet once, his hatte is like his head, of the old blocke, he buies no gloves but of a groat a

26

paire, and having worne them two daies hee
quarrels with the poore Glover that they are too
wide, or too ill stitched, & by base scolding and
lordly words gets his money againe, and the wearing of so much leather for nothing. He will be
knowne by a paire of white pumpes some 16. or
20. yeares, onely by repairing their decaied com-
plection w' a peece of chalke.

Hospitalitie pictured

. . . an old Lord (that is now no Courtier) for hee
keeps a place in the Countrey, & all the chimnies
in it smoke : he spends his money as he spends the
water that passeth to his house, it comes thither in
great pipes, but it is all consumed in his kichin,
his name *Hospitality*. It is a grave & reverend
counteneance; he weares his beard long of purpose,
that the haires being white, & still in his eie, he
may be terrified fro doing any thing unworthy
their honor : his apparrel is for warmth, not
bravery : if he thinke ill at any time, he presently
thinks wel : for just upon his breast he wears his
Reprehension. As a jewel comprehends much
treasure in a little roome; and as that nut-shell held
all *Homers Iliads* smally written in a peece of
Vellum. So, though the tree of his vertues grow
high, and is laden with goodly fruit, yet the top-
bough of all, and the fairest Apple of all he
counteth his *Hospitality:* His bread was never too
stale, his drinke was never sowre, no day in the
yeare was to them that are hungry, *A fasting day*,
yet he observes them all : Hee gives moderately
every houre, but in reverence of one season in the
yeare, all that come may freely take.

Thofe that keepe mee, I keepe, if can, will fill :

Heé's a true Iaylor ftrips the Divell in ill.

THE JAYLOR

GEFFRAY MYNSHUL (?1594–1668)

Essayes and Characters of a Prison and Prisoners. Written
  by G. M. of Grayes-Inne Gent. ... London ...
  1618. 4to. Reprinted 1638 and 1821.
[The illustration is the frontispiece to the 1618 4to
  edition.]

We have altogether twelve essays and nine characters
of Mynshul's. Four of the essays borrow much from
Dekker without acknowledgement. In the present
selection only Mynshul's work is given.

The book is mostly grouped into pairs, of an essay
followed by a character, which form a fairly consecutive
account of the author's experiences in prison. He pleads
strongly that the debtors should be clearly distinguished
from the thieves and other criminals. The intensity of
feeling displayed throughout atones a good deal for the
tendency to wordiness and for the trailing sentences. We
welcome such stirrings of the latent spirit of the real essay
as the passage in ' Mercilesse Jailors ' for which the text
is ' Thou dost preserve the stars from wrong ! '

A Prison

A Prison is a grave to bury men alive, and a
place wherein a man for halfe a yeares experience
may learne more law, then hee can at *Westminster*
for an hundred pound.

It is a *Microcosmus*, a little world of woe, it is
a map of misery, it is a place that will learne a
young man more villainy, if he be apt to take it,
in one halfe yeare, then he can learne at twenty
dicing-houses, bowling-allies, Brothell-houses or
Ordinaries; and an old man more policie then if he
had been Pupill to *Machiavel*.

It is a place that hath more diseases predominant
in it, then the Pest-house in the Plague-time, and

it stinkes more then the Lord Mayors Dogge-house or Paris-garden in August.

It is a little common-wealth, although little wealth be common there; it is a desart where desert lyes hood-winckt; it is a famous Citie wherein are all Trades, for here lies the Alchymist that can rather make *ex auro non aurum*, then *ex non auro aurum*.

It is as intricate a place as *Rosamonds* Labyrinth, and is as full of blinde Meanders, and crooked turnings that it is unpossible to finde the way out, except he be directed by a silver Clue, and can never overcome the *Minotaure* without a golden ball to worke his owne safety.

It is as Innes of Court: for herein Lawyers inhabit, that have crochets to free other men, yet all their quirks and quiddities cannot enfranchize themselves.

It is the Doctors-Commons, where skilfull Physitians frequent, who like *Aesculapius* can cure other mens diseases, yet cannot Quintessence out of all their Vegetals and Minerals, a Balsamum or Elyxir to make a soveraigne plaister to heale the surfet the Mace hath given them.

It is the Chyrurgions-Hall, where many rare Artists live, that can search other mens wounds, yet cannot heale the wound the Serjeant hath given them.

It is your Bankrupts banquetting-house, where he sits feasting with the sweete meates borrowed from other mens tables, having a voluntary disposition never to repay them againe.

It is your Prodigals *Ultimum refugium*, wherein he may see himselfe as in a glasse what his excesse hath brought him to; and lest he should surfet, comes hither to physicke himselfe with moderate dyet, and least that his bed of Downe should breed too many diseases, comes hither to change his bed, where he is scarce able to lye downe.

It is a Purgatory which doth afflict a man with more miseries then ever he reaped pleasures.

It is a Pilgrimage to extenuate sinnes, and absolve offences: for here be Seminaries and Masse-Priests, which doe take down the pride of their flesh more, then a voyage to the Holy Land, or a hayre shirt in Lent.

It is an exile which doth banish a man from all contentments, wherein his actions doe so terrifie him, that it makes a man grow desperate.

To conclude, what is it not? In a word, it is the very Idea of all misery and torments, it converts joy into sorrow, riches into povertie, and ease into discontentments.

A Prisoner

A Prisoner is an impatient Patient, lingring under the rough hands of a cruell Phisitian, his creditor having cast his water knowes his disease, and hath power to cure him, but takes more pleasure to kill him. He is like *Tantalus*, who hath freedome running by his doore yet cannot enjoy the least benefit thereof, his greatest griefe is, that his credit was so good and now no better: his lande is drawne within the compass of a sheepes skin, and his owne hand the fortification that barres him of entrance: hee is fortunes tossing-bal, an object that would make mirth melancholly: to his friends an abject, and a subject of nine dayes

wonder in every Barbers shop: and a mouthfull of
pitty (that he had no better fortune) to Midwives
and talkative Gossips; and all the content that this
transitory life can give him, seemes but to flout
him, in respect the restraint of liberty barres the
true use.   To his familiars hee is like a plague,
whom they dare scarce come nigh for feare of infection, he is a monument ruined by those which
raysed him, hee spends the day with a *hei mihi*, *ve
miserum*, and the night with a *Nullis est medica-
bilis herbis*.

Of Visitants

VISITANTS are men for the most part composed
all of protesting promises, and little or no performance, they are like your Almanacks, which when
they prognosticate faire weather, it is a million to
a mite if it prove not contrary: they are like the
German clocks which seldome goe right, their
tongues run faster then the clocke on Shrove-
tuesday, the pissing Conduit in Cheapside, or an
Irish mans paire of heeles when hee runnes on a
wager.   They will tyre thine eares more in one
howre with their loud protestations, then a Scholler,
Citizen or Taylor will a hackney horse in halfe a
dayes riding, but in performance will bee as slow
as a Snayle in her pace, and when thy messenger
comes to them for money, then they will bee sure
to have the Strangullion, or Chollick that they
cannot speake, and looke as rustily on thy messenger, as a Lawyer will on his clyent which sueth
under *forma pauperis*, your letters as acceptable as
water into a Shippe, the Kings privie seale to an

Usurer, a Subpoena to a Country Gentleman, or a Catch pole amongst the friendly society of Gallants.

They are like the rings and chaines bought at S. Martines, that weare faire for a little time, but shortly after will prove Alchimy, or rather pure Copper.

Lastly, they are like the Apples which grow on the bankes of *Gomorrah*, they have crimson and beautiful rindes, but when they come to gather them they crumble all to dust.

Of Entertainment in Prison

As soone as thou commest before the gate of the Prison, doe but thinke thou art entring into Hell, and it will extenuate somewhat of thy misery, for thou shalt be sure not only to find hell, but fiends and ugly monsters, which with continuall torments will afflict thee, for at the gate there stands *Cerberus*, a man in shew, but a dogge in nature, who at thy entrance will fawne upon thee, bidding thee welcome in respect of the golden crust which hee must have cast him, then he opens the doore with all gentlenes, shewing thee the way to misery is very facile, and being once in, hee shuts it with such fury, that it makes the foundations shake and the doore and windowes so barricadoed, that a man so looseth himselfe with admiration that hee can hardly finde the way out and be a sound man. Now for the most part your Porter is either some broken Cittizen, who hath plaid Jack of all trades, some Pander, Broker or Hangman, that hath plaid the knave with all men, and for the more certainty his Embleme is

a red Beard, to which Sacke hath made his Nose
cousin German.

No sooner shall a man passe this fury, but hee
is conducted to little ease his chamber, where hee
no sooner hath entred, but (hard usage) his chamberlaine salutes him, and protests hee hath lodged
thee with as honest a man as himselfe, when as in
truth a paire of Sheres cannot part the knave
betwixt them, and protesteth thou shalt have a
cleane paire of sheetes, and of the best, who having
no sooner fingred thy coyne, but sends thee a paire
of sheets, fitter for a horse then a man, who having
plaid the Jade so with thee, then leaves thee. Hee
no sooner departs, but thredbare and monilesse
thy chamber-fellowes, come upon thee for a Gar-
nish, which if thou deny them or hast no money,
then _Exit_ cloake from thy shoulders, and enter
two douzen of pots, and one douzen of pipes, this
is the pillow which shall be given thee to sleepe
on the first night: now thou must be saluted in
the morning, or else peradventure thou wilt thinke
thy selfe not welcome.

In the morning at thy uprising, _(Pothearbe)_ the
Gardiner appeares in his likenesse and hee will have
unguentum aureum, for the narrow path thou hast
to walke in.

Then to whet on thy stomach to dinner comes
(Cut-throat) the Steward for his crowne, who professeth much kindnesse hee will shew thee, for
thou hast bound him with thy courtesie, to cousen
thee, not onely in thy meat but money.

Next after this comes (Mistresse _Mutton-chops,_)
the head Cooke, who protesteth thou shalt command her, who having no sooner greased her

fingers with thy silver, but ever after shee will have a hand in thy dish, doe what thou canst to prevent it, so on all sides the blood of thy purse must bee poured out to maintaine such mercilesse Blood-hounds, and continuall purse-leaches.

These Furies, as they have divers shapes, so have they severall kindes of temptations, for after thou hast beene some fortnight in Prison, they will come to thee to cheere thee, least thou shouldst adde melancholly to discontentment, and will tell thee they wish thee well, and thou shalt command them, and in their opinion the sight of the Street will much content thee, and they will attend thee to the Taverne within the rule, where thou must quench their thirst with Sacke, and what is got of thee is well got being obtained by rule, for he that lives by rule cannot erre.

Suppose thou either perceivest these things by others, or by thy owne experience, and so refuse this profered curtesie of theirs, purchased for their pleasures at thy owne cost. Then if at any time upon just occasion thou desirest it, thou must give them a Cup of *aurum potabile*, or else expect not the least favour or smallest courtesie, for no penny no Pater-noster, no gold no friendship.

If thou continually be offered injuries beare them patiently, or else thou shalt be laid in Irons for satisfaction.

If they perceive thou art like to continue and hast good meanes, thou shalt want no content that prison can yeeld, but every dram of content will cost thee a pound of silver.

When they heare thou art upon discharge, then will they bee very sorry and make all the best meanes that possibly they can to detaine thee, but if there be no remedy but thou must needs depart, then what with their three halfe pence a pound for Action money, and three in the pound for Execution, they will make such a large bill which will be more unconscionable then a Taylors, for hee will abate of the *Summa totalis*, but in this heere is nothing to bee abated, all their speech is *legem pone*, or else with their ill custome they will detaine thee, for thy denyall is an execution without triall by law, for notwithstanding that amongst just men, *malus usus abolendus est*, heere *conservandus et preservandus*, and so the entrance into prison, the continuance in prison, and the discharge out of Prison, will be nothing but racking the heartstrings of poore prisoners, and exhausting the substance of the distressed, whatsoever their wants be, holding it for a maxime, that *Summa injuria est summum jus*.

Of mercilesse Jaylors

A VOYCE lowd as thunder had need to roare and to awaken them. One Venny more, and if that hit, so, if not (but if their hearts are not to bee peirced,) I will lay down the Bucklers, and suffer them to take them up, yet fall back, fall edge, thus traverse wee our ground.

I love to see a Mother hugge her Infant, or a Father stroake his Sonne on the head, these are bonds in nature so strangely and strongly sealed, that to infringe them violates the very lawes of heaven : but when I see man exercise wilful tiranny upon man it is as if the Stars should in envy burne

one another to extinguish one anothers light, and
so confound that Spheare in malicious darkenes.

Barbarous cruelty is a Belluine[1] quality: Tygers,
Panthers, Beares, and Bandogs have it by naturall
inclination, it is no shame for them, it is in them
a baseness if they degenerate to mildnesse, and
loose their courages: they have mouths, jawes,
teeth, pawes and limbes, proportionable to their
savage disposition.

But Man is borne weake, gentle, unapt to do
hurt, unable to offer violence, and to fall from that
goodnes is to fall with the Angells, how much then
doe they derogate from their noble Creation, who
turne the sharpeness of their nailes which God
armes them with for their own beauty and defence,
to draw blood upon the bosomes of Christians
made like themselves? Such are mercilesse in-
exorable Jaylors, (I exempt those tender hearted
ones, which I never found other) but most certaine
such may bee found within a small compasse, who
use and exercise all cruelty.

Cruelty becomes them worst of all men: a
Prisoner is a poore weather-beaten Bird, who
having lost the Shoare, is driven by tempest to
hang upon the sailes and tacklings of a prison:
the Jaylor is the Saylor, and if hee beate that Bird
off to sinke her in the Seas, when by climbing up
to the Maine top, or perhaps by lifting up his hand,
hee may take it and lend it heat from his warme
bosome, it is an argument that his heart is made
of the same rocks, that lie in wait to destroy ships
in the Ocean.

Pitty is a Godlike property, but hardnes of

[1] brutal.

heart, selfe-willd tyranny, currish-dealing, and imperious domineering over men dejected, argue base, ignoble, cowardly, and divellish dispositions.

It is a *Maxime* in the Schoole of valour, that no Coward can be an honest man; what then are flint-breasted Jaylors, who dare not strike but when they see men lye fettered at their feet: So dead Lions may bee bitten and torne in pieces by Curres, which before durst not quetch[2] for terror of their pawes; so that hee who descends to that poverty of minde, as to fat himselfe by other mens misery, can no longer write Man, but *Misanthropos*, Man-hater, or rather *Anthropophagus*, Man-eater.

If remorselesse Keepers of Prisons, (for drawing now mine Arrow, beare witnes you who give ayme, that I shoot at none) or if marble-hearted Jaylors were so haplesse happy as to bee mistaken, and bee made Kings, they would instead of Iron to their grates have barres made of mens ribbes, Death should stand at doore for Porter, and the Divell every night come gingling of Keyes, and rapping at doors to lock men up.

The ten-penny and nine-penny Ordinaries should never bee more in the Fleet, Gate-house, or the two infernal Compters, for Hunger would lay the cloth, and Famine should play the leane fac'd Servingman to take away the trenchers.

Neroes cruelty in respect of these would be counted the peaceable Raigne of *Augustus Cesar*, the persecutions of the Romane Emperours upon the Primitive Christians should be painted Tragedies to reall Massacres, compared to the inhuman bloodthirsty exercises which these Tyrants would

[2] stir

put prisoners to, if they durst doe, what they have minde to doe.

Ob. It may happily bee thought that I am too bitter, and write untruths out of a malicious pen.

Res. Let the world bee judge: for when I see or heare that many noble brave and generous spirits, borne to great fortunes, well descended, of courages not to bee baffled, but by the arme of base fortune, and the inresistable violence of Lawes fighting against them for debts: when I say, I see or heare that such Gentlemen, upon one afternoones going abroad, might free themselves from bondage, and offer to goe pinyoned, peradventure with leashes of Keepers, and giving besides proffered security of worthy friends, oaths, faiths, honors and reputations of Gentlemen to come back safe, when an inflexible Jaylor can with a word let them goe, yet spitefully stops them: Oh misery! what shall I speake of this, on whom complaine?

Are there no such Keepers of Prisons in this Kingdome, then I doe none wrong.

ROBERT BURTON (1557–1640)

The Anatomy of Melancholy, What it is. With all the
Kindes, Causes, Symptomes, Prognostickes, and
severall Cures of it. . . . By Democritus Junior.
. . . At Oxford, . . . 1621. 4to. [P6ᵛ-7, P8]

The structure of the book is indicated in the title.
It is under the third section more especially, *Symptoms
or Signs*, that many characters, of a free type, can be found,
just as in 1616 they were to be found in Thomas Adams's
Diseases of the Soule, for Burton's great discourse is built,
ultimately, on the same skeleton plan as Adams's sermon.

Fearful Men

MOST part *they are afraid, they are bewitched,
possessed, or poisoned by their enemies,* and sometimes they suspect their nearest friends: *he thinks
something, speakes or talkes within him, or to him,
and he belcheth of the poison.* . . . Some are
afraid that they shall have every fearefull disease
they see others have, heare of, or read. If they
see one possessed, bewitch't, or an Epileptick
Paroxisme, a man shaking with the palsy, or giddy-
headed, reeling, or standing in a dangerous place
&c. for many dayes after it runs in their mindes,
they are afraid they shal be so too, they are in the
like danger, as *Perkins cap.* 12. *sec.* 2 well observes
in his Cases of conscience. And many times by
Imagination they produce it. They cannot endure
to see any terrible object, as a Monster, a man
executed, a carcase, or heare the divell named, or
any Tragicall relation, but they quake for feare,
hecates somniare sibi videntur, Lucian, they dreame
of hobgoblins, and cannot get it out of their mindes
a long time after: they applie all they see, heare,

read, to themselves; . . . they complaine of toyes
and feare without a cause. As really tormented
and perplexed for toyes and trifles, (such things as
they will after laugh at themselves) as if they were
most materiall and essentiall matters indeed worthy
to bee feared, and will not be satisfied. Pacifie
them with one, they are instantly troubled with
some other feare, they are alwayes afraid of something or other, which they foolishly imagine or
conceive to themselves, [which never peradventure
was, never can be, never likely will be;] [1] troubled
in mind upon every small occasion, still complaining, grieving, vexing, suspecting, discontent, and
cannot be freed so long as melancholy endureth: . . .

Suspition and *Jelousie*, are generall symptomes,
they are commonly distrustfull, apt to mistake,
facilè Irascibiles, testy, pettish, peevish, and ready
to snarle upon every smal occasion, *cum amicis-
simis*, and without a cause. If two talke together
and whisper, or jest, or tell a tale in generall, he
thinkes presently they meane him, applies all to
himselfe, *de se putat omnia dici*. Or if they talke
with him, hee is ready to misconster every word
they speake, and interpret it to the worst he cannot
endure any man to looke steedily on him, speak to
him almost, or laugh, jest, or be familiar, or hem,
or point, or cough, spit, or make a noyse sometimes, &c. He thinks they laugh or point at him,
or doe it in disgrace of him, circumvent him, contemne him, he is pale, red, and sweats for feare
and anger least some body should observe him.
Hee workes upon it, and long after this false conceit of an abuse troubles him.

[1] 6th edition, 1651-2.

DOCTOR ANDREWS (fl.? 1629)

A Character upon a Monsieur.   Harl. Ms. 4955. fol. 87*b*.

This amusing and unusual sketch of a Frenchman occurs at the end of a collection of poems by 'Dr. Andrewes,' whose name seems to have been Francis (v. fol. 87). No more is known of him, nor do his poems appear to have been printed. The piece preceding this character is dated 'London Aug. 14. 1629.'

A Character upon a Monsieur

I WOULD not flatter, neither would I erre,
In giveing Monsieur a true character.
Monsieur I meane a Gentle-man of France.
Whom Birth and Breeding justly doe advance.
   A comely person and a bigot mind,
Which a brave Genius doth togeather bind.
An Eye to glance, a Head made to dispute,
A foote to Dance, a Hand to execute.
A Voice to sing, a Garbe to please at Court,
An Hart to batter, or defend a Forte.
A countenance Undaunted, and a Spright,
Fitt for all motions, full of all delight.
To fight at Feild, to revell in the Hall,
To dance at Balle, or els to play at Ball.
Disgrace him not, for he will in a spirt.
Challendge the feild, & fight it in his shirt.
At Pen a Mercury, as a Mars at duell.
At song Apollo, and at Venus fewell.
At Horsemanship a Centaure, hee sitts on,
As if the Horse and Hee, were all but one.
They move togeather justly every Time,
Hee part of the horse, or els the Horse of him.

The Irish quicknes, and the Germaine strength.
The English Valour, and the Polish length.
The Naples temper, and Italian neatnesse,
The Belgique freenes, and the Spanish greatnesse.
All Nations els haue somewhat of the Hen,
Onely the French is Chantic-cleere of Men.

These all are Noble parts, taken asunder
But meeting all in one, they make a wonder.

THOMAS ADAMS (1612–53)

Diseases of the Soule : A Discourse Divine, Morall, and
   Physicall. ... London, ... 1616. 4to.

Mystical Bedlam, or The World of Mad-Men. ...
   London ... 1615. 4to.

The Workes of Tho: Adams. ... London, ... 1629.
   fol.

The Works ... Edinburgh : ... 1861. 8vo.

   20 characters.

The Diseases of the Soule are divided, each into four
sections, The Disease, Cause, Signs and Symptomes,
Cure. The characters are found under 'Signes and
Symptomes,' whence are taken the first five pieces in the
selection, the sixth from *Mystical Bedlam.*

'Our bookes may come to bee seene, where our selves
shall never be heard,' so Adams writes in one of his
prefaces. But in these prefaces, from which we learn
the friendly terms on which he stood with his chief
contemporaries in church and state, and in his books,
where an original-minded and humorous personality
discloses itself, he lives for us more truly than do many
we see and hear. It is then unimportant that except
that he was preacher under St. Paul's and occasionally
at Whitehall during the years 1618-23, we know little
else about him, for, as we turn the pages of his enormous
Workes we feel we know the man himself.

The Braine-sicke Novelist.[1]   *One drunke with opinion*

1. Lowd speech hee loves not, except from his
own lippes. All noise is tedious to him, but his
owne : and that is most tedious to the companie.
Hee loves to heare himselfe talke out of measure.

[1] innovator.

He wonders, that the senses of all his hearers doe not get up into their eares, to watch and catch his mysteries with attention and silence; when as yet himselfe is more *Non-resident* from his theme, then a discontinuer is from his charge.

2. The cleere light he cannot endure, for his braine is too light already. He presumes, that his head containes more knowledge then tenne Bishops; and wonders that the Church was so over-seene, as to forget him, when offices were dis-posing, or places a dealing; and because he can get none, railes at all for Antichristian. He is the only wise man, if he might teach all men to judge him, as he judgeth himselfe : and no starre should shine in our Orbe, without borrowing some of his light. Hee offers to reforme that man, that would informe him; and presumes of so much light, that if him-selfe were set, our world would be left without a Sunne.

3. Wine he hates, specially when it is poured into his wounds : (as the *Fathers* interpret the *Samaritans wine* to the *wounded man*, to clense and purge him.) Reproofe and he are utter enemies; no man is good enough to chide him : wholesome counsell, which is indeed Wine to a weake soule, he accounts Vineger; nothing so pleaseth him as his owne Lees. *Opinion* hath brewed him ill, and he is like water scared out of the wits.

4. He must not bee moved, nor removed from what hee holdes : his will is like the Persian law, unalterable. You may move him to choler, not to knowledge : his braine is turned, like a Bell rung too deepe, and cannot be fetcht backe againe. His

owne affectation is his pully, that can move him; no engine else stirres him. A man may like him at first, as one that never heard musicke doth the Tinkers note on his kettle; but after a while they are both alike tedious. There is no helpe for his auditour, by any excuses to shift him off; if he have not the patience to endure an impertinent discourse, hee must venter the censure of his manners, and run away. His discourse is so full of parentheses, as if he were troubled with the rhume, and could not spette. He is ever tying hard knots, and untying them, as if no body had hired him, and therefore he must finde himselfe worke. If hee light on the sacred Writ, he conceitedly allegorizes on the plainest subject, and makes the Scripture no more like it selfe, then *Michols* image in the bed upon a pillow of Goates haire, was like *David*. He carries bread at his backe and feedes upon stones. Like a full fedde Dogge, he leaves the soft meate to lye gnawing vpon bones : that wee may say of him, this man hath a strong wit, as wee say, that dogge hath good teeth.

The Fearful Man

HE conceives what is good to be done, but fancies difficulties and dangers, like to knots in a bul-rush, or rubbes in a smooth way. Hee would bowle well at the marke of Integrity, if he durst venture it. Hee hath no journey to goe, but either there are bugges, or he imagines them. Had he a pardon for his brother (being in danger of death) and a Hare should crosse him in the way, he would no further, though his brother hang'd for it. He owes God some good will, but he dares not shew it: when a poore plaintiffe cals him for a witnesse, hee dares not reveale the truth, lest he offend the great adversary. He is a new *Nicodemus*, and would steale to Heaven, if no body might see him. He makes a good motion bad by his fearefulnesse and doubting; and he cals his *trembling* by the name of *conscience*. He is like that Collier, that passing thorow *Smithfield*, and seeing some on the one side hanging, he demaunds the cause; answere was made, for denying the Supremacie to King *Henry:* on the other side some burning, he askes the cause; answered, for denying the reall presence in the Sacrament: some, quoth he, hang'd for Papistry, and some burn'd for Protestancie? then hoyte on a Gods name: chill bee ne're nother. His Religion is primarily his Princes, subordinately his Land-lords. Neither deliberates he more to take a new religion, to rise by it; then he feares to keepe his old, lest he fall by it. All his care is for a *ne noceat*. Hee is a busie inquirer of all Parliament acts, and quakes as they are read, lest hee be found guilty. He is sicke, and afraid to dye, yet holds the potion in a trembling hand, and quakes to drinke his recovery. His thoughts are an ill ballance, and will never be equally poysed. Hee is a light vessell, and every great mans puffe is ready to overturne him. Whiles *Christ* stands on the battlements of heaven, and beckens him thither by his word, his heart answeres, I would faine be there, but that some troubles stand in my way. He would ill with *Peter* walke to him on the pavement of the Sea, or thrust out his hand with *Moses*, to take up a crawling Serpent, or hazard the losse of himselfe, to find his *Saviour*. His minde is ever in suspicion, in suspension, and dares not give a confident determination either way.

Resolution, and his hart are utter enemies, and all his Philosophy is to be a *Scepticke.* . . . A Souldier, a Husband-man, and a Marchant should be ventrous. He would be Gods Husband-man, and sow the seeds of obedience, but for *observing the wind & weather* of great mens frownes. He would be Gods factor, but that he feares to lose by his *Talent*, and therefore *buries it.* He would be Gods souldier, but that the *world* and the *divell* are two such shrewd and sore enemies. He once began to prosecute a deed of charitie, and because the event crossed him, he makes it a rule to do no more good by. . . .

Hee knowes nothing by himselfe but evill, and according to that rule measures others. Hee would faine bee an Vsurer, but that hee dares not trust the Law with waxe and paper. He sweares damnably to the truth of that he affirms; as fearing otherwise not to be beleeved, because without that othing it, he will credit none himself. The bastardy of swearing lays on him the true fatherhood. Hee will trust neither man nor God without a pawne : nor so much as his Taylor with the stuffe to make his clothes : he must be a Broker, or no neighbour. He hath no faith; for he beleeves nothing, but what he knowes; and knowledge nullifies beleefe. If others laugh, he imagines himselfe their ridiculous object : if there bee any whispering, *conscius ipse sibi*, *&c.* it must be of him without question. If he goes to law, he is the advocates sprite, and haunts him worse then his owne *malus genius.* Hee is his owne Cater, his owne Receiver, his owne Secretary; and takes such paines, as if necessitie forced him, because all servants hee thinks theeves. Hee dares not trust his mony above ground for feare of men; nor under ground for feare of rust. When he throwes his censures at actions, his lucke is still to goe out: and so whiles he playeth with other mens credits, he cousins himselfe of his owne. His opinion lights upon the worst sense still; as the Flye, that passeth the sound parts to fasten on a scab; or a Dorre, that ends his flight in a dunghil. Without a *Subpoena* these timorous cowherds dare not to London, for feare lest the citie aire should conspire to poison them: where they are ever crying, *Lord, have mercie on us*, when as *Lord, have mercie on us* is the special thing they feared. The ringing of bels tunes their hearts into melancholy; and the very sight of a corps is almost enough to turne them into corpses. On the Thames they dare not come, because they have heard some there drowned: nor neere the Parliament-house, because it was once in danger of blowing vp. Home this Embleme of diffidence comes, and there lives with distrust of others, and dies in distrust of himselfe; onely now finding death a certaine thing to trust to.

The Ambitious Man

THE *cause* of *Ambition* is a strong opinion of honour; how well he could become a high place, or a high place him. It is a proud covetousnesse, a glorious and Court-madnes. The head of his reason caught a bruise on the right side, his understanding; and ever since he followes affection, as his principall guide. Hee professeth a new quality,

called the art of climbing: wherin he teacheth
others by patterne, not so much to aspire, as to
breake their neckes. No staire pleaseth him, if
there be a higher; and yet ascended to the top,
he complaines of lownesse. He is not so soone layd
in his bed of honour, but hee dreames of a higher
preferment, and would not sit on a seate, long
enough to make it warme. His advancement gives
him a fresh provocation; and he now treades on
that with a disdainefull foote, which ere-while hee
would have kissed to obtaine. Hee climbes falling
towers, and the hope to scale them, swallowes all
feare of toppling downe. Hee is himselfe an Intelligencer to greatnes, yet not without under-officers
of the same ranke. You shall see him narrow-eyed
with watching, affable and open-brested like
Absolon, full of insinuation so long as he is at
the staire-foot: but when authoritie hath once
spoken kindly to him, with *Friend, sit up higher*,
he lookes rougher then *Hercules;* so bigge, as if
the river of his bloud would not bee banked within
his veines. His tongue is *flabellum Diaboli*, and
flagellum justi: bent to scourge some, flatter
others, infect, infest all. *Agrippina*, *Neros* mother,
being told by an Astrologer, that her sonne should
be Emperour, but to her sorrow: answered, *Let
my sorrow be what it will, so my sonne may get
the Empire*. He hath high desires, low deserts.
As *Tully* for his *Pindinessus*, he spends much
money about a little preferment; and with greater
cost then the captain bought his Burges-ship, hee
purchaseth incorporeall fame; which passeth away
as swift, as time doth swallow motion; & whose
weight is nothing but in her name, wheras a lower

place well managed, leaves behinde it a deathlesse memory. Like a great winde, he blowes downe all friends that stand in his way to rising. Policy is his post-horse, and he rides all upon the spurre, till he come to *None-such*.[1] His greatest plague is a Rivall.

> *Nec quemquam jam ferre potest Cæsarve*
> *   priorem,*
> *Pompeisve parem.*
> *Tolluntur in altum, ut lapsu graviore ruant.*
> > Juven. Sat. 2.

He is a childe in his gaudy desires, and great Titles are his rattles, which still his crying, til he see a new toy. He kisses his wits, as a Courtier his hand, when any wished fortune salutes him: and it tickles him, that he hath stolne to promotion without Gods knowledge: *Ambitio ambientium crux.* Ambition is the racke, whereon hee tortureth himselfe. The court is the sea, wherein he desires to fish: but the net of his wit and hope breakes, and there he drownes himselfe. An old courtier being asked what he did at Court, answered, *I doe nothing, but undoe my selfe.*

A Vaine-glorious Man

You shall easily know a *vaine-glorious* man: his owne commendation rumbles within him, till he hath bulked it out; & the ayre of it is unsavory. In the field, he is touching heaven with a launce; in the street, his eye is still cast over his shoulder. He stands up so pertly, that you may know he is not laden with fruite. If you would drinke of his

[1] *Nonsuch*, near Epsom. Obsolete.

wisedome, knocke by a sober question at the barrell, and you shall finde by the sound, his wits are
emptie. In al companies, like chaffe he will be
uppermost: hee is some surfet in natures stomake,
& cannot be kept down. A goodly Cipresse tree,
fertile onely of leaves. He drinks to none beneath
the salt; and it is his Grammar rule without exception, not to conferre with an inferiour in publike.
His impudence will over-rule his ignorance to talke
of learned principles; which come from him, like a
treble part in a base voyce, too bigge for it. Living
in some under-staire office, when he would visite
the countrey, he borrowes some Gallants cast sute
of his servant, and therein (Player-like) acts that
part among his besotted neighbours. When he
rides his masters great horse out of ken, hee vaunts
of him as his owne, and brags how much he cost
him. He feeds upon others curtesie, others meat:
and (whether more?) either fats him. At his Inne
he cals for chickens at spring, and such things as
cannot be had; whereat angry, he sups according
to his purse with a red Herring. Farre enough
from knowledge he talkes of his castle (which is
either in the aire, or inchanted) of his lands,
which are some pastures in the Fairy-ground, invisible, no where. He offers to· purchase Lord-
ships, but wants money for earnest. He makes
others praises as introductions to his own, which
must transcend; and cals for wine, that he may make
knowne his rare vessell of deale, at home: not forgetting to you, that a Dutch Marchant sent it him,
for some extraordinary desert. He is a wonder
every where; among fooles, for his bravery, among
wisemen for his folly. He loves an *Herald* for a

new *Coate*, and hires him to lye upon his Pedigree. All Nobility, that is ancient, is of his allyance; and the Great man is but of the first head, that doth not call him, *Cousin*. When his beames are weakest, like the rising and setting Sunne, hee makes the longest shadowes: whereas bright knowledge, like the Sunne at highest, makes none at all; though then most resultance of heat, and reflection of light. He takes great paines to make himselfe derisory; yet (without suspecting it) both his speech and silence cries, Behold mee. He discommends earned worth with a shrugge, and lispes his enforced appro-bation. Hee loves humility in all men, but himselfe, as if hee did wish well to all soules but his owne.

There is no matter of consequence, that Policy begets, but he will be Gossip to, and give it a name; and knowes the intention of all projects, before they be full hatched. Hee hath somewhat in him, which would bee better for himselfe, and all men, if hee could keepe it in. In his hall, you shall see an old rusty sword hung up, which he swears killed *Glendower* in the hands of his Grand-sire. He fathers upon himselfe some villanies, because they are in fashion; and so vilifies his credit, to advance it. If a newe famous *Cour-teghian* be mentioned, he deeply knowes her; whom indeed he never saw. He will be ignorant of nothing, though it be a shame to know it. His barrell hath a continuall spigot, but no tunnell; and like an unthrift, he spends more then he gets: His speech of himselfe is ever historicall, histrionicall. He is indeed admirations creature, and a circum-stantiall Mountebanke.

The Curious Man

IF this *Itching* curiositie take him in the *Cephalica* veine, and possesse the understanding part, he mootes more questions in an houre, then the seven *Wise men* could resolve in seven yeeres. There is a kinde of downe or curdle on his wit, which is like a Gentlewomans traine, more then needes. Hee would sing well, but that he is so full of Crotchets. His questions are like a plume of feathers, which fooles wil give any thing for, wise-men nothing. He hath a greater desire to know where Hell is, then to scape it: to know what God did before he made the world, then what he will do with him when it is ended. For want of correcting the garden of his inventions, the weedes choke the herbes; and he suffers the skimme of his braine to boile into the broth. He is a dangerous Prognosticator, and propounds desperate riddles; which he gathers from the conjunction of Planets, *Saturne* and *Jupiter;* from doubtfull Oracles out of the hollow vaults and predictions of *Merlin.* He dreames of a cruell Dragon, whose head must bee in England, and taile in Ireland; of a headlesse crosse, of a popish curse. And *Our Lord lights in our Ladies lappe, and therefore England must have a clappe.* But they have broken day with their Creditors, and the Planets have proved honester, then their reports gave them. Thus as *Bion* said of *Astronomers,* he sees not the fishes swimming by him in the water, yet sees perfectly those shining in the *Zodiacke.* Thus if the *Itch* hold him in the theoricall part. If in the practicall;

His actions are polypragmaticall,[1] his feete peri-pateticall.[2] *Erasmus* pictures him to the life. *He knows what every Marchant got in his voyage, what plots are at Rome, what stratagems with the Turke, &c. Hee knowes strangers troubles, not the tumul-tuous fightings in his owne bosome, &c.* His neigh-bours estate he knowes to a penny; and wherein he failes, he supplyes by intelligence from their flattered servants: he would serve well for an Informer to the Subsidie-book. He delayes every passenger with inquiry of newes; and because the countrey cannot satiate him, hee travels every terme to Lon-don for it: whence returning without his full lode, himself makes it up by the way. He buyes letters from the great citie with Capons; which he weares out in three dayes, with perpetuall opening them to his companions. If he heares but a word of some State-act, he professeth to know it & the intention, as if he had bene of the Counsell. He heares a lie in private, and hastes to publish it; so one knave guls him, hee innumerable fooles, with the strange *Fish* at *Yarmouth*, or the *Serpent in Sussex*. Hee can keepe no secret in, without the hazzard of his button. He loves no man a moment longer, then either he will tell him, or hears of him newes. If the spirit of his tong be once raised, all the com-pany cannot conjure it downe. He teaches his neighbor to worke unsent for, and tels him of some dangers without thankes. He comments upon every action, and answers a question ere it be halfe propounded. *Alcibiades* having purchasd a dogge at an unreasonable price, cut off his tayle, and let him run about *Athens;* whiles every man wondred

---

[1] meddlesome.   [2] have a strutting walk.

at his intent, he answered, that his intent was their wonder, for he did it onely to be talk'd of. The same Author reports the like of a gawish[1] Traveller that came to *Sparta*, who standing in the presence of *Lacon* a long time upon one leg, that he might be observed & admired, cryed at the last: *Oh Lacon, thou canst not stand so long upon one legge.* True, said *Lacon, but everie Goose can.*

His state, belike, is too little to finde him worke; hence he busieth himselfe in other mens common wealths: as if he were Towne-taster; hee scalds his lips in every neighbours pottage. If this *Itch* proceed from some inflammation, his bleach is the breaking out of contention. Then he hath *humorem in cerebro, in corde tumorem, rumorem in lingua.* His braine is full of humour, his heart of tumour, his toung of rumour. He spits fire at every word, and doth what hee can to set the whole world in combustion. He whispers in his neighbours eare how such a man slandred him: and returnes to the accused party (with like secrecy) the others invective. He is hated of all, as being indeed a friend to none, but Lawyers and the Divell.

The Busie-body

ALL will confesse a *mad-man:* for hee friskes up and downe, like a nettled horse, & wil stand on no ground. He hath a charge of his owne properly distinguished: yet hee must needs trouble his head, with alien and unnecessary affayres. Hee admits all mens businesses into his brayne, but his owne: and comes not home for his owne, till he hath set all his neighbors ploughes a-going. Hee hurries

[1] gaping.

up and downe, like *Jehu* the *sonne* of *Nimshi* in his Chariot, or as a Gallant in his new Caroch, driving as if he were *mad*.

He loves not to sleepe in his owne dores; and hinders the common-wealth with frivolous questions. He is an universal solicitor for every mans sute; and would talke a *Lawyer* himselfe *madde*. There is not a Boate, wherein hee hath not an Oare; nor a Wheele, wherein hee will not challenge a Spoake. He lives a perpetuall affliction to himselfe and others; and dies without pitty; save that they say, it is pitty hee died no sooner. He is his neighbours *malus genius*, and a plague to melancholy. Hee is the common supervisor to all the wils made in his parrish: and when hee may not be a counseller, hee will bee an intelligencer. If you let him not in to interrupt, hee will stand without to evesdroppe. He is a very *madman;* for he takes great paines without thankes, without recompence, of God, or man, or his owne conscience. Hee is luxurious of businesse, that concernes him not: Lay hands on him, shackle him; there are some lesse *mad* in *Bedlam*. I will be rid of him with this Distich.

Hee cleaves to those he meddles with, like pitch:
Hee's quicke silver, good onely for mens itch.

THOMAS FULLER (1608-1661)

The Holy State. By Thomas Fuller, ... Cambridge :
... 1642. fol.

[section title]. The Profane State. [then as above].

The Holy State and the Profane State.... London,
Chiswick. 1840.

48 characters.

Logic might insist that Fuller's essays are hardly
characters : and it is true that only if the ' maximes '
were collected together could a formal character emerge.
But it is tempting, in spite of logic, which has, after all,
but a small place in literature, to let oneself be swayed
by such connexion with the character-form as there is
in these delightful essays, and to print them here as they
were written, essays though they are.

The Controversiall Divine

HE is Truths Champion to defend her against
all adversaries, Atheists, Hereticks, Schismaticks,
and Erroneous persons whatsoever. His sufficiency
appears in Opposing, Answering, Moderating, and
Writing.

Maxime 1. *He engageth both his judgement,
and affections in opposing of falsehood.* Not like
countrey Fencers, who play onely to make sport,
but like Duellers indeed, at it for life and limbe;
chiefly if the question be of large prospect, and
great concernings, he is zealous in the quarrell. Yet
some, though their judgement weigh down on one
side, the beam of their affections stands so even,
they care not which part prevails.

2. *In opposing a truth, he dissembles himself
her foe, to be her better friend.* Wherefore he

counts himself the greatest conquerour when Truth hath taken him captive. With Joseph having sufficiently sifted the matter in a disguise, he discovereth himself, *I am Joseph your brother*, and then throws away his visard.

Dishonest they, who though the debt be satisfied will never give up the bond, but continue wrangling, when the objection is answered.

3. *He abstains from all foul and railing language.* What? make the Muses, yea the Graces scolds? Such purulent spittle argues exulcerated lungs. Why should there be so much railing about the body of Christ? when there was none about the body of Moses in the Act kept betwixt the devil and Michael the Archangel.

4. *He tyrannizeth not over a weak and undermatch'd Adversary;* but seeks rather to cover his weaknesse if he be a modest man. When a Professour pressed an Answerer (a better Christian then a Clerk) with an hard argument, *Reverende Professor* (said he) *ingenue confiteor me non posse respondere huic argumento.* To whom the Professour, *Recte respondes.*

5. *In answering he states the question, and expoundeth the terms thereof.* Otherwise the disputants shall end, where they ought to have begun, in differences about words, and be Barbarians each to other, speaking in a Language neither understand. If the Question also be of Historicall cognizanse, he shews the pedigree thereof, who first brew'd it, who first broch'd it, and sends the wandring Errour with a pasport home to the place of its birth.

6. *In taking away an objection he not onely puts*

by the thrust, but breaks the weapon. Some rather escape then defeat an argument, and though by such an evasion they may shut the mouth of the Opponent, yet may they open the difficulty wider in the hearts of the hearers. But our Answerer either fairly resolves the doubt; or else shews the falsenesse of the argument, by beggering the Opponent to maintain such a fruitfull generation of absurdities, as his argument hath begotten; or lastly returns and retorts it back upon him again. The first way unties the knot; the second cuts it asunder; the third whips the Opponent with the knot himself tyed. Sure 'tis more honour to be a clear Answerer, then a cunning Opposer, because the latter takes advantage of mans ignorance, which is ten times more then his knowledge.

7. *What his answers want in suddennesse they have in solidity.* Indeed the speedy answer adds lustre to the disputation, and honour to the disputant; yet he makes good payment, who though he cannot presently throw the money out of his pocket, yet will pay it, if but going home to unlock his chest. Some that are not for speedy may be for sounder performance. When Melanchthon at the disputation of Ratisbon was pressed with a shrewd argument by Ecchius, I will answer thee, said he, to morrow. Nay, said Ecchius, do it now or it's nothing worth. Yea, said Melanchthon, I seek the Truth, and not mine own Credit, and therefore it will be as good if I answer thee to morrow by Gods assistance.

8. *In moderating he sides with the Answerer, if the Answerer sides with the truth.* But if he be conceited, & opinioned of his own sufficiency, he lets

him swound before he gives him any hot water.
If a Paradox-monger, loving to hold strange yea
dangerous Opinions, he counts it charity to suffer
such a one to be beaten without mercy, that he may
be weaned from his wilfulnesse. For the main, he
is so a staff to the Answerer, that he makes him
stand on his own legs.

9. *In writing, his Latine is pure, so farre as the
subject will allow.* For those who are to climb the
Alpes are not to expect a smooth and even way.
True it is that Schoolmen, perceiving that fallacy
had too much covert under the nap of flourishing
Language, used thredbare Latine on purpose, and
cared not to trespasse on Grammar, and tread down
the fences thereof to avoid the circuit of words, and
to go the nearest way to expresse their conceits.
But our Divine though he useth barbarous School-
terms, which like standers are fixt to the controversie, yet in his moveable Latine, passages, and
digressions his style is pure and elegant.

10. *He affects clearnesse and plainnesse in all
his writings.* Some mens heads are like the world
before God said unto it, *Fiat lux.* These dark-
lanterns may shine to themselves, and understand
their own conceits, but no body else can have light
from them. Thus Matthias Farinator Professour
at Vienna, assisted with some other learned men,
as the Times then went, was thirty years making
a book of applying Plato's, Aristotle's, and Galen's
rules in Philosophy, to Christ and his Prophets,
and 'tis call'd *Lumen animæ; quo tamen nihil est
caliginosius, labore magno, sed ridiculo, & inani.*
But this obscurity is worst when affected, when
they do as Persius, of whom one saith, *Legi voluit*

quæ scripsit, intelligi noluit quæ legerentur. Some affect this darknesse, that they may be accounted profound, whereas one is not bound to believe that all the water is deep that is muddy.

11. *He is not curious in searching matters of no moment.* Captain Martin Frobisher fetcht from the farthest northern Countries a ships lading of minerall stones (as he thought) which afterwards were cast out to mend the high wayes. Thus are they served, and misse their hopes, who long seeking to extract hidden mysteries out of nice questions, leave them off, as uselesse at last. Antoninus Pius, for his desire to search to the least differences, was called *Cumini sector*, the Carver of cumine seed. One need not be so accurate: for as soon shall one scowr the spots out of the moon, as all ignorance out of man. When Eunomius the Heretick vaunted that he knew God and his divinity, S. Basil gravells him in 21 questions about the body of an ant or pismire: so dark is mans understanding. I wonder therefore at the boldnesse of some, who as if they were Lord Marshalls of the Angels place them in ranks and files. Let us not believe them here, but rather go to heaven to confute them.

12. *He neither multiplies needlesse, nor compounds necessary Controversies.* Sure they light on a labour in vain, who seek to make a bridge of reconciliation over the μέγα χάσμα betwixt Papists and Protestants; for though we go 99 steps, they (I mean their Church) will not come one to give us a meeting. And as for the offers of Clara's and private men (besides that they seem to be more of the nature of baits then gifts) they may make

large profers, without any Commission to treat, and so the Romish Church not bound to pay their promises. In Merionethshire in Wales there are high mountains, whose hanging tops come so close together that shepherds on the tops of severall hills may audibly talk together, yet will it be a dayes journey for their bodies to meet, so vast is the hollownesse of the vallies betwixt them. Thus upon sound search shall we find a grand distance and remotenesse betwixt Popish and Protestant tenents to reconcile them, which at the first view may seem near, and tending to an accomodation.

13. *He is resolute and stable in fundamentall points of Religion.* These are his fixed poles, and axle-tree about which he moves, whilest they stand unmovable. Some sail so long on the Sea of controversies, toss'd up and down, to and fro, *Pro* and *Con*, that the very ground to them seems to move, and their judgements grow scepticall and unstable in the most settled points of Divinity. When he cometh to Preach, especially if to a plain Auditory, with the Paracelsians he extracts an oyl out of the driest and hardest bodies, and knowing that knotty timber is unfit to build with, he edifies people with easie and profitable matter.

The Good Merchant

Is one who by his trading claspeth the iland to the continent, and one countrey to another. An excellent gardiner, who makes England bear wine, and oyl, and spices; yea herein goes beyond Nature in causing that *Omnis fert omnia tellus.* He wrongs neither himself nor the Commonwealth, nor private chapmen which buy commodities of him.

As for his behaviour towards the Commonwealth, it farre surpasses my skill to give any Rules thereof; onely this I know, that to export things of necessity, and to bring in forrein needlesse toyes, makes a rich Merchant, and a poore Kingdome: for the State loseth her radicall moysture, and gets little better then sweat in exchange, except the necessaries which are exported be exceeding plentifull, which then though necessary in their own nature become superfluous through their abundance. We will content our selves to give some generall advertisements concerning his behaviour towards his chapmen, whom he useth well in the quantity, quality, and price of the commodities he sells them.

Maxime 1. *He wrongs not the buyer in Number, Weight, or Measure*. These are the Landmarks of all trading, which must not be removed: for such cosenage were worse then open felony. First, because they rob a man of his purse, and never bid him stand. Secondly, because highway-thieves defie, but these pretend justice. Thirdly, as much as lies in their power, they endeavour to make God accessary to their cosenage, deceiving by pretending his weights. For God is the principall clark of the market, *All the weights of the bag are his work*.

2. *He never warrants any ware for good but what is so indeed*. Otherwise he is a thief, and may be a murtherer, if selling such things as are apply'd inwardly. Besides, in such a case he counts himself guilty if he selleth such wares as are bad, though without his knowledge, if avouching them for good; because he may, professeth, & is bound

to be Master in his own mystery, and therefore in conscience must recompense the buyers losse, except he gives him an Item to buy it at his own adventure.

3. *He either tells the faults in his ware, or abates proportionably in the price he demands:* for then the low value shews the viciousnesse of it. Yet commonly when Merchants depart with their commodities, we heare (as in funerall orations) all the virtues but none of the faults thereof.

4. *He never demands out of distance of the price he intends to take:* If not alwayes within the touch, yet within the reach of what he means to sell for. Now we must know there be foure severall prices of vendible things. First, the Price of the market, which ebbes and flows according to the plenty or scarcity of coyn, commodities, and chapmen. Secondly, the Price of friendship, which perchance is more giving then selling, and therefore not so proper at this time. Thirdly the Price of fancie, as twenty pounds or more for a dog or hauk, when no such inherent worth can naturally be in them, but by the buyers and sellers fancie reflecting on them. Yet I believe the money may be lawfully taken. First, because the seller sometimes on those terms is as loth to forgo it, as the buyer is willing to have it. And I know no standard herein whereby mens affections may be measured. Secondly, it being a matter of pleasure, and men able and willing, let them pay for it, *volenti non fit injuria.* Lastly, there is the Price of cosenage, which our Merchant from his heart detests and abhorres.

5. *He makes not advantage of his chapmans*

ignorance chiefly if referring himself to his honesty: where the sellers conscience is all the buyers skill, who makes him both seller and judge, so that he doth not so much ask as order what he must pay. When one told old Bishop Latimer that the Cutler had cosened him, in making him pay two-pence for a knife not (in those dayes) worth a peny; *No,* quoth Latimer, *he cosen'd not me but his own conscience.* On the other side S. Augustine tells us of a seller, who out of ignorance asked for a book farre lesse then it was worth, and the buyer (conceive himself to be the man if you please) of his own accord gave him the full value thereof.

6. *He makes not the buyer pay the shot for his prodigality;* as when the Merchant through his own ignorance or ill husbandry hath bought dear, he will not bring in his unnecessary expences on the buyers score: and in such a case he is bound to sell cheaper then he bought.

7. *Selling by retail he may justifie the taking of greater gain:* because of his care, pains, and cost of fetching those wares from the fountain, and in parcelling and dividing them. Yet because retailers trade commonly with those who have least skill what they buy, and commonly sell to the poorer sort of people, they must be carefull not to grate on their necessity.

But how long shall I be retailing our rules to this Merchant? It would employ a Casuist an apprenticeship of years: take our Saviours whole-sale rule, *Whatsoever ye would have men do unto you, do you unto them; for this is the Law, and the Prophets.*

The good Sea-Captain

CONCEIVE him now in a Man of warre, with his letters of mart, well arm'd victuall'd and appointed, and see how he acquits himself.

Maxime 1. *The more power he hath, the more carefull he is not to abuse it.* Indeed a Sea-captain is a King in the Iland of a ship, supreme Judge, above appeal, in causes civill and criminall, and is seldome brought to an account in Courts of Justice on land, for injuries done to his own men at sea.

2. *He is carefull in observing of the Lords day.* He hath a watch in his heart though no bells in a steeple to proclaim that day by ringing to prayers. Sr Francis Drake in three years sailing about the world lost one whole day, which was scarce considerable in so long time. 'Tis to be feared some Captains at sea lose a day every week, one in seven, neglecting the Sabbath.

3. *He is as pious and thankfull when a tempest is past, as devout when 'tis present:* not clamorous to receive mercies, and tongue-tied to return thanks. Many mariners are calm in a storm, and storm in a calm, blustring with oathes. In a tempest it comes to their turn to be religious, whose piety is but a fit of the wind, and when that's allayed, their devotion is ended.

4. *Escaping many dangers makes him not presumptuous to run into them.* Not like those Seamen who (as if their hearts were made of those rocks they have often sayled by) are so alwayes in death they never think of it. These in their navigations observe that it is farre hotter under the

Tropicks in the coming to the Line, then under the Line it self, & in like manner they conceive that the fear & phancy in preparing for death is more terrible then death it self, which makes them by degrees desperately to contemne it.

5. *In taking a prize he most prizeth the mens lives whom he takes;* though some of them may chance to be Negroes or Savages. 'Tis the custome of some to cast them overbord, and there's an end of them: for the dumbe fishes will tell no tales. But the murder is not so soon drown'd as the men. What, is a brother by the half bloud no kinne? a Savage hath God to his father by creation, though not the Church to his mother, and God will revenge his innocent bloud. But our Captain counts the image of God neverthelesse his image cut in ebony as if done in ivory, and in the blackest Moores he sees the representation of the King of heaven.

6. *In dividing the gains he wrongs none who took pains to get them.* Not shifting off his poore mariners with nothing, or giving them onely the garbage of the prize, and keeping all the flesh to himself. In time of peace he quietly returns home, and turns not to the trade of Pirates, who are the worst sea-vermine, and the devils water-rats.

7. *His voyages are not onely for profit, but some for honour and knowledge;* to make discoveries of new countreys, imitating the worthy Peter Columbus. Before his time the world was cut off at the middle; Hercules Pillars (which indeed are the navell) being made the feet, and utmost bounds of the continent, till his successefull industry inlarged it.

Primus ab infusis quod terra emerserat undis
  Nuncius adveniens ipsa Columba fuit.
Occiduis primus qui terram invenit in undis
  Nuncius adveniens ipse Columbus erat.

Our Sea-captain is likewise ambitious to perfect
what the other began. He counts it a disgrace,
seeing all mankind is one familie, sundry countreys
but severall rooms, that we who dwell in the parlour (so he counts Europe) should not know the
out-lodgings of the same house, and the world be
scarce acquainted with it self before it be dissolved
from it self at the day of judgement.

8. *He daily sees, and duly considers Gods wonders
in the deep.* Tell me, ye Naturalists, who sounded
the first march and retreat to the Tide, *Hither shalt
thou come, and no further?* why doth not the
water recover his right over the earth, being higher
in nature? whence came the salt, and who first
boyled it, which made so much brine? when the
winds are not onely wild in a storm, but even stark
mad in an herricano, who is it that restores them
again to their wits, and brings them asleep in a
calm? who made the mighty whales, who swim in
a sea of water, and have a sea of oyl swimming
in them? who first taught the water to imitate the
creatures on land? so that the sea is the stable of
horse-fishes, the stall of kine-fishes, the stye of hog-
fishes, the kennell of dog-fishes, and in all things
the sea the ape of the land. Whence growes the
amber-greece in the Sea? which is not so hard to
find where it is, as to know what it is. Was not
God the first ship-wright? and all vessels on the
water descended from the loyns (or ribs rather) of
Noahs ark; or else who durst be so bold with a

few crooked boards nayled together, a stick standing upright, and a rag tied to it, to adventure into
the ocean? what loadstone first touched the loadstone? or how first fell it in love with the North,
rather affecting that cold climate, then the pleasant
East, or fruitfull South, or West? how comes
that stone to know more then men, and to find
the way to the land in a mist?   In most of these
men take sanctuary at *Occulta qualitas*, and com-
plain that the room is dark, when their eyes are
blind.   Indeed they are Gods Wonders; and that
Seaman the greatest Wonder of all for his blockish-
nesse, who seeing them dayly neither takes notice
of them, admires at them, nor is thankfull for them.

ULPIAN FULWEL (*fl.* 1598)

A pleasant Enterlude, intituled, Like will to Like quoth the Devill to the Collier. ... Made by Ulpian Fulwel. ... London ... 1587. 4to. [B4]
First edition, 1568 [Bodleian].
Dodsley's Old Plays, iii. 1874.

Tom Tospot

FROM morning til night I sit tossing the black bole:
then come I home and pray for my fathers soule.
Saying my praiers with wounds, bloud, guts and
     hart,
Swearing and staring thus play I my parte.
If any poore man have in a whole week earn'd a
     grote:
He shal spend it in one houre in tossing the pot.
I use to call servants and poore men to my company,
and make them spend all they have unthriftily.
So that my company they think to be so good:
that in short space their haire growes through their
     hood.

BEN JONSON (1573-1637)

The Fountaine of Selfe-Love. Or Cynthias Revels. . . .
 London . . . 1601. 4to.

The Magnetick Lady : Or, Humors Reconcil'd. . . .
 London, 1640. fol.

Cynthia's Revels is a lengthy discussion of the typical failings of certain classes of courtiers. In Act II, Mercury and Cupid, disguised as pages, watch various courtiers as they exhibit their humours in turn, and as they go out, Mercury describes them to Cupid. The 'heavenly pair' —as if they were giving a ruling for the Overburians who soon were to try their wits in the game—determine ' not to utter a phrase but what shall come forth steep'd in the very brine of conceit, and sparkle like salt in fire.'

A typical humour is that of Asotus, the citizen's heir, who wishes to become a courtier. He has been receiving social hints from Amorphous, a traveller, and as he goes out with his preceptor, Mercury gives the character of the traveller and then of Criticus, who next comes in.

In *Every Man Out of His Humour*, 1599, Jonson attaches brief tags which he calls ' The Characters of the Persons ' to the list of his dramatis personae. There is no character-sketch in the play itself. In 1633, in *The Magnetick Lady*, he returns to some of the undramatic character-devices of his youth and gives set descriptions of his chief personages, especially Palate and Rut.

A Traveller

ONE so made out of the mixture and shreds of formes, that himselfe is truely deformed : Hee walkes most commonlye with a *Clove* or *Pick-toothe* in his mouth, Hee's the very Minte of *Complement;* All his behaviours are printed, his face is another volume of *Essayes;* and his beard

an *Aristarchus*. He speakes all creame, skimd, &
more affected then a dozen of waiting women;
Hee's his owne promooter in every place: The
wife of the *Ordinary* gives him his diet to maintaine her table in discourse, which (indeed) is a
meere Tiranny over her other guests: for he will
usurp all the talke: Ten Cunstables are not so
tedious. He is no great shifter; once a yeare his
apparell is ready to revolt; He doth use much to
arbitrate quarrells, and fights himselfe exceeding
well (out at a window.) He will lie cheaper then
any Begger, and lowder then most Clockes; for
which he is right properly accommodated to the
Whetstone his page. The other gallant is his *Zani*,
& doth most of these tricks after him; sweats to
imitate him in every thing (to a haire) except a
Beard, which is not yet extant: he doth learne to
eat *Anchoves*, & *Caveare* because he loves 'hem,
speakes as he speakes; lookes, walkes, goes so in
Cloathes and fashion, is in al, as he were moulded
of him. Marry (before they met) he had other
very pretty sufficiencies, which yet he retaines some
light Impression of: As frequenting a dauncing
schoole, and grievously torturing strangers, with
inquisition after his grace in his Galliard; He buyes
a fresh acquaintance at any rate; his Eye, and his
Raiment confer much together as he goes in the
street; He treads nicely, like a fellow that walkes
upon ropes, especially the first Sunday of his Silk-
stockings, and when he is most neate and new, you
shal stripp him with commendations.

Criticus, The True Critic

A CREATURE of a most perfect and divine temper; One, in whom the *Humors* & *Elements* are peaceably met, without æmulation of Precedencie: he is neither too fantastickly *Melancholy;* too slowly *P[h]legmatick*, too lightly *Sanguine*, or too rashly *Cholerick*, but in al, so composd and order'd; as it is cleare, Nature was aboute some full worke, she did more then make a man when she made him; His discourse is like his behaviour, un-common, but not unpleasing; he is prodigall of neither: He strives rather to be (that which men call) Judicious, then to be thought so; and is so truely learned that he affects not to shew it: He wil thinke, & speak his thought, both freely; but as distant from depraving any other mans Merrit, as proclaiming his owne: For his valor, tis such, that he dares as little to offer an Injury, as receive one. In sum, he hath a most Ingenious and sweet spirit, a sharp and season'd wit, a streight judge-ment, and a strong minde; constant and unshaken: *Fortune* could never breake him, or make him lesse, he counts it his pleasure to despise pleasures, and is more delighted with good deedes then Goods, It is a competencie to him that he can be vertuous. He doth neither covet, nor feare; he hath too much reason to do either: and that com-mends all things to him.

Parson Palate

I CAN gi' you his Character.
Hee, is the Prelate of the Parish, here;
And governes all the Dames; appoints the cheere;

Writes downe the bils of fare; pricks all the Guests;
Makes all the matches and the marriage feasts
Within the ward; drawes all the parish wils;
Designes the Legacies; and strokes the Gills
Of the chiefe Mourners; And (who ever lacks)
Of all the kindred, hee hath first his blacks.
Thus holds hee weddings up, and burials,
As his maine tithing; with the Gossips stals,
Their pewes; He's top still, at the publique messe;
Comforts the widow, and the fatherlesse,
In funerall sack!   Sits 'bove the Alderman!
For of the Ward-mote *Quest*, he better can,
The mysterie, then the Levitick Law:
That peece of Clark-ship doth his Vestry awe.
Hee is as he conceives himselfe, a fine
Well furnish'd, and apparaled Divine.

ANONYMOUS

The Returne from Pernassus. . . .   At London, 1606.
4to.   [D3ᵛ, E4, F1]

Reprinted in the Temple Dramatists, 1896.

The Returne from Pernassus is a satirical play dealing
with the discontents of scholars.   There are about four
or five distinct character-sketches in the text.   And in a
general way, the affinity of the whole play to the popular
character-satire of the time is marked.   Most of its
personages represent the various typical callings which
are vainly discussed or essayed by the pilgrims.   There
are too, on almost every page, jesting allusions to the
single qualities of a type, or to the type itself, until the
whole atmosphere of aspirants to fame and position in
the university, in the church and in the court becomes
clearly felt.

A Meere Scholler

I HEARD a courtier once define a meere scholler,
to be *animall scabiosum*, that is, a living creature
that is troubled with the itch : or a meere scholler
is a creature that can strike fire in the morning at
his tinder-box, put on a paire of lined slippers, sit
rewming till dinner, and then goe to his meate
when the Bell rings, one that hath a peculiar gift
in a cough, and a licence to spit : or if you will
have him defined by negatives : he is one that
cannot make a good legge, one that cannot eate a
messe of broth cleanly, one that cannot ride a
horse without spur-galling : one that cannot salute
a woman, and looke on her directly, one that
cannot——

The Linguist-Gallant

THIS great linguist my Maister, will march through Paules Church-yard. Come to a booke binders shop, and with a big Italian looke and spanish face aske for these bookes in spanish and Italian, then turning through his ignorance, the wrong ende of the booke upward use action, on this unknowne tongue after this sort, first looke on the title and wrinckle his brow, next make as though he read the first page and bites a lip, then with his naile score the margent as though there were some notable conceit, and lastly when he thinkes hee hath gulld the standers by sufficiently, throwes the booke away in a rage, swearing that he could never finde bookes of a true printe since he was last in *Joadna*, enquire after the next marte, and so departs.

A Courtier

HE is one, that will draw out his pocket glasse thrise in a walke, one that dreames in a night of nothing, but muske and civet, and talke[s] of nothing all day long but his hawke, his hound, and his mistresse, one that more admires the good wrinckle of a boote, the curious crinkling of a silke stocking, then all the wit in the world : one that loves no scholler but him whose tyred eares can endure halfe a day togither his fliblow sonnettes of his mistresse, and her loving pretty creatures, her munckey and her puppet.

JOSEPH HALL (1574-1656)

Characters of Vertues and Vices. In two Bookes. By Joseph Hall. London ... 1608. 8vo.

[7 editions in England in the seventeenth century, 3 in the nineteenth, all except the first two of 1608, included in collections of Hall's works. The 1621 edition is the first to contain the 'Happie Man.'] French editions in 1610, 1619, 1634.

26 characters.

The Vertues, which include the 'Good Magistrate,' are in the main vague and theoretical, if regarded as characters, but contain much that is finely said if they are thought of as belonging to Hall's sermons. The Vices are very different in effect, chiefly because Hall has here been able to imitate Theophrastus.

The first French edition of the characters, beautifully printed in Paris in 1610, describes itself as 'La première traduction de l'Anglois jamais imprimée en aucun vulgaire.' Sir Sidney Lee confirms this so far as France and England were concerned, for he calls it 'the first English book of literary interest which is known to have appeared in a French translation.' (*Bibliog. Soc. Trans.* viii. 1907.)

He is an Happie Man

THAT hath learn'd to reade himself more than all Books; and hath so taken out this Lesson, that he can never forget it; That knowes the World, and cares not for it; That after many traverses of thoughts, is growne to know what he may trust to, and stands now equally armed for al events: That hath got the masterie at home, so as hee can crosse his will without a mutinie, and so please it, that hee makes it not a Wanton: That in earthly things

78

wishes no more than nature; in spirituall, is ever
graciously ambitious: That for his condition,
stands on his owne feete, not needing to leane
upon the great; and can so frame his thoughts to
his estate, that when he hath least, hee cannot want,
because hee is as free from desire, as superfluitie:
That hath seasonably broked the head-strong resti-
nesse of prosperitie, and can now menage it at
pleasure: Upon whom, all smaller crosses light as
haile-stones upon a roofe; and for the greater cala-
mities, he can take them as Tributes of life, and
tokens of love; and if his Ship bee tossed, yet
hee is sure his Anchor is fast. If all the World
were his, he could be no other than he is;
no whit gladder of himselfe, no whit higher
in his carriage, because he knowes, contentment
lyes not in the things he hath, but in the minde
that values them. The powers of his resolution
can either multiply, or subtract at pleasure. Hee
can make his Cottage a Mannor, or a Palace when
hee lists; and his Home-close, a large Dominion,
his staind-cloth, Arras; his Earth, Plate, and can
see State in the attendance of one Servant; as one
that hath learned, a mans greatnesse or basenesse
is in himselfe; and in this hee may even contest
with the proud, that he thinkes his owne the best.
Or if he must be outwardly great, he can but turne
the other end of the Glasse, and make his stately
Mannor a low and strait Cottage; and in all his
costly furniture hee can see not richnesse, but use;
hee can see drosse in the best mettall, and Earth
thorow the best clothes, & in all his troupe, hee
can see himselfe his owne Servant. Hee lives
quietly at home, out of the noyse of the World,

and loves to enjoy himselfe alwayes, and sometimes
his friend, and hath as full scope to his thoughts as
to his eyes. He walkes ever even, in the midway
betwixt hopes and feares, resolved to feare nothing
but God, to hope for nothing but that which hee
must have. Hee hath a wise and vertuous minde
in a serviceable bodie; which that better part affects
as a present Servant, and a future companion; so
cherishing his flesh, as one that would scorne to
bee all flesh. He hath no enemies, not for that all
love him, but because hee knowes to make a gaine
of malice. Hee is not so ingaged to any earthly
thing, that they two cannot part on even tearmes;
there is neither laughter in their meeting, nor in
their shaking of hands, teares. He keepes ever
the best companie, the God of Spirits, & the Spirits
of that God; whom he entertaynes continually in
an awfull familiaritie, not being hindred, either
with too much light, or with none at all. His conscience and his hands are friends, and (what Devill
soever tempt him) will not fall out. That divine
part goes ever uprightly and freely, not stooping
under the burden of a willing sin, not fettered with
the Gyves of unjust scruples. He would not, if
he could, runne away from himselfe, or from God;
not caring from whom hee lyes hid, so hee may
looke these two in the face. Censures and ap-
plauses are Passengers to him, not ghests; his eare
is their thorow-fare, not their harbour; he hath
learned to fetch both his counsell, and his sentence
from his owne brest. Hee doth not lay weight
upon his own shoulders, as one that loves to torment himselfe with the honour of much imployment; but as hee makes worke his game, so doth

he not list to make himselfe worke. His strife is
ever to redeeme, and not to spend time. It is his
trade to doe good; and to thinke of it, his recreation. Hee hath hands enow for himselfe, and
others, which are ever stretched forth for beneficence; not for need. He walkes cheerefully in
the way that God hath chalked, and never wishes
it more wide, or more smooth. Those very tenta-
tions whereby he is foyled, strengthen him; hee
comes forth crowned, and triumphing out of the
spirituall Battels, and those skarres he hath, make
him beautifull. His soule is every day dilated to
receive that God, in whom he is; and hath attayned
to love himselfe for God, and God for his owne
sake. His eyes sticke so fast in Heaven, that no
earthly object can remove them; yea, his whole
selfe is there before his time, and sees with *Steven*,
and heares with *Paul*, and enjoyes with *Lazarus*,
the glorie that he shall have; and takes possession
before-hand of his room amongst the Saints: and
these heavenly contentments have so taken him up,
that now hee lookes downe displeasedly upon the
Earth, as the Region of his sorrow and banish-
ment; yet joying more in hope, then troubled with
the sense of evils; he holds it no great matter to
live, and his greatest businesse to dye; and is so
well acquainted with his last Ghest, that hee feares
no unkindnesse from him : neither makes hee any
other of dying, then of walking home when he is
abroad, or of going to bed when hee is wearie of
the day. Hee is well provided for both Worlds,
and is sure of peace here, of glory hereafter; and
therefore hath a light heart, and a cheereful face.
All his fellow-creatures rejoyce to serve him; his

betters, the Angels, love to observe him; God himselfe takes pleasure to converse with him, and hath
Sainted him afore his death, and in his death
crowned him.

The Hypocrite

An Hypocrite is the worst kinde of player, by
so much as he acts the better part; which hath
alwayes two faces, oft times two hearts: That
can compose his forhead to sadnesse and gravitie,
while hee bids his heart be wanton and carelesse
within, and (in the meane time) laughs within himselfe, to think how smoothly he hath couzened the
beholder. In whose silent face are written the
characters of Religion, which his tongue & gestures
pronounce, but his hands recant. That hath a
cleane face and garment, with a foule soule; whose
mouth belies his heart, and his fingers belie his
mouth. Walking early up into the Citie, he turnes
into the great Church, and salutes one of the pillars
on one knee, worshipping that God which at home
hee cares not for; while his eye is fixed on some
window, on some passenger, and his heart knowes
not whither his lips goe. He rises, and looking
about, with admiration, complains of our frozen
charitie, commends the ancient. At Church hee will
ever sit where hee may bee seene best, and in the
midst of the Sermon pulles out his Tables in haste,
as if he feared to leese that note; when hee writes
either his forgotten errand or nothing: then he
turnes his Bible with a noise, to seeke an omitted
quotation; and foldes the leafe, as if he had found
it; and askes aloud the name of the Preacher, and
repeats it; whom hee publikely salutes, thanks,

praises, invites, entertaines with tedious good counsell, with good discourse, if it had come from an honester mouth. Hee can commaund teares, when hee speaks of his youth, indeed because it is past, not because it was sinfull: himselfe is now better, but the times are woorse. All other sinnes he reckens up with detestation, while hee loves and hides his darling in his bosome. All his speech returnes to himselfe, and every occurrent drawes in a storie to his owne praise. When he should give, he looks about him, and sayes, WHO SEES ME? No almes, no prayers fall from him without a witnesse; belike, lest God should denie, that hee hath received them: and when hee hath done (lest the world should not know it) his owne mouth is his trumpet to proclame it. With the superfluitie of his usurie he builds an Hospitall, and harbours them whom his extortion hath spoiled: so while hee makes many beggers, he keeps some. He turneth all Gnats into Camels, and cares not to undoe the world for a circumstance. Flesh on a Friday is more abomination to him than his neighbours bed: Hee abhorres more, not to uncover at the name of Jesus, than to sweare by the name of God. When a Rimer reads his Poeme to him, he begges a Copie, and perswades the Presse; there is nothing that hee dislikes in presence, that in absence hee censures not. He comes to the sicke bed of his stepmother, & weeps, when hee secretly feares her recoverie. He greets his friend in the street with so cleere a countenance, so fast a closure, that the other thinks hee reades his heart in his face; and shakes hands, with an indefinite invitation of *When will you come?* and when his backe is turned, joyes that hee is so well rid of a guest: yet if that guest visit him unfeared, hee counterfeits a smiling welcome, and excuses his chere, when closely he frownes on his wife for too much. Hee shewes well, and sayes well; and himselfe is the worst thing he hath. In briefe, hee is the strangers saint, the neighbours disease, the blot of goodnesse, a rotten sticke in a darke night, a poppie in a corne field, an ill tempered candle with a great snuffe, that in going out smelles ill; an Angell abroad, a Divell at home: and worse when an Angell, than when a Divell.

The Superstitious

SUPERSTITION is Godlesse religion, devout impietie. The superstitious is fond in observation, servile in feare, he worships God but as he lists: he gives God what he asks not, more than he askes; and all but what he should give; and makes more sinnes than the Ten Commandements. This man dares not stirre foorth till his brest be crossed, and his face sprinckled. If but an Hare crosse him the way, he returnes; or if his journey began unawares on the dismall day; or if hee stumbled at the threshold. If hee see a snake unkilled, he feares a mischiefe; if the salt fall towards him, hee lookes pale and red, and is not quiet till one of the waiters have powred wine on his lappe; and when hee sneeseth, thinks them not his friends that uncover not. In the morning he listens whether the Crow crieth eeven or odde, and by that token presages of the weather. If hee heare but a Raven croke from the next roofe, hee makes his will, or if a Bittour flie over his head by night:

but if his troubled fancie shall second his thoughts with the dreame of a faire Garden, or greene rushes, or the salutation of a dead friend, hee takes leave of the world, and sayes hee can not live. Hee will never set to Sea but on a Sunday; neither ever goes without an *Erra Pater* in his pocket. Saint Pauls day and Saint Swithunes with the Twelve are his Oracles; which he dares beleeve against the Almanacke. When hee lies sicke on his death-bed, no sinne troubles him so much as that hee did once eat flesh on a Friday, no repentance can expiate that; the rest need none. There is no dreame of his without an interpretation, without a prediction; and if the event answer not his exposition, hee expounds it according to the event. Every dark groave and pictured wall strikes him with an awfull but carnall devotion. Olde wives and starres are his counsellers; his night-spell is his guard, and charmes his Physitians. He weares Paracelsian Characters for the tooth-ache, and a little hallowed wax is his Antidote for all evils. This man is strangely credulous, and calles impossible things, miraculous : If hee heare that some sacred blocke speakes, moves, weepes, smiles, his bare feet carrie him thither with an offering : and if a danger misse him in the way, his saint hath the thanks. Some wayes he will not go, & some he dares not; either there are bugs, or he faineth them; every lanterne is a ghost, & every noise is of chaines. He knowes not why, but his custome is to goe a little about, and to leave the crosse stil on the right hand. One event is enough to make a rule; out of these rules he concludes fashions proper to himselfe; and nothing can turne him out of his owne course. If he have done his taske hee is safe, it matters not with what affection. Finally, if God would let him be the carver of his owne obedience, hee could not have a better subject, as he is he can not have a worse.

The Covetous

HEE is a servaunt to himselfe, yea to his servant; and doth base homage to that which should be the worst drudge. A livelesse peece of earth is his master, yea his God, which hee shrines in his coffer, and to which hee sacrifices his heart. Every face of his coine is a new image, which he adores with the highest veneration; yet takes upon him to be protectour of that he worshippeth: which he feares to keepe, and abhorres to lose: not daring to trust either any other God, or his own. Like a true Chymist hee turnes everie thing into silver, both what hee should eat, and what hee should weare; and that hee keepes to looke on, not to use. When hee returnes from his field, he asks, not without much rage, what became of the loose crust in his cup-boord, and who hath rioted amongst his leekes? He never eats good meale, but on his neighbors trencher; and there hee makes amends to his complaining stomacke for his former and future fasts. He bids his neighbours to dinner, and when they have done, sends in a trencher for the shot. Once in a yeere perhaps, he gives him-selfe leave to feast; and for the time thinks no man more lavish; wherein hee lists not to fetch his dishes from farre; nor will bee beholden to the shambles: his owne provision shall furnish his boord with an insensible cost; and when his guests are parted, talkes how much every man devoured, and how many cups were emptied, and feeds his familie with the moldie remnants a moneth after. If his servant breake but an earthen dish for want of light, hee abates it out of his quarters wages. He chips his bread, & sends it backe to exchange for staler. He lets money, and selles Time for a price; and will not be importuned either to prevent or defer his day; and in the meane time looks for secret gratuities, besides the main interest; which hee selles and returnes into the stocke. He breeds of money to the third generation; neither hath it sooner any being, than hee sets it to beget more. In all things hee affects secrecie and proprietie : hee grudgeth his neighbor the water of his well : and next to stealing hee hates borrowing. In his short and unquiet sleepes hee dreames of theeves, & runnes to the doore, and names more men than hee hath. The least sheafe hee ever culles out for Tithe; and to rob God holds it the best pastime, the cleerest gaine. This man cries out above other, of the prodigalitie of our times, and telles of the thrift of our forefathers : How that great Prince thought himselfe royally attired, when he bestowed thirteen shillings & foure pence on halfe a sute. How one wedding gown served our Grandmothers, till they exchanged it for a winding sheet; and praises plainnesse, not for lesse sinne, but for lesse cost. For himselfe hee is still knowen by his fore-fathers coat, which hee meanes with his blessing to bequeath to the many descents of his heires. Hee neither would be poore, nor be accounted rich. No man complaines so much of want, to avoid a Subsidie; no man is so importunate in begging, so

cruell in exaction; and when hee most complaines
of want, hee feares that which he complaines to
have.   No way is indirect to wealth, whether of
fraud or violence : Gaine is his godlinesse, which
if conscience go about to prejudice, and grow
troublesome by exclaiming against, he is condemned
for a common barretor.   Like another Ahab hee is
sicke of the next field, and thinks he is ill seated,
while he dwelles by neighbours.   Shortly, his
neighbours doe not much more hate him, than he
himselfe.   He cares not (for no great advantage)
to lose his friend, pine his bodie, damne his soule;
and would dispatch himselfe when corne falles, but
that hee is loth to cast away money on a cord.

The Vaine-glorious

ALL his humor rises up into the froth of ostentation; which if it once settle, falles downe into a
narrow roome.   If the excesse be in the understanding part, all his wit is in print; the Presse
hath left his head emptie; yea, not only what he
had, but what he could borrow without leave.   If
his glorie be in his devotion, he gives not an
Almes but on record; and if hee have once done
well, God heares of it often; for upon every unkindnesse hee is readie to upbraid him with his
merits.   Over and above his owne discharge hee
hath some satisfactions to spare for the common
treasure.   Hee can fulfill the law with ease, and
earne God with superfluitie.   If hee have bestowed but a little sum in the glazing, paving,
parieting of Gods house, you shall finde it in the
Church-window.   Or, if a more gallant humour
possesse him, hee weares all his land on his backe,

and walking high, looks over his left shoulder, to see if the point of his rapier follow him with a grace. Hee is proud of another mans horse; and wel mounted, thinks every man wrongs him, that looks not at him. A bare head in the street doth him more good than a meales meat. Hee sweares bigge at an Ordinarie, and talkes of the Court with a sharpe accent; neither vouchsafes to name anie not honourable, nor those without some terme of familiaritie, and likes well to see the hearer looke upon him amazedly; as if he sayd, How happie is this man that is so great with great ones! Under pretence of seeking for a scroll of newes, hee drawes out an handfull of letters indorsed with his owne stile, to the height; and halfe reading every title, passes over the latter part, with a murmur; not without signifying what Lord sent this, what great Ladie the other; and for what sutes: the last paper (as it happens) is his newes from his honourable friend in the French Court. In the midst of dinner, his Lacquay comes sweating in, with a sealed note from his creditour, who now threatens a speedie arrest, and whispers the ill newes in his Masters eare, when hee aloud names a Counseller of State, and professes to know the imployment. The same messenger hee calles with an imperious nod, and after expostulation, where he hath left his fellowes, in his eare sends him for some new spur-leathers or stockings by this time footed, and when he is gone halfe the roome, recalles him, and sayth aloud, *It is no matter, let the greater bagge alone till I come;* and yet again calling him closer, whispers (so that all the table may heare) *that if his crimson sute be readie against the day, the rest need no haste.* He picks his teeth when his stomacke is emptie, and calles for Pheasants at a common Inne. You shall finde him prizing the richest jewels, and fairest horses, when his purse yeelds not money enough for earnest. He thrusts himselfe into the prease before some great Ladies; and loves to be seene neere the head of a great traine. His talke is how many Mourners hee furnish't with gownes at his fathers funerals, how many messes; how rich his coat is, and how ancient, how great his alliance: what challenges hee hath made and answered; what exploits hee did at *Cales* or *Nieuport:* and when hee hath commended others buildings, furnitures, sutes, compares them with his owne. When hee hath undertaken to be the Broker for some rich Diamond, he weares it, and pulling off his glove to stroke up his haire, thinks no eye should have any other object. Entertaining his friend, he chides his Cooke for no better cheere, and names the dishes he meant, and wants. To conclude, hee is ever on the stage, and acts still a glorious part abroad, when no man carries a baser heart, no man is more sordid and carelesse at home. He is a Spanish souldier on an Italian Theater; a bladder full of winde, a skin full of words; a fooles wonder, and a wise mans foole.

SIR THOMAS OVERBURY
(1581-1613)

Sir Thomas Overburye His Wife . . . New Characters, . . . London, 1622. 8vo.

[This is the first complete edition, of 82 characters and an Essay of Valour. No characters added afterwards. Though the text is from this edition, the characters are given here in the order in which they originally appeared.]

The first edition, 1614 ; in all, 17 editions before 1700.

A big step has at last been taken which has not only helped to determine the authorship of the Overburian collection, but has given us some prose that John Webster wrote. For the conclusions of the interesting evidence to this effect, independently contributed by Mr. H. Dugdale Sykes and Baron A. F. Bourgeois to 'Notes and Queries' in 1913-15, seem highly probable. These writers suggest that Webster wrote the 32 characters added, with a separate titlepage, to the 6th edition of Overbury's 'Wife' in 1615. [From 'A Noble-Housekeeper' to 'A Franklin' in this selection.] It is interesting to note that 'one-fifth' of the 'Milkmaid' is borrowed in Webster's fashion, from Sidney's *Arcadia, e.g.* 'Philoclea so bashful, as though her excellencies had stolen into her before she was aware' (*Arcadia,* i. p. 13), or 'telling them it was shame for them to mar their complexions, yea and conditions too with lying long abed' (*Arcadia,* ii. p. 151, quoted by H. D. Sykes from Routledge's edition).

Early in 1615 John Stephens, a lawyer, printed an unfriendly sketch of 'A Common Player.' A reply was made at once. For a 'friend of the actors' wrote 'An excellent Actor' and this was one of the new group of 32 characters added to Overbury's that year. Into this character was inserted a disconnected passage directly and abusively attacking Stephens for his hostile sketch. Stephens at once rushed out a second edition of his ' Characters ' in which he elaborately attacked ' the actor's friend ' for his ' scurrilous retort ' and declared he had not meant to insult the London companies. The next edition of Overbury (1616) omitted the offending passage and it was never reprinted.

The ' Excellent Actor ' is a sympathetic picture of an actor long ago supposed to be Richard Burbage, whose love of painting is noted, and by itself it was the best answer to the criticism directed against the players.

The Quacksalver carried on his notorious practices, with little change, for generations. *The Infallible Mountebank and Quack Doctor* [1] of the illustration is caught at the moment of his proclamation to his dupes,

See Sirs, see here !
A Doctor Rare,
Who travels much at home !
Here take my Bills
I cure all Ills
Past, Present and to come,

and he goes on to repeat the old lying tags. He is standing on an improvised platform, with Harlequin to support him, and the scene is probably part of the performances of a group of travelling mountebanks, in which the quack doctor was usually the leading figure.

The vivid woodcut is likely to be of Italian origin and of earlier date than its letterpress.

A Courtier

To all mens thinking is a man, and to most men the finest : all things else are defined by the understanding, but this by the sences; but his surest marke is, that hee is to be found onely about Princes. He smells; and putteth away much of

[1] [London : Printed by H. Hills, in Black-Fryars, near the Water-side. 1707, fol.]

his judgement about the scituation of his clothes. He knowes no man that is not generally knowne. His wit, like the *Marigold*, openeth with the *Sunne*, and therefore he riseth not before ten of the clocke. He puts more confidence in his words than meaning, and more in his pronunciation than his words. *Occasion* is his *Cupid*, and he hath but one receipt of making love. Hee followes nothing but inconstancie, admires nothing but beauty, honours nothing but fortune. Loves nothing. The sustenance of his discourse is Newes, and his censure like a shot depends upon the charging. He is not, if he be out of Court, but fish-like breathes destruction, if out of his owne element. Neither his motion, or aspect are regular, but he moves by the upper *Spheres*, and is the reflection of higher substances.

If you finde him not here, you shall in *Pauls*, with a picke-tooth in his Hat, a cape cloke, and a long stocking.

An Affectate Traveller

Is a speaking fashion; hee hath taken paines to be ridiculous, & hath seene more then he hath perceived. His attire speakes *French* or *Italian*, and his *gate* cries, *Behold me*. He censures all things by countenances, and shrugs, and speaks his owne language with shame and lisping: he will choake rather than confesse *Beere* good drinke: and his pick-tooth is a maine part of his behaviour. He chuseth rather to be counted a *Spie*, than not a *Politician*: and maintaines his reputation by naming great men familiarly. He chuseth rather to tell lies, then not wonders, and talkes with men singly: his discourse sounds big, but meanes nothing: & his boy is bound to admire him howsoever. He comes still from great Personages, but goes with meane. He takes occasion to shew Jewels given him in regard of his vertue, that were bought in S. *Martines:* and not long after having with a *Mountbanks* method, pronounced them worth thousands, empawneth them for a few shillings. Upon festivall daies he goes to Court, and salutes without resaluting: at night in an Ordinary he canvasseth the businesse in hand, and seemes as conversant with all intents & plots, as if he begot them. His extraordinary account of men is, first to tel them the ends of all matters of consequence, and then to borrow money of them; hee offereth courtesies, to shew them, rather then himselfe humble. Hee disdaines all things above his reach, and preferreth all Countries before his owne. Hee imputeth his want and poverty to the ignorance of the time, not his owne unworthinesse: and concludes his discourse with halfe a period, or a word, and leaves the rest to imagination. In a word, his religion is fashion, and both body and soule are governed by fame, he loves most voices above truth.

A Noble Spirit

HATH surveied and fortified his disposition, and converts all occurrents into experience, betweene which experience and his reason, there is marriage; the issue are his actions. He circuits his intents, and seeth the end before he shoot. Men are the instruments of his Art, and there is no man without his use: occasion incites him, none enticeth

him: and he moves by affection, not for affection;
he loves glory, scornes shame, and governeth and
obeyeth with one countenance; for it comes from
one consideration. He cals not the varietie of the
world chances, for his meditation hath travelled
over them; and his eye mounted upon his understanding, seeth them as things underneth. He
covers not his body with delicacies, nor excuseth
these delicacies by his body, but teacheth it, since
it is not able to defend its owne imbecilitie, to shew
or suffer. He licenceth not his weaknesse, to weare
Fate, but knowing reason to be no idle gift of
Nature, he is the Steeres-man of his owne destinie.
Truth is his Goddesse, and he takes pains to get
her, not to look like her. He knowes the condition of the world, that he must act one thing like
another, and then another. To these he carries his
desires, & not his desires him; and stickes not fast
by the way (for that contentment is repentance) but
knowing the circle of all courses, of all intents, of
all things, to have but one center or period, without all distraction, he hasteth thither and ends
there, as his true and naturall element. He doth
not contemne Fortune, but not confesse her. He
is no Gamester of the world (which only complaine
and praise her) but being only sensible of the
honestie of actions, contemnes a particular profit
as the excrement or scum. Unto the societie of
men he is a *Sunne*, whose cleerenesse directs their
steps in a regular motion: when he is more particular, he is the wise mans friend, the example of
the indifferent, the medicine of the vicious. Thus
time goeth not from him, but with him: and he
feeles age more by the strength of his soule, than

the weaknesse of his bodie: thus feeles he no paine, but esteemes all such things as friends, that desire to file off his fetters and helpe him out of prison.

A Country Gentleman

Is a thing out of whose corruption the generation of a Justice of peace is produced. He speaks statutes & husbandry well enough, to make his neighbours thinke him a wise man; he is well skilled in *Arithmeticke* or rates: and hath eloquence enough to save two-pence. His conversation amongst his Tenants is desperate; but amongst his equals full of doubt. His travell is seldom farther then the next market Towne, and his inquisition is about the price of Corne: when he travelleth, he will goe ten mile out of the way to a Cousins house of his to save charges; and rewards the Servants by taking them by the hand when hee departs. Nothing under a *Sub-pena* can draw him to *London:* and when hee is there, he sticks fast upon every object, casts his eyes away upon gazing, and becomes the prey of every Cutpurse. When he comes home, those wonders serve him for his Holy-day talke. If he goe to Court, it is in yellow stockings; and if it be in Winter in a slight tafetie cloake, and pumps and pantofles. He is chained that wooes the usher for his comming into the presence, where hee becomes troublesome with the ill managing of his Rapier and the wearing of his girdle of one fashion, & the hangers of another; by this time he hath learned to kisse his hand, and make a legge both together, and the names of Lords and Counsellors;

he hath thus much toward entertainment and courtesie, but of the last he makes more use; for by
the recitall of *my Lord*, he conjures his poore
Countrimen. But this is not his element, he must
home againe, being like a Dor, that ends his flight
in a dunghill.

A Melancholy Man

Is a strayer from the drove: one that Nature
made a sociable, because she made him man, and
a crazed disposition hath altered. Impleasing to
all, as all to him; stragling thoughts are his content, they make him dreame waking, there's his
pleasure. His imagination is never idle, it keepes
his minde in a continuall motion, as the poise the
clocke: he windes up his thoughts often, and as
often unwindes them; *Penelopes* webbe thrives
faster. He'le seldome be found without the shade
of some grove, in whose bottome a river dwels.
He carries a cloud in his face, never faire weather:
his outside is framed to his inside, in that hee
keepes a *Decorum*, both unseemely. Speake to
him; hee heares with his eyes, eares follow his
minde, and that's not at leasure. Hee thinkes
businesse, but never does any; hee is all contemplation, no action. He hewes and fashions his
thoughts, as if hee meant them to some purpose,
but they prove unprofitable, as a peece of wrought
timber to no use. His Spirits and the Sunne are
enemies; the Sunne bright and warme, his humour
blacke and cold: varietie of foolish apparitions
people his head, they suffer him not to breathe,
according to the necessities of nature; which makes
him sup up a draught of as much aire at once, as

would serve at thrice. Hee denies nature her due in sleepe, and over-payes her with watchfulnesse: nothing pleaseth him long, but that which pleaseth his owne fantasies: they are the consuming evills, and evill consumptions that consume him alive. Lastly, hee is a man onely in shew, but comes short of the better part; a whole reasonable soule, which is mans chiefe preheminence, and sole marke from creatures sensible.

The Character of a happy life

By Sir H.[enry] W.[otton]

How happy is he borne or taught,
That serveth not anothers will;
Whose Armour is his honest thought,
And silly *Truth* his highest skill.

Whose passions not his Masters are,
Whose soule is still prepar'd for death:
Untyed unto the world with care
Of Princely love, or vulgar breath.

Who hath his life from rumors freed,
Whose conscience is his strong retreit:
Whose state can neither flatterers feed,
Nor ruine make accusers great.

Who envieth none whom chance doth raise,
Or vice: who never understood,
How deepest wounds are given with praise,
Not rules of state, but rules of good.

Who GOD doth late and early pray,
More of his grace, then gifts to lend;
Who entertaines the harmelesse day
With a well chosen Booke or Friend.

This man is free from servile bands,
Of hope to rise, or feare to fall;
Lord of himselfe, though not of Lands:
And having nothing, he hath All.

A Tinker

Is a mooveable; for hee hath no abiding place;
by his motion he gathers heat, thence his chol-
lericke nature. Hee seemes to bee very devout,
for his life is a continuall pilgrimage, and sometimes in humility goes barefoot, therein making
necessity a vertue. His house is as ancient as
Tubal Caines, and so is a runnagate by antiquity:
yet hee prooves himselfe a Gallant, for hee carries
all his wealth upon his backe; or a Philosopher,
for he beares all his substance about him. From
his Art was Musicke first invented, and therefore
is hee alwaies furnisht with a song: to which his
hammer keeping tune, proves that he was the first
founder of the Kettle-drumme. Note that where
the best Ale is, there stands his musicke most upon
crotchets. The companion of his travels is some
foule sunne-burnt Queane, that since the terrible
Statute recanted Gypsisme, and is turned Ped-
leresse. So marches he all over England with his
bag and baggage. His conversation is unreprove-
able; for hee is ever mending. Hee observes truely
the Statutes, and therefore hee had rather steale
then begge, in which hee is unremoveably constant
in spight of whips or imprisonment: and so a
strong enemy to idlenesse, that in mending one
hole, hee had rather make three then want worke;
and when hee hath done, hee throwes the Wallet of
his faults behind him. Hee embraceth naturally

ancient customes, conversing in open fields, and lowly Cottages. If he visit Cities or Townes, tis but to deale upon the imperfections of our weaker vessels. His tongue is very voluble, which with Canting proves him a *Linguist*. Hee is entertain'd in every place, but enters no further then the doore, to avoid suspicion. Some would take him to be a Coward; but beleeve it, hee is a Lad of mettle, his valor is commonly three or foure yards long, fastned to a pike in the end for flying off. Hee is very provident, for he will fight but with one at once, and then also hee had rather submit then bee counted obstinate. To conclude, if he scape Tyburne and Banbury, he dies a begger.

[By J. Cocke]

An Innes of Court man

HE is distinguished from a Scholler by a paire of silke stockings, and a Beaver Hat, which makes him contemne a Scholler as much as a Scholler doth a Schoolemaster. By that he hath heard one mooting, and seene two plaies, he thinkes as basely of the *University*, as a young *Sophister* doth of the *Grammer-schoole*. Hee talkes of the *University*, with that state, as if he were her Chauncellour; findes fault with alterations, and the fall of *Discipline*, with an *It was not so when I was a Student;* although that was within this halfe yeare. Hee will talke ends of *Latine* though it bee false, with as great confidence, as ever *Cicero* could pronounce an Oration, though his best authors for 't, be *Tavernes* and *Ordinaries*. Hee is as farre behinde a *Courtier* in his fashion, as a Scholler is behinde

him: and the best grace in his behaviour, is to
forget his acquaintance.

Hee laughes at every man whose Band fits not
well, or that hath not a faire shoo-tie, and he is
ashamed to be seene in any mans company that
weares not his cloathes well. His very essence
he placeth in his out-side, and his chiefest prayer
is, that his revenues may hold out for Taffata
cloakes in the Summer, and Velvet in the Winter.
For his recreation, he had rather goe to a Citizens
Wife, then a Bawdy-house, onely to save charges:
and hee holds Fee-taile to bee absolutely the best
tenure. To his acquaintance he offers two quarts
of wine, for one he gives. You shall never see
him melancholly, but when hee wants a new Suite,
or feares a Seargeant: At which times onely, he
betakes himselfe to *Ploydon*. By that he hath
read *Littleton*, he can call *Solon, Lycurgus*, and
Justinian, fooles, and dares compare his Law to a
Lord Chiefe Justices.

A Noble and retired House-keeper

Is one whose bounty is limited by *reason*, not
ostentation: and to make it last, he deales it dis-
creetly, as wee sowe the *furrow*, not by the sacke,
but by the handfull. His word and his meaning
never shake handes and part, but alway goe together. Hee can survay good, and love it, and
loves to doe it himselfe, for its owne sake; not for
thankes. Hee knowes there is no such miserie as
to out-live good name; nor no such folly as to put
it in practise. His minde is so secure, that *thunder*
rockes him asleepe, which breaks other mens slum-
bers. *Nobility* lightens in his eyes; and in his

face and gesture is painted, *The god of Hospi-talitie*. His great houses beare in their front more durance, then state; unlesse this adde the greater state to them, that they promise to out last much of our new phantasticall building. His *heart* never growes old, no more then his *memorie*, whether at his booke or on horsebacke; he passeth his time in such noble exercise, a man cannot say, any time is lost by him : nor hath he only *yeares*, to approve he hath lived till hee bee old, but *vertues*. His thoughts have a *high aime*, though their dwelling bee in the *Vale of an humble heart*, whence, as by an *Engine* (that raises water to fall, that it may rise the higher) hee is heightned in his humility. The *Adamant* serves not for all Seas, but this doth; for hee hath, as it were, put a gird about the whole world, and sounded all her *quicke-sands*. Hee hath this hand over *Fortune*, that her injuries, how violent or sudden soever, they doe not daunt him; for whether his time call him to live or die, hee can doe both nobly : if to fall, his descent is breast to breast with vertue; and even then, like the *Sunne* neere his Set, hee shewes unto the world his *clearest countenance*.

An Intruder into favour

Is one that builds his reputation on others infamy : for slaunder is most commonly his morn-ing prayer. His passions are guided by *Pride*, and followed by *Injustice*. An inflexible anger against some poore sutor, hee falsely calles a *Couragious constancy*, and thinks the best part of gravity to consist in a ruffled forehead. Hee is the most slavishly submisse; though envious to those are in better place then himselfe; and knowes the Art of words so well, that (for shrowding dishonesty under a faire pretext) hee seemes to preserve mudde in Chrystall.   Like a man of a kinde nature, hee is first good to himselfe; in the next file, to his French Taylor, that gives him all his perfection: for indeed, like an *Estridge*, or *Bird of Paradise*, his feathers are more worth then his body.   If ever hee doe good deede (which is very seldome) his owne mouth is the *Chronicle* of it, least it should die forgotten.   His whole body goes all upon *screwes*, and his face is the *vice* that moves them.   If his *Patron* be given to musicke, hee opens his chops, and *sings*, or with a wrie necke, falls to tuning his instrument: if that faile, hee takes the height of his Lord with a Hawking pole. Hee followes the mans fortune, not the man: seeking thereby to encrease his owne.   Hee pretends hee is most undeservedly envied, and cries out, remembring the game, *Chesse*, that a Pawne before a King is most plaid on.   Debts hee owes none, but shrewd turnes, and those hee payes ere hee be sued.   Hee is a flattering *Glasse* to conceale age, and wrinckles.   Hee is *Mountains Monkie*, that climbing a tree, and skipping from bough to bough, gives you backe his face; but come once to the toppe, hee holds his nose up into the winde, and shewes you his tayle: yet all this gay glitter shewes on him, as if the Sunne shone in a puddle; for he is a small wine that will not last, and when he is falling, hee goes of himselfe faster then misery can drive him.

A fayre and happy Milke-mayd

Is a Countrey Wench, that is so farre from making her selfe beautifull by Art, that one looke of hers is able to put all *face-Physicke* out of countenance. She knowes a faire looke is but a *dumb Orator* to commend vertue, therefore mindes it not. All her excellencies stand in her so silently, as if they had stolne upon her without her knowledge. The lining of her apparell (which is her selfe) is farre better than outsides of *Tissew:* for though she be not arraied in the spoile of the *Silke-worme*, shee is deckt in *innocencie*, a far better wearing. Shee doth not, with lying long a bed spoile both her *complexion* and *Conditions;* nature hath taught her, too *immoderate sleepe is rust to the Soule:* shee rises therefore with *Chaunticleare*, her Dames Cocke, and at night makes the *Lambe* her *Corfew.* In milking a Cow, and strayning the Teates through her fingers, it seemes that so sweet a Milke-presse makes the Milke the whiter, or sweeter; for never came *Almond Glove* or *Aromatique Oyntment* on her Palme to taint it. The golden eares of corne fall and kisse her feete when shee reapes them, as if they wisht to bee bound and led prisoners by the same hand fell'd them. Her breathe is her owne, which sents all the yeere long of *June*, like a new-made Hay-cocke. Shee makes her hand hard with labour, and her heart soft with pitty: and when winter evenings fall early (sitting at her merry wheele) shee sings a defiance to the giddie *wheele of Fortune.* She doth all things with so sweet a grace, it seemes *ignorance* will not suffer her to doe ill, being her minde is to doe well. Shee bestowes her yeares wages at next faire; and in choosing her Garments, counts no bravery i' th' world like decencie. The *Garden* and *Bee-hive* are all her *Physicke* and *Chyrurgerie*, and shee lives the longer for 't. Shee dares goe alone, and unfold sheepe i' th' night, and feares no manner of ill, because shee meanes none: yet to say truth, she is never alone, for shee is still accompanied with old *songs*, *honest thoughts*, and *prayers*, but short ones; yet they have their efficacy, in that they are not pauled with insuing idle cogitations. Lastly, her dreames are so chaste, that shee dare tell them: onely a Fridaies dreame is all her *superstition:* that shee conceales for feare of anger. Thus lives shee, and all her care is shee may die in the *Spring-time*, to have store of flowers stucke upon her winding sheet.

An Arrant Horse-courser

Hath the tricke to blow up Horse-flesh, as a Butcher doth Veale, which shall wash out againe in twice riding twixt *Waltham* and *London*. The Trade of Spurre-making had decayed long since, but for this ungodly tyre-man. He is curst all over the foure ancient High-waies of England; none but the blind men that sell switches i' th' Road are beholding to him. His Stable is fill'd with so many Diseases, one would thinke most part about Smithfield were an Hospitall for Horses, or a slaughter-house of the common hunt. Let him furnish you with a Hackney, 'tis as much as if the Kings Warrant overtooke you within ten miles to stay your journey. And though a man cannot say, hee cozens you directly; yet any Ostler

within ten miles, should hee be brought upon his
Booke-oath, will affirme hee hath layd a bayt for
you. Resolve when you first stretch your selfe
in the stirrops, you are put as it were upon some
Usurer, that will never beare with you past his
day. Hee were good to make one that had the
Collicke alight often, and (if example will cause
him) make urine; let him only for that say,
Gr'amercy Horse. For his sale of horses, hee
hath false covers for all manner of Diseases, onely
comes short of one thing (which hee despaires not
utterly to bring to perfection) to make a horse goe
on a woodden legge and two crutches. For pow-
dring his eares with Quicksilver, and giving him
suppositories of live Eeles he's expert. All the
while you are a cheaping hee feares you will not
bite; but hee laughs in his sleeve when he hath
cozened you in earnest. French-men are his best
Chapmen, hee keepes amblers for them on purpose,
and knowes hee can deceive them very easily. Hee
is so constant to his Trade that while hee is awake,
he tires any man he talkes with, and when hee's
asleepe he dreams very fearefully of the paving of
Smithfield, for hee knowes it would founder his
occupation.

An Improvident young Gallant

There is a confederacy betweene him and his
clothes, to bee made a puppy : view him well, and
you'll say his Gentry fits as ill upon him, as if he
had bought it with his penny. He hath more
places to send money to, then the Devill hath to
send his Spirits : and to furnish each Mistrisse,
would make him runne besides his wits, if hee had

any to lose. Hee accounts bashfulnesse the wickedst thing in the world; and therefore studies Impudence. If all men were of his minde, all honesty would be out of fashion: hee withers his Cloathes on the Stage, as a Sale-man is for'ct to doe his sutes in Birchin-lane; and when the Play is done, if you marke his rising, 'tis with a kinde of walking Epilogue betweene the two candles, to know if his Suite may passe for currant: hee studies by the direction of his Barber, to frizle like a Baboone: three such would keepe three the nimblest Barbers in the towne, from ever having leisure to weare net-Garters: for when they have to doe with him, they have many Irons in th' fire. He is travelled, but to little purpose; onely went over for a squirt, and came backe againe, yet never the more mended in his conditions, 'cause hee carried himselfe along with him: a Scholler hee pretends himselfe, and sayes he hath sweat for it: but the truth is, he knowes *Cornelius*, farre better than *Tacitus:* his ordinary sports are Cock-fights; but the most frequent, horse-rases, from whence hee comes home drie-foundered. Thus when his purse hath cast her calfe, hee goes downe into the Country, where he is brought to milke and white cheese like the *Switzers*.

A Devillish Usurer

Is sowed as *Cummin* or *Hemp seede*, with curses; and he thinkes he thrives the better. Hee is better read in the *Penall Statutes*, then the Bible; and his evill Angell perswades him, hee shall sooner be saved by them. Hee can bee no mans friend; for all men hee hath most interest in, hee undo's; and a double-dealer hee is certainly; for by his good will he ever takes the forfeit. Hee puts his money to the unnaturall Act of generation; and his Scrivener is the supervisor Bawd to 't. Good Deeds he loves none, but Seal'd and Delivered; nor doth he wish any thing to thrive in the Countrey, but Bee-hives; for they make him waxe rich. Hee hates all but Law-Latine; yet thinkes he might bee drawne to love a Scholler, could hee reduce the yeere to a shorter compasse, that his use-money might come in the faster: he seems to be the son of a Jaylor, for all his estate is most heavie and cruell bonds. He doth not give, but sell daies of payment; and those at the rate of a mans undoing: he doth onely feare, the day of Judgement should fall sooner, than the paiment of some great sum of money due to him: hee removes his lodging when a subsidie comes; and if hee be found out, and pay it, hee grumbles Treason; but tis in such a deformed silence, as Witches raise their Spirits in. Gravity hee pretends in all things, but in his private Whore; for hee will not in a hundreth pound take one light sixe-pence; and it seemes hee was at *Tilbury Campe*, for you must not tell him of a *Spaniard*. Hee is a man of no conscience; for (like the *Jakes-farmer* that swounded going into Bucklersbury) hee fals into a cold sweat, if hee but looke into the Chauncerie: thinkes in his Religion, wee are in the right for every thing, if that were abolisht: hee hides his money as if hee thought to finde it againe at last day, and then begins old trade with it. His clothes plead prescription; and whether they or his body are more rotten, is a question: yet should hee live to bee hang'd in

them, this good they would doe him, The very
Hangman would pittie his case. The Table
hee keepes is able to starve twenty tall men; his
servants have not their living, but their dying from
him, and that 's of Hunger. A spare diet he
commends in all men, but himselfe: hee comes to
Cathedrals onely for love of the singing boyes,
because they looke hungry. Hee likes our Religion best, because tis best cheape; yet would faine
allow of Purgatorie, 'cause 'twas of his Trade, and
brought in so much money: his heart goes with
the same snaphance[1] his purse doth, tis seldome
open to any man: friendship hee accounts but a
word without any signification; nay, he loves all
the world so little, that, and it were possible, hee
would make himselfe his owne Executor: for certaine, hee is made Administrator to his owne good
name while he is in perfect memorie, for that dies
long afore him; but he is so farre from being at the
charge of a Funerall for it, that hee lets it stinke
above ground. In conclusion, for Neighbourhood,
you were better dwell by a contentious Lawyer.
And for his death, 'tis rather Surfet, the Pox, or
despaire, for seldome such as he die of Gods
making, as honest men should doe.

A Water-man

Is one that hath learnt to speake well of himselfe; for alwaies hee names himselfe, The first Man.
If he had betane himselfe to some richer Trade, hee
could not have chos'd but done well: for in this
(though it bee a meane one) he is still plying it,
and putting himselfe forward. He is evermore

---

[1] a spring-catch.

telling strange newes; most commonly lies. If he bee a Sculler, aske him if hee bee married, hee'l equivocate and sweare hee's a single man. Little trust is to bee given to him, for he thinkes that day he does best when hee fetches most men over. His daily labour teaches him the Arte of dissembling; for like a fellow that rides to the Pillorie, he goes not that way hee lookes: hee keepes such a bawling at *Westminster*, that if the Lawyers were not acquainted with it, an order would be tane with him. When he is upon the water, hee is Fare-company: when he comes a shore, he mutinies; and contrary to all other trades, is most surly to Gentlemen, when they tender payment. The Play-houses only keepe him sober; and as it doth many other Gallants, make him an afternoones man. London-Bridge is the most terriblest eye-sore to him that can bee. And to conclude, nothing but a *great Presse*, makes him flye from the River; nor any thing, but a great *Frost*, can teach him any good manners.

A reverend Judge

Is one that desires to have his greatnes, only measur'd by his goodnesse: his care is to appeare such to the people, as he would have them be; and to be himselfe such as hee appeares; for vertue cannot seeme one thing, and bee another: hee knowes that the hill of greatnesse yeeldes a most delightfull prospect, but withall that it is most subject to lightning, and thunder: and that the people, as in ancient *Tragedies*, sit and censure the actions of those are in authority: he squares his owne therefore, that they may farre bee above their pity:

hee wishes fewer Lawes, so they were better ob-
serv'd : and for those are Mulctuarie, hee understands their institution not to bee like briers or
springes, to catch every thing they lay hold of;
but like Sea-markes (on our dangerous *Goodwin*)
to avoid the ship-wracke of ignorant passengers:
hee hates to wrong any man; neither hope, nor
despaire of preferment can draw him to such an
exigent : he thinkes himselfe then most honourably
seated, when hee gives mercy the upper hand :
hee rather strives to purchase good name then land;
and of all rich stuffes forbidden by the Statute,
loathes to have his Followers weare their cloathes
cut out of bribes and extortions.   If his Prince call
him to a higher place, there hee delivers his minde
plainely, and freely, knowing for truth, there is no
place wherein dissembling ought to have lesse
credit, than in a Princes Councell.   Thus honour
keepes peace with him to the grave, and doth not
(as with many) there forsake him, and goe backe
with the Heralds : but fairely sits ore him, and
broods out of his memory, many right excellent
Common-wealths men.

A Quacksalver

Is a Mountebanke of a larger bill then a Taylor;
if hee can but come by names enow of Diseases, to
stuffe it with, tis all the skill hee studies for.   Hee
tooke his first being from a Cunning woman, and
stole this blacke Art from her while hee made her
Sea-coale fire.   All the diseases ever sinne brought
upon man, doth he pretend to bee Curer of; when
the truth is, his maine cunning is Corne-cutting.   A
great plague makes him; what with rayling against

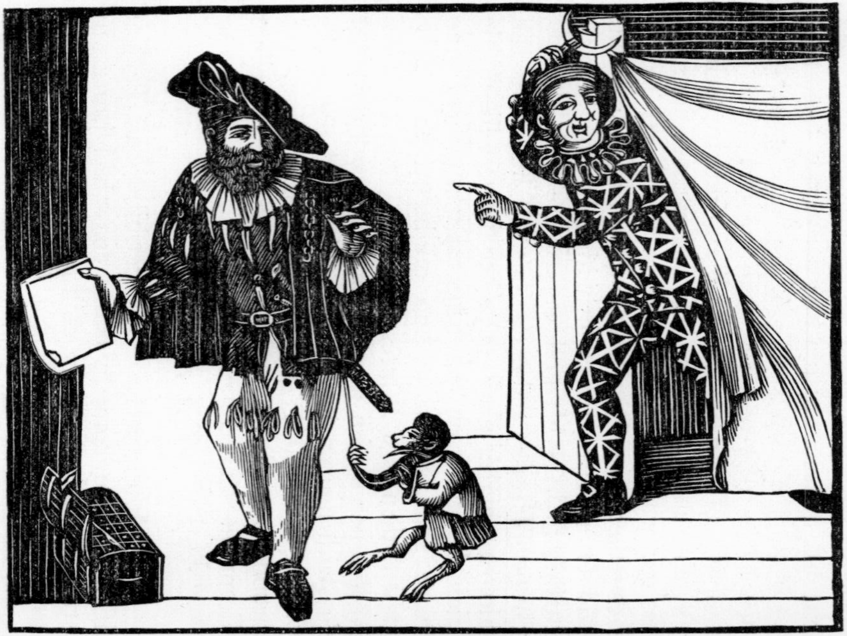

THE QUACK-DOCTOR

such, as leave their cures for feare of infection, and
in friendly breaking Cake-bread, with the Fish-
wives at Funerals, hee utters a most abominable
deale of musty *Carduus-water*, and the Conduits
cry out, All the learned Doctors may cast their
Caps at him. Hee parts stakes with some Apothecary in the Suburbes, at whose house hee lies:
and though he be never so familiar with his wife,
the Apothecary dare not (for the richest horne in
his shop) displease him. All the Mid-wives in the
Towne are his intelligencers; but Nurses and young
Marchants Wives (that would faine conceive with
childe) these are his Idolaters. Hee is a more
unjust Bone-setter, then a Dice-maker; hath put
out more eyes then the small Pox; made more deafe
then the *Cataracts* of *Nilus;* lamed more then the
Gout; shrunke more sinewes, then one that makes
Bow-strings; and kild more idly, then Tobacco.
A Magistrate that had any way so noble a spirit,
as but to love a good horse well, would not suffer
him to be a Farrier. His discourse is vomit; and
his ignorance, the strongest purgation in the world:
to one that would be speedily cured, hee hath more
delayes, and doubles then a Hare, or a Law-suit:
he seekes to set us at variance with nature, and
rather then hee shall want diseases he'le beget
them. His especiall practise (as I said afore) is
upon women; labours to make their mindes sicke,
ere their bodies feele it, and then there's worke for
the Dogleach. Hee pretends the cure of madmen;
and sure he gets most by them, for no man in his
perfect wit would meddle with him. Lastly, hee
is such a Juggler with Urinals, so dangerously un-
skilfull, that if ever the City will have recourse to

him for diseases that need purgation, let them
employ him in scouring *Moreditch*.

An excellent Actor

WHATSOEVER is commendable in the grave
Orator, is most exquisitly perfect in him; for by
a full and significant action of body, he charmes
our attention: sit in a full Theater, and you will
thinke you see so many lines drawne from the
circumference of so many eares, whiles the *Actor*
is the *Center*. He doth not strive to make nature
monstrous, shee is often seene in the same Scene
with him, but neither on Stilts nor Crutches; and
for his voice tis not lower then the prompter; nor
lowder then the Foile and Target. By his action
hee fortifies morall precepts with example; for what
wee see him personate, wee thinke truely done
before us: a man of a deepe thought might apprehend, the Ghosts of our ancient *Heroes* walk't
againe, and take him (at severall times) for many
of them. Hee is much affected to painting, and
tis a question whether that make him an excellent
Player, or his playing an exquisite Painter. Hee
addes grace to the Poets labours: for what in the
Poet is but ditty, in him is both ditty and musicke.
He entertaines us in the best leasure of our life,
that is betweene meales, the most unfit time either
for studie or bodily exercise. The flight of Hawkes
and chase of wilde beasts, either of them are
delights noble: but some thinke this sport of men
the worthier, despight all *calumny*. All men have
beene of his occupation: and indeed, what hee doth
fainedly, that doe others essentially: this day one
playes a Monarch, the next a private person. Here

one acts a Tyrant, on the morrow an Exile: A Parasite this man to night, to morrow a Precisian, and so of divers others. I observe, of all men living, a worthy Actor in one kinde is the strongest motive of affection that can be: for when hee dies, wee cannot be perswaded any man can doe his parts like him. But to conclude, I value a worthy Actor by the corruption of some few of the quality, as I would doe gold in the oare; I should not minde the drosse but the purity of the mettall.

A Franklin

His outside is an ancient Yeoman of England, though his inside may give armes (with the best Gentleman) and ne're see the Herald. There is no truer servant in the house then himselfe. Though he bee Master he sayes not to his servants, goe to field, but let us goe; and with his owne eye, doth both fatten his flocke, and set forward all manner of husbandrie. Hee is taught by nature to bee contented with a little; his owne folde yeelds him both food and rayment: hee is pleas'd with any nourishment God sends whilest curious gluttonie ransackes, as it were, *Noahs Arke* for food, onely to feed the riot of one meale. He is nere knowne to goe to Law; understanding, to bee Law-bound among men, is like to bee hide-bound among his beasts; they thrive not under it: and that such men sleepe as unquietly, as if their pillowes were stuft with Lawyers pen-knives. When hee builds, no poore Tenants cottage hinders his prospect: they are indeed his Almes-houses, though there be painted on them no such superscription. Hee never sits up late, but when he

hunts the Badger, the vowed foe of his Lambes:
nor uses hee any cruelty, but when he hunts the
Hare, nor subtilty but when hee setteth snares
for the Snipe, or pitfals for the Blacke-bird; nor
oppression, but when in the moneth of July, hee
goes to the next river, and sheares his sheepe.
Hee allowes of honest pastime, and thinkes not
the bones of the dead any thing bruised, or the
worse for it, though the country Lasses dance in
the Church-yard after Even-song. Rocke-Mon-
day, and the Wake in Summer, shrovings, the
wakefull ketches on Christmas Eve, the Hoky,
or Seed-cake, these he yerely keeps, yet holds
them no reliques of Popery. Hee is not so in-
quisitive after newes derived from the privie closet,
when the finding an eiery of Hawkes in his owne
ground, or the foaling of a Colt come of a good
straine, are tydings more pleasant, more profitable. He is Lord paramount within himselfe,
though hee hold by never so meane a Tenure;
•and dyes the more contentedly (though hee leave
his heire young) in regard hee leaves him not
liable to a covetous Guardian. Lastly, to end
him; he cares not when his end comes; hee needes
not feare his Audit, for his *Quietus* is in heaven.

A Prison

IT should be Christs Hospitall: for most of
your wealthy citizens are good benefactors to it;
and yet it can hardly bee so, because so few in
it are kept upon almes. Charities house and this
are built many miles asunder. One thing notwithstanding is heere praise-worthy, for men in
this persecution cannot chuse but prove good

Christians, in that they are a kinde of Martyrs and suffer for the truth. And yet it is so cursed a peece of land, that the sonne is ashamed to bee his fathers heire in it. It is an infected pest-house all the yeare long: the plague sores of the law are the diseases heere hotly raigning. The Surgeons are Atturneyes and Pettifoggers, who kill more then they cure. *Lord have mercy upon us*, may well stand over these doores, for debt is a most dangerous and catching City pestilence. Some take this place for the walkes in Moorefields, (by reason the mad men are so neere) but the crosses heere and there are not alike. No: it is not halfe so sweet an ayre: for it is the dunghill of the law, upon which are throwne the ruines of Gentry, and the nasty heapes of voluntary-decayed Bankerupts: by which meanes it comes to be a perfect meddall of the iron age; sithence nothing but gingling of keies, ratling of shackles, bolts and grates are heere to be heard. It is the horse of Troy in whose wombe are shut up all the mad Greekes that were men of action. *The Nullum vacuum* (unlesse in prisoners bellies) is heere truely to be proved. One excellent effect is wrought by the place it selfe, for the arrantest coward breathing, being poasted hither, comes in three dayes to an admirable stomacke. Does any man desire to learne musicke? every man heere sings *Lachrymae* at first sight, and is hardly out; hee runnes division upon every note, and yet (to their commendations be it spoken) none of them (for all that division) doe trouble the Church; They are no Anabaptists; if you aske under what Horizon this Climate lies, the Bermudas and it are both under one and the same height. And whereas some suppose that this Iland (like that) is haunted with Devils, it is not so: for those Devils (so talked of and feared) are none else but hoggish Jailors. Hither you neede not saile, for it is a ship of it selfe: the Masters side is the upper decke: They in the common Jayle lie under hatches and helpe to ballast it; Intricate cases are the tacklings, Executions the Anchors, Capiasses the Cables, Chancerie-bils the huge Sailes, A long Terme the Mast, Law the Helme, a Judge the Pylot, a Councel the Purser, an Atturney the Boatswaine, his fleeting Clarke the Swabber, Bonds the Waves, Outlawries gusts, The Verdicts of Juries rough Windes, Extents the Rockes that split all in peeces. Or if it be not a Ship, yet this and a Shippe differ not much in the building; the one is a mooving misery, the other a standing. The first is seated on a Spring, the second on Pyles. Either this place is an Embleme of a Bawdy-house, or a Bawdy-house of it; for nothing is to be seene (in any Roome) but scurvy Beds and bare walles. But (not so much to dishonor it) it is an University of poore Schollers, in which three Arts are chiefly studied: To pray, to curse, and to write letters.

A Common cruel Jaylor

Is a creature mistaken in the making, for hee should be a Tyger, but the shape being thought too terrible, it is covered; and hee weares the vizor of a man, yet retaines the qualities of his former fiercenes, currishnesse, and ravening. Of that red earth, of which man was fashioned, this peece was

the basest, of the rubbish which was left, and
throwne by, came this Jaylor, his descent is then
more ancient, but more ignoble, for hee comes of
the race of those Angels that fell with *Lucifer*
from heaven, whither he never (or very hardly)
returnes. Of all his bunches of keyes not one
hath wards to open that doore; For this Jaylours
soule stands not upon those two Pillers that support heaven, (*Justice* and *Mercy*) it rather sits
upon those two foot-stooles of hell, *Wrong* and
Cruelty. Hee is a Judges slave, and a prisoner's
his. In this they differ, he is a voluntary one, the
other compeld. He is the *Hang-man* of the law
(with a lame hand) and if the law gave him all his
limbs perfect, hee would strike those on whom he
is glad to fawne. In fighting against a Debtor,
hee is a Creditors second; but observes not the
lawes of the *Duello*, for his play is foule, and on
all base advantages. His conscience and his
shackles hang up together, and are made very
neere of the same mettle, saving that the one is
harder then the other, and hath one property above
Iron, for that never melts. Hee distils money out
of poore mens teares, and growes fat by their
curses. No man comming to the practicall part of
Hell, can discharge it better, because here hee does
nothing but study the Theoricke of it. His house
is the picture of Hell in little, and the originall
of the letters Patents of his office stand exem-
plified there. A chamber of lowsie beds is better
worth to him then the best acre of corne-land in
England. Two things are hard to him (nay almost
impossible) viz : To save all his prisoners that
none ever escape, and to bee saved himselfe. His

eares are stopt to the cries of others, and Gods to his: and good reason, for lay the life of a man in one Scale, and his fees on the other, hee will lose the first to finde the second. He must looke for no mercy (if he desires Justice to be done him) for hee shewes none, and I thinke hee cares the lesse, because hee knowes heaven hath no neede of suche Tenants, the doores there want no Porters, for they stand ever open. If it were possible for all creatures in the world to sleepe every night, he only and a Tyrant cannot. That blessing is taken from them, and this curse comes in the steade, to bee ever in feare, and ever hated: what estate can be worse?

What a Character is

IF I must speake the Schoole-masters language, I will confesse that Character comes of this Infinitive moode χαραξω, which signifies to engrave, or make a deepe Impression. And for that cause, a letter (as A. B.) is called a Character.

Those Elements which wee learne first, leaving a strong seale in our memories.

Character is also taken for an Ægyptian Hieroglyphicke, for an imprese, or short Embleme; in little comprehending much.

To square out a Character by our English levell, it is a picture (reall or personall) quaintly drawne, in various colours, all of them heightned by one shadowing.

It is a quicke and soft touch of many strings, all shutting up in one musicall cloze: It is wits descant on any plaine song.

A Dunce

HE hath a soule drowned in a lumpe of flesh, or is a peece of earth that *Prometheus* put not halfe his proportion of fire into. A thing that hath neither edge of desire, nor feeling of affection in it; the most dangerous creature for confirming an *Atheist*, who would sweare his soule were nothing but the bare temperature of his body. He sleepes as he goes, and his thoughts seldome reach an inch further then his eies. The most part of the faculties of his soul lie fallow, or are like the restive Jades, that no spur can drive forwards towards the pursuit of any worthy designes. One of the most unprofitable of Gods creatures being as he is, a thing put cleane besides his right use, made fit for the cart and the flayle; and by mis-chance intangled amongst bookes and papers. A man cannot tell possibly what he is now good for, save to move up and downe and fill roome, or to serve as *animatum instrumentum*, for others to work withall in base imploiments, or to be foile for better wits, or to serve (as they say Monsters doe) to set out the varietie of nature, and orna-ment of the universe. He is meere nothing of himselfe, neither eates, nor drinkes, nor goes, nor spits, but by Imitation, for all which he hath set-formes and fashions, which he never varies, but stickes to, with the like plodding constancie, that a mill-horse followes his trace. Both the Muses and the Graces are his hard Mistresses, though he daily invocate them, though he sacrifice *Heca-tombs*, they still look asquint. You shall note him oft (besides his dull eye, and lowting head, and a certaine clammy benummed pace) by a faire displaied beard, a night cap, and a gowne, whose very wrincles proclaime him the true *Genius* of formalitie. But of all others his discourse, and compositions best speake him, both of them are much of one stuffe and fashion. Hee speakes just what his bookes or last company said unto him, without varying one whit, and very seldome understands himself. You may know by his discourse where he was last, for what he heard or read yesterday, he now dischargeth his memory or Note-book of, not his understanding, for it never came there. What hee hath he flings abroad at all adventures, without accomodating it to time, place, persons, or occasions. He commonly loseth himself in his tale, and flutters up and down windlesse without recovery, and whatsoever next presents it selfe, his heavy conceit seizeth upon and goeth along with, how ever *Heterogeneall* to his matter in hand. His Jests are either old flead *Proverbs*, or lean-sterv'd-hackney-*Apophthegms*, or poore verball quips, outworne by Servingmen, Tapsters, and Milkemaides, even laid aside by Balladers. Hee assents to all men that bring any shadow of reason, and you may make him when hee speakes most Dogmatically, even with one breath, to averre poore contradictions. His compositions differ only *terminorum positione* from dreames; nothing but rude heaps of immateriall, incoherent, drossie, rubbish stuffe, promiscuously thrust up together. Enough to infuse dulnesse and barrennesse of conceit into him that is so prodigall of his eares as to give the hearing. Enough to make a mans memory ake with suffering such durty stuffe cast into it. As unwelcome to any true conceit, as sluttish morsels, or wallowish potions to a nice stomacke, which whiles hee empties himselfe of, it stickes in his teeth, nor can hee bee deliuered without sweat, and sighes, and hems, and coughs, enough to shake his Grandams teeth out of her head. He spits, and scratches, and sprawles, and turnes like sicke men from one elbow to another, and deserves as much pitty during his torture, as men in fits of *Tertian Fevers*, or selfe-lashing Penitentiaries. In a word, rippe him quite asunder, and examine every shred of him, you shall finde him to bee just nothing, but the subject of nothing: the object of contempt; yet such as hee is you must take him, for there is no hope he should ever become better.

[By John Donne]

JOHN STEPHENS (fl. 1615)

Satyrical Essayes Characters And Others. Or Accurate and quick Descriptions, fitted to the life of their Subjects.... John Stephens. London,...1615. 8vo. 2nd edition 1615, reissued 1631. *A Friend* first in this.

50 characters.

Stephens' characters have an historical rather than a purely literary appeal. He preserves many details of permanent interest in connexion with the law or with country life, but though some of his sketches are freshly observed, his style is too often wordy and vague to have much attraction.

His 'common Player' was the torch in that bonfire which consumed for a time good feeling between the players and the lawyers : but we can be grateful for it, since by its light we can at last discern the figure of John Webster and can recognise him as the 'leader' of the players, and part-author of the Overburian collection.

The essay *Of Poetrie* contains a passage which is a pendant to the 'worthy Poet,' and beautiful in itself :—
'Poore and Prodigall haue been a Poets Titles : these have been fixt with a contemptive meaning : but I imagine they advance his qualitie ; for therefore he neglects wealth, because he feeles in himselfe a Jewell which can redeeme his bondage in adversitie.'

A worthy Poet

Is the purest essence of a worthy Man: He is confident of nature in nothing but the form, and an ingenious fitnesse to conceive the matter. So he approves nature as the motive, not the foundation or structure of his worthinesse. His workes doe every way pronounce both nourishment, delight,

and admiration to the readers soule : which makes
him neither rough, effeminate, nor windy : for by
a sweet contemperament of Tune and Ditty, hee
entices others to goodnesse; and shewes himselfe
perfect in the lesson.   Hee never writes upon a
full stomacke, and an empty head; or a full head,
and an emptie stomacke.   For he cannot make so
Divine a receptacle stoope to the sordid folly of
gall or envy, without strength : or strength of
braine stoope, and debase it selfe with hunting out
the bodies succour.   Hee is not so impartiall as
to condemne every new fashion, or taxe idle circumstance; nor so easie as to allow vices, and
account them generous humours.   So hee neither
seekes to enlarge his credit of bitternesse, by a
snarling severitie; nor to augment his substance
by insinuating courtshippe.   Hee hath more
debttors in knowledge among the present Writers,
then Creditors among the ancient Poets.   Hee is
possessed with an innocent libertie, which excludes
him from the slavish labour and meanes of setting
a glosse upon fraile commodities.   Whatsoever
therefore proceeds from him, proceedes without
a meaning to supply the worth, when the worke
is ended; by the addition of preparative verses at
the beginning; or the dispersed hire of acquaintance to extoll things indifferent.   He does not
therefore passionately affect high patronage, or any
further then hee may give freely; and so receive
back honest thankes.   The dangerous name and
the contempt of Poets, sprung from their multitude of corruptions, proves no disadvantage or
terrour to him : for such be his antidotes that he
can walke untouched, even through the worst

infection. He is no miserable selfe-lover, nor no unbounded prodigall: for he can communicate himselfe wisely to avoide dull reservednesse, but not make every thought common, to maintaine his market. It must be imputed to his perfect eye-sight, that he can see error, and avoide it without the hazard of a new one: As in Poems, so in projects, by an easie conjecture. Hee cannot flatter, nor bee flattered: If hee gives *Desert*, hee gives no more; and leaves *Hyperbole* in such a matter of importance: As for himselfe, he is so well knowne unto him-selfe, that neither publicke fame, nor yet his owne conceite, can make him overvalued in himselfe. Hee is an enemy to Atheists; for he is no Fatist nor Naturalist: hee therefore excludes *Lucke* and *Rime*, from the acceptance of his Poems; scorning to acknowledge the one as an efficient, the other as an essence, of his Muses favour. Hee paies back all his imitation with interest; whilst his Authors (if revived) would confesse their chiefe credit was to bee such a patterne: otherwise (for the most part) he proves himselfe the patterne, and the project in hand: Silver onely and sound mettall comprehends his nature: rubbing, motion, and customary usage, makes the brightnesse of both more eminent. No mervaile though he be Immortall, seeing he converts poyson into nourishment; even the worst objects and societies to a worthy use. When he is lastly silent (for he cannot die) hee findes a Monument prepared at others cost and remembrance, whilst his former actions bee a living Epitaph.

A common Player

Is *a slow Payer, seldome a Purchaser, never a Puritan.* The Statute hath done wisely to acknowledge him a Rogue: for his chiefe Essence is, *A dayly Counterfeite:* Hee hath been familiar so long with out-sides, that hee professes himselfe, (beeing unknowne) to bee an apparant Gentleman. But his thinne Felt, and his Silke Stockings, or his foule Linnen, and faire Doublet, doe (in him) bodily reveale the Broaker: So beeing not sutable, hee proves a *Motley:* his minde observing the same fashion of his body: both consist of parcells and remnants: but his minde hath commonly the newer fashion, and the newer stuffe: hee would not else hearken so passionatly after new Tunes, new Trickes, new Devises: These together apparrell his braine and understanding, whilest hee takes the materialls upon trust, and is himselfe the Taylor to take measure of his soules liking. If hee cannot beleeve, hee doth conjecture strongly; but dares not resolve upon particulars, till he hath either spoken, or heard the *Epilogue;* unlesse he be prevented; neither dares hee entitle good things *Good,* unlesse hee bee heartned on by the Multitude: till then, hee saith faintly what hee thinkes, with a willing purpose to recant or persist: So howsoever he pretends to have a royall Master, or Mistresse, his wages and dependance prove him to bee the servant of the people. The cautions of his judging humour (if hee dares undertake it) bee a certaine number of lying jests against the common Lawyer; hansome conceits against the fine Cour-

tiers; delicate quirkes against the rich Cuckold a
Cittizen; shadowed glaunces for good innocent
Ladies and Gentlewomen; with a nipping scoffe
for some honest Justice, who hath once imprisoned
him: or some thriftie Trades-man, who hath
allowed him no credit: alwayes remembred, his
object is, *A new Play*, or *A Play newly revived*.
Other Poems hee admits, as good fellowes take
Tobacco, or ignorant Burgesses give a voyce, for
company sake; as things that neither maintaine,
nor bee against him. Hee can seeme no lesse then
one in honour, or at least one mounted: for unto
miseries which persecute such, hee is most incident.
Hence it proceedes, that in the prosperous fortune
of a Play frequented, hee proves immoderate, and
falles into a Drunkards paradise, till it be *last* no
longer. Otherwise when adversities come, they
come together: For Lent and Shrove-tuesday bee
not farre asunder: then hee is dejected daily and
weekely: his blessings be neither lame nor monstrous: they goe upon foure legges; but move
slowly: and make as great a distance betweene
their steppes, as betweene the foure Tearmes. If
he marries, hee mistakes the Woman for the Boy
in Womans attire, by not respecting a difference in
the mischiefe. But so long as hee liues unmarried,
he mistakes the Boy, or a Whore for the Woman;
by courting the first on the stage, or visiting the
second at her devotions. Take him at the best,
he is but a shifting companion: for he lives effec-
tually by putting on, and putting off. If his profession were single, hee would thinke himselfe a
simple fellow, as hee doth all professions besides
his owne: His owne therefore is compounded of

all Natures, all Humours, all professions. Hee is politick enough to perceive the Common-wealths doubts of his licence, and therefore in spight of Parliaments or Statutes he incorporates himselfe by the title of a Brother-hood. I need not multiply his character; for boyes and every one, will no sooner see men of this Faculty walke along, but they will (unasked) informe you what hee is by the vulgar denomination.

A Friend

Is one of the waightiest sillables (God excepted) that English or any Language doth afford. He is neerer to me then marriage, or naturall kindred of the same bloud; because love without kindred or ceremony, is more to be admired; and by the consequent more precious. Marriage and Kindred goes oftentimes no further then the Name or Body; but friendship is annexed with unanimity. My Friend therfore is either disposed (as I am) well: or well disposed to make me better. His multitude of acquaintance doth not extenuate his love, nor devide his affection. His lower fortunes be not distasted, nor dissembled, nor swolne bigger then they bee. He must not be imployed in trifles and continually, like a servant; nor with expectation, like a Sonne: For an absolute Friend will finish (when importance calles) before he can be requested. He therefore among all, confutes the saying of *Wares proffer'd:* For what a Friend gives freely, (either to prevent request, or to supply a modest silence) inchants the party. Hee is much dearer, then my leggs and armes, for he is my body and my soule together. His honour is true love: which being so, hee loves because he *will not*, & not because he *cannot* alter: That man *cannot alter*, who cannot with honesty disclaime affection; as being tyed with dotage or favours above merrit and requitall: But friends *will not*: which signifies that their love depends upon approbation of the naked man. A Friend therefore must be freely chosen not painfully created: for jealousies and feares intrude when favours be not mutuall; if favours bee the first beginning. He is manifest to me, whilst invisible to the world: and is indeed much about the making of this Character; little in worth and little pleasing at the first sight. Hee is able and willing, to councell, to perform. A second meeting thinkes him fitt; A second tryall knowes him a fit Friend. The meere imagination of a friends love is an inchanted armor: my heart is impenetrable whilst I weare the comfort: for whether I survive or dye, my Friend pre-serves me. Time nor anger can dissolve his amity: for either he submits and I pardon, or I submit & he pardons. Hee is like a true Christian, that undertakes & suffers for Christs sake as a friend for his friends sake with equall joy, both credit and discredit, rest and travaile. Being once had, a friend is full enough, and true a needles epithite: for *I am his, he mine:* and being so, we are one to another the best or no friends. It is foolish Paganisme to worship the suns rising, which doth regard al alike with his Idolaters: and it is crazy dotage for any to honour that friend, who prostitutes his favour to the worlds liking. A perfect friend, thinkes friendship his felicity: without which estimation, the neerest friendship, is but a sociable custome: for man hath never made an action perfect, unlesse he drew felicitie from his actions nature.

NICHOLAS BRETON (?1545-?1626)

Characters Upon Essaies Morall, and Divine, ...
London ... 1615.   8vo.

16 characters (containing *Warre*).

The Good and the Badde, or Descriptions of the Worthies
and Unworthies of this Age. ... London, ... 1616.
4to.

50 characters (containing *A Worthy Marchant*).

Fantasticks : Serving for a Perpetuall Prognostication. ...
London, ... 1626.   4to.

36 characters.

> ' Nor will it irk thee, now and then to look
> On old-world pictures of his warbled prose
> Quaint Talks in Green Lanes and by Fire-side
> Nook.'
>   A. B. GROSART.

The device of contrast that Breton uses in *The Good and
the Badde* was a favourite one among the character-writers,
and Milton was in the fashion with his L'Allegro and
Il Penseroso.

Fantasticks contains thirty-seven short accounts ' in
description of the twelve houres, the twelve moneths, and
some special dayes in the yere.' [1]   In these prose pictures
Breton found himself.   They are dewy and sweet.

Fantasticks was in part reprinted and enlarged in 1661
as *The Twelue Moneths* ... By M. Stevenson, ... London,
Printed by M. S. for Thomas Jenner.   No reference was
made to Breton.   'Augustus' is one of the twelve attractive woodcuts added to this edition.

Warre

WARRE is a scourge of the wrath of God, which
by famine, fire, or sword, humbleth the spirits of

---

[1] Cf. Leigh Hunt's two essays called ' A Now.'

the Repentant, tryeth the patience of the Faith-full, and hardneth the hearts of the ungodly: it is the misery of Time, and the terror of Nature, the dispeopling of the Earth, and the ruine of hir Beauty: Hir life, is Action, hir food, Bloud, hir honour, Valor, and hir joy, Conquest. Shee is Valors exercise, and Honors adventure, Reasons trouble, and Peaces enemy: shee is the stout mans love, and the weake mans feare, the poore mans toile, and the rich mans plague: shee is the Armourers Benefactor, and the Chirurgions agent, the Cowards ague, and the Desperats overthrow: she is the wish of Envy, the plague of them that wish hir, the shipwracke of life, and the agent for death; The best of hir is, that shee is the seasoner of the body, and the manager of the minde, for the induring of labor, in the resolution of action: shee thunders in the Aire, rips up the Earth, cuts thorough the Seas, and consumes with the fire: shee is indeed the invention of Malice, the worke of Mischiefe, the musique of Hell, and the daunce of the Devill: she makes the end of Youth un-timely, and of Age wretched, the Cities sacke, and the Countries beggery: shee is the Captaines pride, and the Captives sorrow, the throat of bloud, and the grave of flesh: shee is the woe of the world, the punishment of sinne, the passage of danger, and, the Messenger of destruction: shee is the wise mans warning, and the fooles paiment, the godly mans griefe, and, the wicked mans game: In summe, so many are her woundes, so mortall her cures, so daungerous her course, and, so devilish her devises, that, I will wade no further in her rivers of bloud, but, only, thus conclude in her description: she is Gods curse, and Mans misery, hells Practise, and earthes Hell.

A Worthy Marchant

A WORTHY Marchant is the heire of adventure, whose hopes hang much upon winde: Upon a wodden horse he rides through the world, and in a merry Gale, makes a path through the Seas: he is a discoverer of Countries, and a finder out of commodities, resolute in his attempts, and royall in his expences: he is the life of Traffick, and the maintainer of Trade, the Sailers Master, and the Souldiers friend; hee is the exercise of the exchange, the honor of credit, the observation of Time, and the understanding of thrift: his studie is number, his care his accounts, his comfort his Consience, and his wealth his good Name: he feares not *Silla*, and sayles close by *Caribdis*, and having beaten out a storme, rides at rest in a harbour: by his Sea gaine, he makes his landpurchase, and by the knowledge of Trade, findes the key of Treasure: out of his travailes, he makes his discourses, and from his eye-observations, brings the Moddels of Architectures; he plants the earth with forraine fruits, and knowes at home what is good abroad: he is neat in apparell, modest in demeanure, dainty in dyet, and civill in his carriage. In summe, hee is the Pillar of a City, the enricher of a Country, the furnisher of a Court, and the worthy servant of a King.

The Spring

IT is now Spring: a time blest of the Heavens for the comfort of the Earth, now begins the

Sunne to give light unto the Ayre, and with the reflexion of his beames to warme the cold earth: the Beasts of the woods looke out into the plaines, and the fishes out of the deepe run up into the shallow waters, the breeding fowles fall to building of their nests, and the senselesse creatures gather life into their bodies, the Birds tune their throats to entertaine the Sunne rising, and the little flies begin to flocke in the ayre: now *Cupid* begins to nocke his Arrowes and sharpe their heads: and *Venus*, if she be, will be knowne what she is: Now *Pallas* and her Muses try the Poets in their Pamphlets, and *Diana*, if shee bee to bee seene, is a grace to her fayrest Nymph: Time is now gracious in Nature, & Nature in time: the Ayre wholesome, and the earth pleasant, and the sea not uncomfortable: the Aged feele a kind of youth, & Youth, the Spirit ful of life: it is the messenger of many pleasures: the Courtiers progresse, and the Farmers profit: the Labourers Harvest, and the Beggers Pilgrimage. In summe there is much good to be spoken of this time: but to avoyd tediousnes, I wil thus conclude of it: I hold it in all that I can see in it, the Jewell of time, and the Joy of Nature. Farewell.

Summer

IT is now Summer, & *Zephirus* with his sweet breath cooles the parching beames of *Titan:* the leaves of the trees are in whisper talkes of the blessings of the aire, while the Nightingale is tuning her throat to refresh the weary spirit of the Travayler: *Flora* now brings out her Wardrob, and richly embroydeth her greene Apron: the

Nymphes of the Woodes in consort with the Muses sing an *Ave* to the Morning, and a *Vale* to the Sunnes setting; the Lambes and the Rabbettes run at base in the sandy Warrens, and the Plow landes are covered with corne: the stately Hart is at Layre in the high wood, while the Hare in a furrow sits washing of her face: The Bull makes his walke like a Master of the field, and the broad-headed Oxe beares the Garland of the market: the Angler with a fly takes his pleasure with the fish, while the little Merline hath the Partridge in the foot: the Hony-dewes perfume the Ayre, and the Sunny-showers are the earths comfort: the Greyhound on the plaine makes the faire course: & the wel-mouthed Hound makes the Musicke of the woods: the Battaile of the field is now stoutly fought, and the proud Rye must stoupe to the Sickle: The Carters whistle cheeres his forehorse, and drinke and sweat is the life of the Labourer: Idle spirits are banished the limits of Honour, while the studious braine brings forth his wonder: the Azure Sky shewes the Heaven is gracious, and the glorious Sunne glads the spirit of Nature: The ripened fruits shew the beauty of the earth, and the brightnesse of the aire the glory of the heavens: In summe, for the world of worth that I find in it, I thus conclude of it: I hold it a most sweet season, the variety of pleasures, and the Paradise of Love. Farewell.

Harvest

It is now Harvest, and the Larke must lead her yong out of the nest: for the Sithe and the Sickle wil down with the grasse and the corne: Now are the hedges ful of Berries, & the highwayes full of Rogues, and the lazy Limmes must sleepe out their dinner: The Ant and the Bee worke for their winter provision, and after a frost, the Grashopper is not seene: Butter, milke and cheese, are the Labourers dyet, and a pot of goode Beere quickens his spirit. If there be no plague, the people are healthy, for continuance of motion is a preservation of nature: The fresh of the morning, and the coole of the Evening are the times of Court walkes; but the poore traveller treads out the whole day: Malt is now above wheat with a number of mad people, and a fine shirt is better then a Frize Jerkin: Peares and Plummes now ripen apace, and being of a watry substance, are cause of much sicknesse: The pipe and the taber now follow the Fayres, and they that have any money, make a gaine of their markets. Bucks now are in season, and Partridges are Rowen-taild, & a good Retriver is a Spaniell worth the keeping. In sum, it is a time of much worth, when, if God bee well pleased, the world will thrive the better. And to conclude, this is all that I will say of it: I hold it the Heavens Bounty, the Earths Beauty, and the Worlds Benefit. Farewell.

Winter

IT is now Winter, and Boreas beginnes to fill his cheekes with breath, shaketh the tops of the high Cedars, and hoyseth the waves of the sea, to the danger of the Saylers comfort: Now is the Earth nipt at the heart with a cold, and her Trees are disrobed of their rich apparell: there is a glasse set upon the face of the Waters, and the fishes are driven to the bottomes of the deepe: The Usurer now sits lapt in his furres, and the poore makes his breath, a fire to his fingers ends: Beautie is maskt for feare of the ayre, and youth runs to Physicke for Restoratives of Nature: The Stagge roares for losse of his strength, and the Flea makes his Castle in the wooll of a blanket: Cards and Dice now begin their harvest, and good Ale and Sack are the cause of civill warres: *Machiavil* and the Devill are in counsell upon destruction, and the wicked of the world make hast to hell: Money is such a Monopoly, that hee is not to be spoken of, and the delay of suits is the death of hope. In it selfe it is a wofull Season, the punishment of Nature's pride, and the play of misery. Farewell.

January

IT is now *January*, and *Time* beginnes to turne the wheel of his Revolution, the Woods begin to lose the beauty of their spreading boughs, and the proud Oke must stoop to the Axe: the Squirrell now surveyeth the Nut and the Maple, and the Hedgehogge rowles up himselfe like a football: an Apple and a Nutmeg make a Gossips cup: and the Ale and the Fagot are the Victuallers merchandise: the Northerne black Dust is the during Fuell, and the fruit of the Grape heats the stomacke of the Aged: Downe beds and quilted cappes are now in the pride of their service, and the Cooke and the Pantler are men of no meane office: the Oxe and the fat Weather now furnish the market, and the Coney is so ferreted, that she cannot keepe in her borough: the Currier & the Lime-rod are the death of the fowle, and the Faulcons bels ring the death of the Mallard: the trotting gelding makes a way through the mire, and the Hare & the Hound put the Huntsman to his horne: the barren Doe subscribes to the dish, and the smallest seed makes sauce to the greatest flesh: the dryed grasse is the horses ordinary, and the meale of the beanes makes him goe through with his trauell: Fishermen now have a cold trade, and travellers a foule journey: the Cook room now is not the worst place in the Ship, and the Shepheard hath a bleake seat on the Mountaine: the Blackbird leaveth not a berry on the thorne, and the garden earth is turned up for her roots, the water floods runne over the proud bankes, and the gaping Oister leaves his shell in the streets, while the proud Peacocke leaps into the pye: *Muscovia* commodities are now much in request, and the water Spaniell is a necessary servant: the Lode horse to the mill hath his full backe burthen; and the Thresher in the barne tryes the strength of his flayle: the Woodcocke and the Pheasant pay their lives for their feed, and the Hare after a course makes his hearse in a pye: the shoulder of a hog is a shooing horne to good drink, and a cold almes makes a begger shrug. To conclude, I hold it a time of little comfort, the rich mans charge, and the poore mans misery. Farewell.

February

IT is now *February*, & the sun is gotten up a Cocke-stride of his climbing, the Valleys now are painted white, and the brookes are full of water: the Frog goes to seeke out the Paddocke, and the Crow and the Rooke begin to mislike their old

Makes: forward Connies begin now to kindle, & the fat grounds are not without Lambes: the Gardiner fals to sorting of his seeds, and the Husbandman falls afresh to scowring of his Ploughshare: the Terme travellers make the Shooemakers Harvest, and the Chaundlers cheese makes the chalke walke apace: The Fishmonger sorts his ware against Lent; and a Lambe-Skinne is good for a lame arme: the waters now alter the nature of their softnes, and the soft earth is made stony hard: The Ayre is sharp and piercing, and the winds blow cold: the Tavernes and the Innes seldom lack Guests, & the Ostler knows how to gaine by his Hay: the hunting Horse is at the heeles of the Hound, while the ambling Nagge carrieth the Physitian and his footcloth: the blood of youth begins to spring, and the honour of Art is gotten by Exercise: The trees a little begin to bud, and the sap begins to rise up out of the root: Physick now hath work among weake bodies, and the Apothecaries drugges are very gainfull: There is hope of a better time not farre off, for this in itselfe is little comfortable: and for the small pleasure that I find in it, I will thus briefly conclude of it: It is the poor mans pick-purse, and the misers cut-throat, the enemy to pleasure, and the time of patience. Farewell.

March

IT is now March, and the Northerne wind dryeth up the Southerne durt: The tender Lippes are now maskt for fear of chopping, and the faire hands must not be ungloved: now riseth the Sunne a pretty step to his faire height, and Saint *Valentine* calls the birds together, where Nature is pleased in the varietie of love: the Fishes and the Frogs fall to their manner of generation, and the Adder dyes to bring forth her young: the Ayre is sharpe, but the Sunne is comfortable, and the day beginnes to lengthen: The forward Gardens give the fine Sallats, and a Nosegay of Violets is a present for a Lady: Now beginneth Nature (as it were) to wake out of her sleepe, and sends the Traveller to survey the walkes of the World: the sucking Rabbit is good for weake stomackes, and the dyet for the Rhume doth make a great Cure: The Farrier now is the horses Physitian, and the fat Dog feeds the Faulcon in the Mew: The Tree begins to bud, and the grasse to peepe abroad, while the Thrush with the Black-bird make a charme in the young Springs: the Milke-mayd with her best beloved, talke away wearinesse to the Market, and in an honest meaning, kind words doe no hurt: the Foot-ball now tryeth the legges of strength, and merry matches continue good fellowship: It is a time of much worke, and tedious to discourse of: but in all I find of it, I thus conclude in it: I hold it the Servant of Nature, and the Schoole-master of Art: the hope of labour, and the Subject of Reason. Farewell.

April

It is now *April*, and the Nightingale begins to tune her throat against May: the Sunny showers perfume the aire, and the Bees begin to goe abroad for honey: the Dewe, as in Pearles, hangs upon the tops of the grasse, while the Turtles sit billing upon the little greene boughes: the Trowt begins to play in the Brookes, and the Sammon leaves the Sea, to play in the fresh waters : The Garden bankes are full of gay flowers, and the Thorne and the Plumme send forth their faire Blossomes; the March Colt begins to play, and the Cosset Lamb is learned to butt. The Poets now make their studies in the woods, & the Youth of the Country make ready for the Morris-dance : the little Fishes lye nibling at a bait, and the Porpas playes in the pride of the tide : the Shepheards pipe entertaines the Princesse of *Arcadia*, and the healthfull Souldier hath a pleasant march. The Larke and the Lambe looke up at the Sun, and the Labourer is abroad by the dawning of the day : Sheepes eyes in Lambs heads, tell kind hearts strange tales, while faith and troth make the true Lovers knot : the aged haires find a fresh life, and the youthfull cheeks are as red as a cherry : It were a world to set doune the worth of this moneth; But in summe, I thus conclude, I hold it the Heavens blessing, and the Earths comfort. Farewell.

May

IT is now *May*, and the sweetnesse of the Aire refresheth every spirit : the sunny beames bring forth faire Blossomes, and the dripping Clouds water *Floraes* great garden : the male Deere puts out the Velvet head, and the pagled Doe is near her fawning : The Sparhawk now is drawne out of the mew, and the Fowler makes ready his whistle for the Quaile : the Larke sets the morning watch, and the evening, the Nightingale : the Barges like Bowers, keep the streams of the sweet Rivers, and the Mackrell with the Shad are taken prisoners in the Sea: the tall young Oke is cut downe for the Maypole: the Sithe and the Sickle are the Mowers furniture, and fayre weather makes the Labourer merry: the Physitian now prescribes the cold Whey, and the Apothecary gathers the dew for a medicine: Butter & Sage make the wholsome breakfast, but fresh cheese and creame are meat for a dainty mouth: and the Strawbery and the Pescod want no price in the market: the chicken and the Ducke are fatned for the market, and many a Goslin never lives to be a Goose. It is the moneth wherein Nature hath her full of mirth, and the Senses are filled with delights. I conclude, It is from the Heavens a Grace, & to the Earth a Gladnesse. Farewell.

June

IT is now *June*, and the Hay-makers are mustered to make an army for the field, where not alwayes in order, they march under the Bagge and the Bottle, when betwixt the Forke and the Rake, there is seene great force of armes: Now doth the broad Oke comfort the weary Laborer, while under his shady Boughes he sits singing to his bread and cheese: the Hay-cocke is the Poore mans Lodging, and the fresh River is his gracious Neighbour: Now the Faulcon and the Tassell try their wings at the Partridge, and the fat Bucke fils the great pasty: the trees are all in their rich aray: but the seely Sheep is turned out of his coat: the Roses and Sweet Herbes put the Distiller to his cunning, while the greene apples on the tree are ready for the great bellied wives: Now begins the Hare to gather up her heeles, and the Foxe lookes about him, for feare of the Hound: the Hooke and

the Sickle are making ready for harvest: the
Medow grounds gape for raine, and the Corne in
the eare begins to harden: the little Lads make
Pipes of the straw, and they that cannot dance, will
yet bee hopping: the Ayre now groweth somewhat
warme, and the coole winds are very comfortable:
the Sayler now makes merry passage, and the
nimble Foot-man runnes with pleasure: In briefe,
I thus conclude, I hold it a sweet season, the senses
perfume, and the spirits comfort. Farewell.

July

It is now *July*, and the sunne is gotten up to
his height, whose heat parcheth the earth, and
burnes up the grasse on the mountaines. Now
begins the Canon of heaven to rattle, and when
the fire is put to the charge, it breaketh out among
the Cloudes: the stones of congealed water cut off
the eares of the Corne: and the blacke stormes
affright the faint-hearted: the Stag and the Bucke
are now in pride of their time, and the hardnesse
of their heads makes them fit for the Horner: Now
hath the Sparhawke the Partridge in the foot, and
the Ferret doth tickle the Cony in the borough.
Now doeth the Farmer make ready his teame and
the Carter with his whip, hath no small pride in
his Whistle? Now doe the Reapers try their
backs and their Armes, and the lusty youthes pitch
the Sheafes into the Cart, The old Partridge calles
her Covey in the morning, and in the evening,
the Shepheard fals to folding of his flocke: the
Sparrowes make a charme upon the greene Bushes,
till the Fowler come and take them by the dozens:
the Smelt now begins to be in season, and the Lam-

prey out of the River leapes into a Pye: the Souldier now hath a hot march, and the Lawyer sweats in his lyned Gowne: The Pedler now makes a long walke, and the *Aqua vitae* Bottle sets his face on a fiery heat: In summe, I thus conclude of it, I hold it a profitable season, the Labourers gaine, and the rich mans wealth. Farewell.

August

IT is now *August*, and the Sunne is somewhat towards his declination, yet such is his heat as hardeneth the soft clay, dries up the standing pondes, wythereth the sappy leaves, and scorcheth the skin of the naked: now beginne the Gleaners to follow the Corne Cart, and a little bread to a great deale of drinke makes the Travailers dinner: the Melowne and the Cucumber is now in request: and Oyle and vinegar give attendance on the Sallet hearbes: the Alehouse is more frequented then the Taverne, and a fresh River is more comfortable then a fiery Furnace: the Bathe is now much visited by diseased bodies, and in the fayre Rivers, swimming is a sweet exercise: the Bow and the Bowle picke many a purse, and the Cockes with their heeles spurne away many a mans wealth: The Pipe and the Taber is now lustily set on worke, and the Lad and the Lasse will have no lead on their heeles: the new Wheat makes the Gossips Cake, and the Bride cup is caried above the heads of the whole Parish: the Furmenty pot welcomes home the Harvest cart, and the Garland of Flowers crownes the Captaine of the Reapers. Oh, 'tis the merry time, wherein honest Neighbours make good cheere, and God is glorified in his blessings on the

Augustus

Dayes-39

earth.   In summe, for that I find, I thus conclude,
I hold it the worlds welfare, and the earths
Warming-pan.   Farewell.

September

IT is now *September* and the Sunne begins to
fall much from his height, the medowes are left
bare, by the mouthes of hungry Cattell, and the
Hogges are turned into the Corne-fields: the
windes begin to knocke the Apples heads together
on the trees, and the fallings are gathered to fill the
Pyes for the Houshold: the Saylers fall to worke
to get afore the winde, and if they spy a storme,
it puts them to prayer: the Souldier now begins
to shrug at the weather, and the Campe dissolved,
the Companies are put to Garison: the Lawyer
now begins his Harvest, and the Client payes for
words by waight: the Innes now begin to provide
for ghests, and the night-eaters in the stable, pinch
the Travailer in his bed: Paper, pen and inke are
much in request, and the quarter Sessions take
order with the way-layers: Coales and wood make
toward the Chimney, and Ale and Sacke are in
account with good fellowes: the Butcher now
knocks downe the great Beeves, and the Poulters
feathers make toward the Upholster: Walflet
Oysters are the Fish wives wealth, and Pippins
fine are the Costermongers rich merchandise: the
flayle and the fan fall to worke in the Barne, and
the Corne market is full of the Bakers: the
Porkets now are driven to the Woods, and the
home-fed Pigges make porke for the market.   In
briefe, I thus conclude of it, I hold it the Winters
forewarning, and the Summers farewell.   Adieu.

October

IT is now *October*, and the lofty windes make bare the trees of their leaves, while the hogs in the Woods grow fat with the falne Acorns: the forward Deere begin to goe to rut, and the barren Doe groweth good meat: the Basket-makers now gather their rods, and the fishers laye their leapes in the deepe: the loade horses goe apace to the Mill, and the Meal-market is seldome without people: the Hare on the hill makes the Greyhound a faire course, & the Foxe in the woods cals the Hounds to a full cry: the multitude of people raiseth the price of wares, and the smooth tongue will sell much: the Saylor now bestirreth his stumps, while the Merchant liveth in feare of the weather: the great feasts are now at hand for the City, but the poore must not beg for feare of the stockes; a fire and a paire of Cards keepe the ghests in the Ordinary, and Tobacco is held very precious for the Rhewme: The Coaches now begin to rattle in the Street: but the cry of the poore is unpleasing to the rich: Muffes and Cuffes are now in request, and the shuttel-Cocke with the Battel-doore is a pretty house-exercise: Tennis & Baloune are sports of some charge, and a quicke bandy is the Court-keepers commodity: dancing and fencing are now in some use, and kind hearts and true Lovers lye close to keep off cold: the Titmouse now keepes in the hollow tree, and the black bird sits close in the bottome of a hedge: In briefe, for the fresh pleasure I find in it, I thus conclude of it: I hold it a Messenger of ill newes, and a second service to a cold dinner. Farewell.

November

IT is now *November*, and according to the old Proverbe, Let the Thresher take his flayle, and the ship no more sayle: for the high winds and the rough seas will try the ribs of the Shippe and the hearts of the Sailers: Now come the Countrey people all wet to the Market, and the toyling Carriers are pittifully moyled: The yong Herne and the Shoulerd are now fat for the great Feast, and the Woodcocke begins to make toward the Cockeshoot: the Warriners now beginne to plie their harvest, and the Butcher, after a good bargaine drinkes a health to the Grasier: the Cooke and the Comfitmaker make ready for Christmas, and the Minstrels in the Countrey, beat their boyes for false fingring: Schollers before breakfast have a cold stomacke to their bookes, and a Master without Art is fit for an *A. B. C.* A red herring and a cup of Sacke, make warre in a weake stomacke, and the poore mans fast is better then the Gluttons surfet: Trenchers and dishes are now necessary servants, and a locke to the Cubboord keepes a bit for a neede: Now beginnes the Goshawke to weede the wood of the Phesant, and the Mallard loues not to heare the belles of the Faulcon: The Winds now are cold, and the Ayre chill, and the poore die through want of Charitie: Butter and Cheese beginne to rayse their prices, and Kitchen stuffe is a commoditie, that every man is not acquainted with. In summe, with a conceit of the chilling cold of it, I thus conclude in it: I hold it the discomfort of Nature, and Reasons patience. Farewell.

December

IT is now *December*, & hee that walkes the streets, shall find durt on his shooes, except hee goe all in bootes: Now doth the Lawyer make an end of his harvest, and the Client of his purse: Now Capons and Hennes, besides Turkies, Geese and Duckes, besides Beefe and Mutton, must all die for the great feast, for in twelve dayes a multitude of people will not bee fed with a little: Now plummes and spice, Sugar and Honey, square it among pies and broth, and Gossip I drinke to you, and you are welcome, and I thanke you, and how doe you, and I pray you bee merrie: Nowe are the Taylors and the Tiremakers full of worke against the Holidayes, and Musicke now must bee in tune, or else never: the youth must dance and sing, and the aged sit by the fire. It is the Law of Nature, and no Contradiction in reason: The Asse that hath borne all the yeare, must now take a little rest, and the leane Oxe must feed till hee bee fat: the Footman now shall have many a foule step, and the Ostler shall haue worke enough about the heeles of the Horses, while the Tapster, if hee take not heed, will lie drunke in the Seller: The prices of meat will rise apace, and the apparell of the proud will make the Taylor rich: Dice and Cardes, will benefit the Butler: And if the Cooke doe not lacke wit, hee will sweetly licke his fingers: Starchers and Launderers will have their hands full of worke, and Periwigs and painting will not be a little set by, strange stuffes will bee well sold, strange tales well told, strange sights much sought, strange things much bought, and what else as fals out.

To conclude, I hold it the costly Purveyour of Excesse, and the after breeder of necessitie, the practice of Folly, and the Purgatory of Reason. Farewell.

GEORGE WITHER (1588-1667)

The Schollers Purgatory, Discovered In the Stationers
 Commonwealth. . . . By Geo : Wither. . . . Imprinted
 for the Honest Stationers. [London, 1625], 8vo.

The Schollers Purgatory is a vigorous account of the
quarrel between Wither and the Stationers' Company.
Wither had obtained a Royal privilege to print his *Hymnes
& Songs of the Church*, and the Stationers had thereupon
' uncivelly abused him,' so jealous were they when a private
author, not being a stationer, thus occasionally derived
some profit from his books.   As a rule the author sold his
work outright.

Wither concludes his case with these two attractive
sketches, written with vivid sincerity.

An honest Stationer

AN honest Stationer is he, that exercizeth his
Mystery (whether it be in printing, bynding, or
selling of Bookes) with more respect to the glory
of God, & the publique advantage, then to his
owne commodity : & is both an ornament, & a
profitable member in a civill Commonwealth.   He
is the Caterer that gathers provision to satisfy the
curious appetite of the Soule, & is carefull to his
powre that whatsoever he provides shalbe such as
may not poyson or distemper the understanding.
And, seeing the State intrusteth him with the dis-
posing of those Bookes, which may both profitt
& hurt, as they are applyed, (like a discreet Apothecary in selling poysnous druggs) he observes by
whom, & to what purpose, such bookes are likely
to be bought up, before he will deliver them out

of his hands.   If he be a Printer, he makes conscience to exemplefy his Coppy fayrely, & truly.
If he be a Booke-bynder; he is carefull his worke
may bee strong & serviceable.   If he be a seller of
Bookes, he is no meere Bookeseller (that is) one
who selleth meerely ynck & paper bundled vp
together for his owne advantage only; but he is
the Chapman of Arts, of wisedome, & of much
experience for a litle money.   He would not publish a booke tending to schisme, or prophannesse,
for the greatest gain: & if you see in his shopp,
any bookes vaine or impertinent; it is not so much
to be imputed his fault, as to the vanity of the
Tymes: For when bookes come forth allowed by
authority, he holds it his duty, rather to sell them,
then to censure them: Yet, he meddles as little
as he can, with such as he is truly perswaded are
pernitious, or altogether unprofitable.

The reputation of Schollers, is as deare unto him
as his owne: For, he acknowledgeth, that from
them, his Mystery had both begining and meanes
of continuance.   He heartely loves & seekes the
prosperity of his owne Corporation: Yet he would
not injure the Universityes, to advantage it, norbe
soe sawcie as to make comparisons betweene them.
He loves a good Author as his Brother, and will
be ready to yeeld him the due portion of his labors,
without wrangling. . . .

In a word, he is such a man that the State ought
to cherish him; Schollers to love him; good Customers to frequent his shopp; and the whole Company of Stationers to pray for him; . . .

A meere Stationer

A MEERE Stationer is he that imagines he was borne altogether for himselfe, and exercizeth his Mystery without any respect either to the glory of God, or the publike advantage. For which cause, he is one of the most pernitious superfluities in a Christian gover[n]ment, and may be well termed the Devills seedman; seeing he is the aptest Instrument to sowe schismes, heresies, scandalls, and seditions through the world. What booke soever he may have hope to gaine by, he will divulge; though it contayne matter against his Prince, against the State, or blasphemy against God; And all his excuse wil be, that he knew not it comprehended any such matter. For (give him his right) he scarcely reads over one page of a booke in seaven yeare, except it be some such history as the Wise men of Gotham; and that he doth to furnish himselfe with some foolish conceits to be thought facetious. He prayseth no booke, but what sells well, and that must be his owne Coppy too or els he will have some flirt at it: No matter, though there be no cause; For, he knowes he shall not be questioned for what hee sayes; or if he be, his impudence is enough to outface it. What he beleeves is prepared for him, in the next world, I know not, but, for his enriching in this life, he is of so large a faith, that he seemes to beleeve, all Creatures and Actions of the world, were ordayned for no other purpose but to make bookes upon, to encrease his trade: And if another man, of his small understanding, should heare him plead his owne supposed right where none might contradict;

He would halfe thinke, that all our Universityes,
and Schooles of Learning, were erected to no other
end, but to breed Schollers to study for the enriching of the Company of Stationers. . . . He
will fawne upon Authors at his first acqu[a]int-
ance, & ring them to his hive, by the promising
sounds of some good entertainement; but assoone
as they have prepared the hony to his hand, he
drives the Bees to seek another Stall. If he be a
Printer, so his worke have such appearance of
being well done, that he may receave his hyre, he
cares not how unworkmanlike it be parformed; nor
how many faults he lett goe to the Authors discredit, & the readers trouble. If his employment
be in bynding bookes; soe they will hold together
but till his worke Maister hath sold them, he
desireth not, they should last a weeke longer : For,
by that meanes a booke of a Crowne is mard in one
Moneth, which would last a hundred yeares, if it
had 2d. more workmanshipp; & so, their gaine &
employment is encreased to the subjects losse. If
he be a seller of Bookes; he makes no conscience
what trash he putts off : nor how much he takes,
for that which is worth nothing. He will not stick
to belye his Authors intentions, or to publish
secretly that there is somewhat in his new ym-
printed books, against the State, or some Honor-
able personages; that so, they being questioned his
ware may haue the quicker sale. He makes no
scruple to put out the right Authors Name, & insert
another in the second edition of a Booke; And
when the impression of some pamphlet lyes upon
his hands, to imprint new Titles for yt, (and so take
mens moneyes twice or thrice, for the same matter

under diverse names) is no injury in his opinion. If he gett any written Coppy into his powre, likely to be vendible; whether the Author be willing or no, he will publish it; And it shall be contrived and named alsoe, according to his owne pleasure: which is the reason, so many good Bookes come forth imperfect, and with foolish titles. Nay, he oftentymes giues bookes such names as in his opinion will make them saleable, when there is litle or nothing in the whole volume sutable to such a Tytle. . . .

To conclude, he is a dangerous excrement, worthy to be cutt off, by the State; to be detested of all Schollers; to be shun'd of all the people; & deserves to be curst, & expeld out of the Company of Stationers.

JOHN EARLE (?1601-1665)

Micro-cosmographie. Or, A Peece of The World Discovered; In Essayes And Characters. London,... for Edward Blount, 1628. 12mo.

54 characters.

The fift edition 1629.

77 characters. The last seven in the selection first appeared in this.

12 editions in the 17th century. Many since. A useful one is in the Temple Classics series, this includes the first reprint of Healey's translation of Theophrastus.

78 characters.

'Overbury' is often intent on playing with the superficial, Earle on registering with quiet humour what the superficial meant. Some of his most skilful analyses are of colourless types which were usually ignored, because their appeal becomes most evident only when such an observer as Earle can treat their situation as a problem of psychology. His sympathetic studies of such as a poor man, or a weak man, not only describe these types, but make them newly intelligible. Earle is the most contemplative writer of all who followed the character-fashion, but, unlike others of this quality, he can make his points with the incisiveness of Overbury at his best. He gives us the Plodding Student in a sentence, 'His Studie is not great but continuall, and consists much in the sitting up till after Mid-night in a rug-gowne, and a Night-cap to the vanquishing perhaps of some sixe lines.'

'Nothing angers' the Shee-precise Hypocrite 'so much as that Women cannot Preach, and in this point onely thinkes the Brownist erroneous.' Her point was touched on by the satirist who chose the inscription on the woodcut for his sketch of a Brownist, or *Lucifers Lacky* ('the 12. of December. 1641'). The cut had already appeared, with another motto, in John Taylor's *A Swarme of Sectaries* (1641). The woodcut has been taken from the latter, the inscription from the former.

A Childe

Is a man in a small Letter, yet the best Copie of *Adam* before hee tasted of *Eve*, or the Apple; and hee is happy whose small practice in the World can only write this Character. Hee is natures fresh picture newly drawn in Oyle, which time and much handling, dimmes and defaces. His Soule is yet a white paper unscribbled with observations of the world, wherewith at length it becomes a blurr'd Note-booke. He is purely happy, because he knowes no evill, nor hath made meanes by sinne, to bee acquainted with misery. Hee arrives not at the mischiefe of being wise, nor endures evils to come by foreseeing them. He kisses and loves all, and when the smart of the rod is past, smiles on his beater. Nature and his Parents alike dandle him, and tice him on with a bait of Sugar, to a draught of Worme-wood. He playes yet, like a young Prentise the first day, and is not come to his taske of melancholly. His hardest labour is his tongue, as if he were loath to use so deceitfull an Organ; and hee is best company with it when hee can but prattle. Wee laugh at his foolish sports, but his game is our earnest: and his drummes, rattles and hobby-horses, but the Emblems, & mocking of mans businesse. His father hath writ him as his owne little story, wherein hee reades those dayes of his life that hee cannot remember; and sighes to see what innocence he has outliv'd. The elder he growes, hee is a stayer lower from

God; and like his first father much worse in his breeches. He is the Christians example, and the old man's relapse: The one imitates his purenesse, and the other fals into his simplicitie. Could hee put off his body with his little Coate, he had got eternitie without a burthen, and exchang'd but one heaven for another.

An Antiquary

HEE is a man strangely thrifty of Time past, & an enemy indeed to his Maw, whence hee fetches out many things when they are now all rotten and stinking. Hee is one that hath that unnaturall disease to bee enamour'd of old age, and wrinckles, and loves all things (as Dutchmen doe Cheese) the better for being mouldy and worme-eaten. He is of our Religion, because wee say it is most ancient; and yet a broken Statue would almost make him an Idolater. A great admirer he is of the rust of old Monuments, and reades onely those Characters, where time hath eaten out the letters. Hee will goe you forty miles to see a Saints Well, or ruin'd Abbey: and if there be but a Crosse or stone foot-stoole in the way, hee'l be considering it so long, till he forget his journey. His estate consists much in shekels, and Roman Coynes, and hee hath more Pictures of Cæsar, then *James* or *Elizabeth*. Beggers coozen him with musty things which they have rak't from dunghils, and he preserves their rags for precious Reliques. He loves no Library, but where there are more Spiders volums then Authors, and lookes with great admiration on the Antique work of Cob-webs. Printed bookes he contemnes, as a novelty of this latter age; but a Manu-script he pores on ever-lastingly especially if the cover be all Moth-eaten, and the dust make a Parenthesis betweene every Syllable. He would give all the Bookes in his Study (which are rarities all) for one of the old Romane binding, or sixe lines of *Tully* in his owne hand. His chamber is hung commonly with strange Beasts skins, and is a kind of Charnel-house of bones extraordinary, and his discourse upon them, if you will heare him shall last longer. His very atyre is that which is the eldest out of fashion, and you may picke a Criticism out of his Breeches. He never lookes upon himself till he is gray-hair'd, and then he is pleased with his owne Antiquity. His Grave do's not fright him, for he ha's been us'd to Sepulchers, and hee likes Death the better, because it gathers him to his Fathers.

A Taverne

Is a degree, or (if you will) a paire of stayres above an Alehouse, where men are drunke with more credit and Apologie. If the Vintners nose be at doore, it is a signe sufficient, but the absence of this is supplyed by the Ivie bush : The rooms are il breath'd, like the drinkers that have bin washt well over night, and are smelt too fasting next morning; not furnisht with beds apt to be defil'd, but more necessary implements, Stooles, Table, and a Chamber-pot. It is a broacher of more newes then hogs-heads, & more jests then newes, which are suckt up heere by some spungy braine, and from thence squeaz'd into a Comedy. Men come heere to make merry, but indeed make a

noise, and this Musicke above is answered with
the clinking below. The Drawers are the civillest
people in it, men of good bringing up, and howsoever wee esteeme of them, none can boast more
justly of their high calling. Tis the best Theater
of natures, where they are truely acted, not plaid,
and the busines as in the rest of the world up and
downe, to wit, from the bottome of the Seller to
the great Chamber. A melancholy Man would
finde heere matter to worke upon, to see Heads
as brittle as Glasses, and ofter broken. Men come
hither to quarrell, and come hither to be made
friends, and if *Plutarch* will lend me his Simile, it
is even *Telephus* his sword that makes wounds,
and cures them. It is the common consumption
of the Afternoone, and the murderer, or maker
away of a rainy day. It is the Torrid Zone that
scorches the face, and Tobacco the gun-powder
that blowes it up. Much harme would be done,
if the charitable Vintener had not Water readie for
these flames. A house of sinne you may call it,
but not a house of darkenesse, for the Candles are
never out, and it is like those Countries far in the
North, where it is as cleare at mid-night as at
mid-day. After a long sitting, it becomes like a
street in a dashing showre, where the spouts are
flushing above, and the Conduits running below,
while the Jordans like swelling rivers overflow
their bankes. To give you the totall reckoning
of it. It is the busie mans recreation, the idle
mans businesse, the melancholy mans Sanctuary,
the strangers welcome, the Innes a Court mans
entertainment, the Schollers kindnesse, and the
Citizens curtesie. It is the studie of sparkling

wits, and a cup of Canary their booke, where we leave them.

An old Colledge Butler

Is none of the worst Students in the house, for he keepes the set houres at his booke more duly then any. His authority is great over mens good names, which hee charges many times with shrewd aspersions, which they hardly wipe off without payment. His Boxe and Counters prove him to be a man of reckoning; yet hee is stricter in his accounts then a Usurer, and delivers not a farthing without writing. He doubles the paine of *Gallo-belgicus*, for his bookes goe out once a quarter, and they are much in the same nature, briefe notes and summes of affaires, and are out of request as soone. His commings in are like a Taylors from the shreds of bread, the chippings and remnants of the broken crust: excepting his vailes from the barrell, which poore folkes buy for their hogs, but drinke themselves. He divides a halfepeny loafe with more subtilty then *Kekerman*, and sub-divides the *a primo ortum* so nicely, that a stomacke of great capacity can hardly apprehend it. Hee is a very sober man considering his mani-fold temptations of drinke and strangers, and if hee be over-seene, tis within his owne liberties, and no man ought to take exceptions. He is never so well pleas'd with his place, as when a Gentle-man is beholding to him for shewing him the Buttery, whom hee greets with a cup of single beere and slyst manchet, and tels him tis the fashion of the Colledge. Hee domineers over Freshmen when they first come to the Hatch, and puzzles them with strange language of Cues and Cees, and some broken Latine which he ha's learnt at his Bin. His faculties extraordinary, is the warming of a paire of Cards, and telling out a doozen of Counters for Post and Paire, and no man is more methodicall in these businesses. Thus he spends his age, till the tappe of it is runne out, and then a fresh one is set abroach.

A downe-right Scholler

Is one that has much learning in the Ore, un-wrought and untryed, which time and experience fashions and refines. He is good mettall in the inside, though rough & unscour'd without, and therefore hated of the Courtier, that is quite con-trarie. The time has got a veine of making him ridiculous, and men laugh at him by tradition, and no unluckie absurdity, but is put upon his profession, and done like a Scholer. But his fault is onely this, that his minde is somewhat much taken up with his mind, and his thoughts not loaden with any carriage besides. Hee has not put on the quaint Garbe of the Age, which is now become a mans Totall. He has not humbled his Meditations to the industrie of Complement, not afflicted his braine in an elaborate legge. His body is not set upon nice Pinnes, to bee turning and flexible for every motion, but his scrape is homely, and his nod worse. He cannot kisse his hand and cry Madame, nor talke idly enough to beare her company. His smacking of a Gentle-woman is somewhat too savory, and he mistakes her nose for her lippe. A very Woodcocke would puzzle him in carving, and hee wants the logicke of a Capon.

He has not the glib faculty of sliding over a tale, but his words come squeamishly out of his mouth, and the laughter commonly before the jest. He names this word Colledge too often, and his discourse bears too much on the University. The perplexity of mannerlinesse will not let him feed, and he is sharpe set at an argument when hee should cut his meate. He is discarded for a gamester at all games but one and thirty, and at tables he reaches not beyond doublets. His fingers are not long and drawne out to handle a Fiddle, but his fist is cluncht with the habite of disputing. Hee ascends a horse somewhat sinisterly, though not on the left side, and they both goe jogging in griefe together He is exceedingly censur'd by the Innes a Court men, for that hainous Vice being out of fashion. Hee cannot speake to a Dogge in his owne Dialect, and understands Greeke better then the language of a Falconer. Hee has beene used to a darke roome, and darke Clothes, and his eyes dazzle at a Sattin Doublet. The Hermitage of his Study, has made him som what uncouth in the world, and men make him worse by staring on him. Thus is hee silly and ridiculous, and it continues with him for some quarter of a yeare, out of the Universitie. But practise him a little in men, and brush him ore with good companie, and hee shall outballance those glisterers as much as a solid substance do's a feather or Gold Gold-lace.

A Player

He knowes the right use of the World, wherein hee comes to play a part and so away, His life is

not idle for it is all Action, and no man need be
more wary in his doings, for the eyes of all men
are upon him. His profession ha's in it a kind of
contradiction, for none is more dislik'd and yet
none more applauded, and hee ha's this misfortune
of some Scholler, too much witte makes him a
foole. He is like our painting Gentle-women,
seldome in his owne face, seldomer in his cloathes,
and hee pleases, the better hee counterfeits, except
onely when hee is disguis'd with straw for gold
lace. Hee do's not only personate on the stage,
but sometime in the Street, for hee is maskd still
in the habite of a Gentleman. His Parts find him
oathes and good words, which he keepes for his
use and Discourse, and makes shew with them
of a fashionable Companion. He is tragicall on
the stage, but rampant in the Tyring-house, and
sweares oathes there which he never con'd. The
waiting women Spectators are over-eares in love
with him, and Ladies send for him to act in their
Chambers. Your Innes of Court men were undone
but for him, hee is their chiefe guest and imployment, and the sole businesse that makes them
Afternoones men; The Poet only is his Tyrant,
and hee is bound to make his friends friend drunk
at his charges. Shrove-tuesday hee feares as much
as the Baudes, and Lent is more damage to him
then the Butcher. Hee was never so much discredited as in one Act, & that was of Parliament,
which gives Hostlers Priviledge before him, for
which hee abhors it more then a corrupt Judge.
But to give him his due, one wel-furnisht Actor
has enough in him for five common Gentlemen,
and if he have a good body, for sixe, and for

resolution, hee shall Challenge any *Cato*, for it has beene his practise to die bravely.

A Cooke

THE Kitchin is his Hell, and hee the Divell in it, where his meate and he frye together. His Revennues are showr'd downe from the fat of the Land, and he enterlards his owne grease among to helpe the drippings. Colericke hee is, not by nature so much as his Art, and it is a shrewd temptation that the chopping knife is so neare. His weapons ofter offensive, are a messe of hot broth and scalding water, and woe bee to him that comes in his way. In the Kitchin he will domineere, and rule the roste, in spight of his Master, and Curses is the very Dialect of his Calling. His labour is meere blustring and furie, and his Speech like that of Sailors in a storme, a thousand businesses at once, yet in all this tumult hee do's not love combustion, but will bee the first man that shall goe and quench it. Hee is never good Christian till a hizzing Pot of Ale has slak't him, like Water cast on a firebrand, and for that time hee is tame and dispossest. His cunning is not small in Architecture, for hee builds strange Fabricks in Paste, Towers and Castles, which are offered to the assault of valiant teeth, and like *Darius* his Pallace, in one Banquet demolisht. Hee is a pittilesse murderer of Innocents, and hee mangles poore foules with unheard of tortures, and it is thought the Martyrs persecutions were devised from hence, sure we are Saint *Lawrence* his Gridiron came out of his Kitchin. His best facultie is at the Dresser, where hee seemes to have great skill in the Tactikes, ranging his Dishes in order, Militarie: and placing with great discretion in the fore-front meates more strong and hardy and the more cold and cowardly in the reare, as quaking Tarts, and quivering Custards, and such milke sop Dishes which scape many times the fury of the encounter. But now the second Course is gone up, and hee downe into the Sellar, where hee drinkes and sleeps till foure a clocke in the afternoone, and then returnes againe to his Regiment.

A Pretender to Learning

Is one that would make others more fooles then himselfe; for though he know nothing, he would not have the world know so much. He conceits nothing in Learning but the opinion, which he seekes to purchase without it, though hee might with lesse labour cure his ignorance, then hide it. He is indeed a kind of Scholler-Mountebank, and his Art, our delusion. He is trickt out in all the accoutrements of Learning, and at the first encounter none passes better. Hee is oftner in his study, then at his Booke, and you cannot pleasure him better, then to deprehend him. Yet he heares you not till the third knocke, and then comes out very angry, as interupted. You find him in his Slippers, and a Pen in his eare, in which formality he was asleep. His Table is spred wide with some Classicke Folio, which is as constant to it as the carpet, and hath laid open in the same Page this halfe yeere. His Candle is alwayes a longer sitter up then himselfe, and the boast of his

Window at Midnight. He walkes much alone in
the posture of Meditation, and ha's a Booke still
before his face in the fields. His pocket is seldome without a Greeke Testament, or Hebrew
Bible, which hee opens only in the Church, and
that when some stander by lookes over. He has
his sentences for Company, some scatterings of
Seneca and *Tacitus*, which are good upon all occasions. If he read anything in the morning, it
comes up all at dinner: and as long as that lasts,
the discourse is his. Hee is a great *Plagiarie* of
Taverne-wit: and comes to Sermons onely that hee
may talke of *Austin*. His Parcels are the meere
scrappings from Company, yet he complains at
parting what time he has lost. He is wondrously
capricious to seeme a judgement, and listens with
a sowre attention, to what hee understands not:
Hee talkes much of *Scaliger* and *Causabone*, and
the Jesuites, and prefers some unheard-of Dutch
name before them all. He has verses to bring in
upon these and these hints, and it shall goe hard
but he will wind in his opportunity. Hee is
criticall in a language hee cannot conster, and
speaks seldome under *Arminius* in Divinity. His
businesse and retirement and caller away is his
Study, and he protests no delight to it comparable.
Hee is a great Nomen-clator of Authors, which
hee has read in generall in the Catalogue, and in
particular in the Title, and goes seldome so farre
as the Dedication. Hee never talkes of any thing
but learning, and learnes all from talking. Three
incounters with the same men pumpe him, and
then hee onely puts in, or gravely sayes nothing.
He ha's taken paines to be an Asse, though not

to be a Scholler, and is at length discovered and
laught at.

A Pot-Poet

Is the dreggs of wit; yet mingled with good
drinke may have some relish. His Inspirations
are more reall then others; for they doe but faine
a God, but hee has his by him. His Verses run
like the Tap, and his invention as the Barrell, ebs
and flowes at the mercy of the spiggot. In thin
drinke hee aspires not above a Ballad, but a cup
of Sacke inflames him, and sets his Muse and Nose
a fire together. The Presse is his Mint, and stamps
him now and then a sixe pence or two in reward
of the baser coyne his Pamphlet. His workes
would scarce sell for three halfe pence, though they
are given oft for three Shillings, but for the pretty
Title that allures the Country Gentleman: and
for which the Printer maintaines him in Ale a
fortnight. His Verses are like his clothes, miserable Cento's and patches, yet their pace is not altogether so hobling as an Almanacks. The death
of a great man or the burning of a house furnish
him with an Argument, and the nine Muses are
out strait in mourning gowne, and *Melpomine
cryes* Fire, Fire. His other Poems are but Briefs
in Rime, and like the poore Greekes collections to
redeeme from captivity. He is a man now much
imploy'd in commendations of our Navy, and a
bitter inveigher against the Spaniard. His frequent'st Workes goe out in single sheets, and are
chanted from market to market, to a vile tune, and
a worse throat: whilst the poore Country wench
melts like her butter to heare them. And these

are the Stories of some men of Tiburne, or a
strange Monster out of Germany: or sitting in
a Baudy-house, hee writes Gods Judgements. Hee
ends at last in some obscure painted Cloth, to
which himselfe made the Verses, and his life like
a Canne too full spils upon the bench. He leaves
twenty shillings on the score, which my Hostesse
looses.

A Blunt Man

Is one whose wit is better pointed then his
behaviour, and that course, and Impollisht not out
of ignorance so much as humour. He is a great
enemy to the fine Gentleman, and these things of
Complement, and hates ceremony in conversation,
as the Puritan in Religion. Hee distinguishes not
betwixt faire and double-dealing, and suspects all
smoothnes for the dresse of knaverie. He starts
at the encounter of a Salutation as an assault, and
beseeches you in choller to forbeare your courtesie.
Hee loves not anything in Discourse that comes
before the purpose, and is alwaies suspicious of a
Preface. Himselfe falls rudely still on his matter
without any circumstance, except hee use an old
Proverbe for an Introduction. Hee sweares olde
out of date innocent othes, as by the Masse, by
our Ladie, and such like, and though there bee
Lords present, he cryes, My Masters. Hee is
exceedingly in love with his Humour, which
makes him always professe and proclaime it, and
you must take what hee sayes patiently, because
he is a plaine man. His nature is his excuse still,
and other mens Tyrant: for hee must speake his
mind, and that is his worst, and craves your pardon

most injuriously for not pardoning you. His
Jests best become him, because they come from
him rudely and unaffected: and hee has the lucke
commonly to have them famous. Hee is one that
will doe more then hee will speake, and yet speake
more then hee will heare: for though hee love to
touch others, he is touchy himselfe, and seldome
to his owne abuses replyes but with his Fists. Hee
is as squeazy of his commendations as his courtesie, and his good word is like an Elogie in a
Satyre. Hee is generally better favour'd then hee
favours, as being commonly well expounded in his
bitternesse, and no man speakes treason more
securely. Hee chides great men with most boldnesse, and is counted for it an honest fellow. Hee
is grumbling much in the behalfe of the Common-
wealth, and is in Prison oft for it with credit. He
is generally honest, but more generally thought so,
and his downe rightnesse credits him, as a man
not well bended and crookned to the times. In
conclusion, hee is not easily bad, in whom this
quality is Nature, but the counterfeit is most dangerous since hee is disguis'd in a humour, that
professes not to disguise.

A weake Man

Is [a child at mans estate][1] one whom Nature
huddled up in haste, and left his best part un-
finish't. The rest of him is growne to bee a man,
onely his braine stayes behind. Hee is a man that
ha's not improov'd his first rudiments, nor attain'd
any proficiencie by his stay in the world: but wee
may speake of him yet, as when hee was in the
budde, a good harmelesse nature, a well meaning

[1] Added in 1629

mind, if hee could order his intentions. It is his misery that hee now most wants a Tutor, and is too old to have one. Hee is two steps above a foole, and a great many mo below a wise-man: yet the foole is oft given him, and by those whom he esteems most. Some tokens of him are: Hee loves men better upon relation then experience: for he is exceedingly enamour'd of Strangers, and none quicklier a weary of his friends. Hee charges you at first meeting with all his secrets, and on better acquaintance growes more reserv'd. Indeed hee is one that mistakes much his abusers for friends, and his friends for enemies, and hee apprehends your hate in nothing so much, as in good counsell. One that is flexible with anything but reason, and then only perverse; & you may better intice then perswade him. A servant to every tale and flatterer, & whom the last man still works over. A great affecter of wits and such pretinesses; and his company is costly to him, for he seldom ha's it but invited. His friendship commonly is begun in a supper and lost in lending money. The Taverne is a dangerous place to him, for to drinke and to be drunke, is with him all one, and his braine is sooner quench'd then his thirst. He is drawn into naughtines with company, but suffers alone, and the Bastard commonly laid to his charge. One that will bee patiently abus'd, and take exceptions a Moneth after when he understands it, and then be abused again into a reconcilement; and you cannot endeare him more then by coozening him, and it is a temptation to those that would not. One discoverable in all sillinesses to all men but himselfe, & you may take any mans knowledge

of him better then his owne.   Hee will promise
the same thing to twenty, and rather then denie
one, breake with all.   One that ha's no power o're
himselfe, o'er his businesse, o're his friends: but
a prey and pitie to all: and if his fortunes once
sinke, men quickly crie, Alas, and forget him.

A Shee precise Hypocrite

Is one in whom good Women suffer, and have
their truth mis-interpreted by her folly.

She is one, she knows not what her selfe if you
aske her, but shee is indeed one that has taken a
toy at the fashion of Religion, and is enamour'd
of the New-fangle.   Shee is a Nonconformist in
a close Stomacher and Ruffe of Geneva Print, and
her puritie consists much in her Linnen.   Shee ha's
heard of the Rag of Rome, and thinkes it a very
sluttish Religion, and rayles at the Whore of
Babylon for a very naughty Woman.   Shee ha's
left her Virginity as a Relique of Popery, and
marries in her Tribe without a Ring.   Her devotion
at the Church is much in the turning up of her
eye, and turning downe the leafe in her Booke
when she heares nam'd Chapter and Verse.   When
she comes home, shee commends the Sermon for
the Scripture, and two houres.   She loves Preaching better then Praying, and of Preachers Lecturers, and thinkes the Weeke-dayes Exercise farre
more edifying then the Sundaies.   Her oftest Gos-
sippings are Sabaoth-dayes journeyes, where
(though an enemy to Superstition) shee will goe in
Pilgrimage five mile to a silenc'd Minister, when
there is a better Sermon in her owne Parish.   Shee
doubts of the Virgin Marie's Salvation, and dare

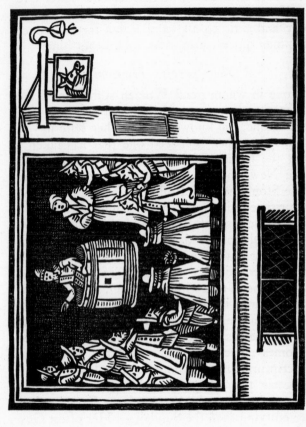

'When Women Preach, and Coblers Pray,
The fiends in Hell, make holiday.'

not Saint her, but knowes her own place in heaven as perfectly, as the Pew shee ha's a key to. Shee is so taken up with Faith, shee ha's no roome for Charity, and understands no good Workes, but what are wrought on the Sampler. She accounts nothing Vices but Superstition, and an Oath, and thinkes Adultery a lesse sinne, then to sweare by my Truely. Shee rayles at other Women by the names of *Jezabel* and *Dalilah:* and calls her owne daughters *Rebecka* and *Abigail*, and not *Anne* but *Hannah*. She suffers them not to learne on the Virginalls, because of their affinity with the Organs, but is reconcil'd to the Bells for the Chymes sake, since they were reform'd to the tune of a Psalme. She over flowes so with the Bible, that she spils it upon every occasion, and wil not Cudgell her Maides without Scripture. It is a question whether shee is more troubled with the Divell or the Divell with her: shee is alwayes challenging and daring him, and her weapons are Spels no lesse potent then different, as being the sage Sentences of some of her owne Sectaries. No thing angers her so much as that Women cannot Preach, and in this point onely thinkes the Brownist erroneous: but what shee cannot at the Church, shee do's at the Table, where she prattles more then any against sense, and Anti-christ, till a Capon wing silence her. Shee expounds the Priests of *Baal* Reading Ministers, and thinkes the Salvation of that Parish as desperate as the Turkes. Shee is a maine derider to her capacitie of those that are not her Preachers, and censures all Sermons but bad ones. If her Husband be a Tradesman, shee helpes him to Customers, however to good cheere, and they are

a most faithfull couple at these meetings for they
never faile. Her Conscience is like others Lust
never satisfied, and you might better answere
Scotus then her Scruples. Shee is one that thinkes
she performes all her duty to God in hearing, and
shewes the fruites of it in talking. Shee is more
fiery against the May-pole then her Husband, and
thinkes he might doe a Phinehas his act to break
the pate of the Fiddler. She is an everlasting
argument; but I am weary of her.

A Contemplative Man

Is a Scholler in this great University the World;
and the same his Booke and Study. Hee cloysters
not his Meditations in the narrow darknesse of a
Roome, but sends them abroad with his Eyes, and
his Braine travels with his Feete. He looks upon
Man from a high Tower, and sees him trulyer at
this distance in his Infirmities and poorenesse. He
scornes to mixe himselfe in men's actions, as he
would to act upon a Stage; but sits aloft on the
Scaffold a censuring Spectator. Nature admits
him as a partaker of her Sports, and asks his
approbation as it were of her owne Workes, and
variety. Hee comes not in Company, because hee
would not be solitary, but findes Discourse enough
with himselfe, and his owne thoughts are his excellent play-fellowes. He lookes not upon a thing
as a yawning Stranger at novelties; but his search
is more mysterious and inward, and hee spels
Heaven out of earth. He knits his observations
together, and makes a Ladder of them all to climbe
to God. He is free from vice, because he has no
occasion to imploy it, and is above those ends that

make men wicked. He ha's learnt all can heere be taught him, and comes now to Heaven to see more.

An Aturney

His Ancient beginning was a blue coat, since a livery, and his hatching under a Lawier; whence though but pen-feather'd, hee hath now nested for himselfe, and with his horded pence purchast an Office. Two Deskes, and a quire of Paper set him up, where he now sits in state for all commers. We can call him no great Author, yet he writes very much, and with the infamy of the Court is maintain'd in his libels. Hee ha's some smatch of a Scholler, and yet uses Latin very hardly, and lest it should accuse him, cuts it off in the midst, and will not let it speake out. He is contrary to great men, maintained by his followers, that is his poore country Clients, that worship him more then their Landlord, and be there never such churles, he lookes for their curtesie. He first racks them soundly himselfe, and then delivers them to the Lawier for execution. His looks are very solicitous importing much hast and dispatch, he is never without his handfull of businesse, that is, of paper. His skin becomes at last as dry as his parchment and his face as intricate as the most winding cause. He talkes Statutes as fiercely, as if he had mooted seven yeers in the Inns of Court; when all his skill is stucke in his girdle, or in his office window. Strife and wrangling have made him rich, and he is thankfull to his benefactor, and nourishes it. If he live in a Country village, he makes all his neighbours good Subjects; for there

shall be nothing done but what there is law for.
His businesse gives him not leave to thinke of
his conscience, and when the time, or terme of his
life is going out, for Doomes-day he is secure; for
he hopes he has a tricke to reverse judgement.

A vulgar-spirited Man

Is one of the heard of the World. One that
followes meerely the common crye, and makes it
louder by one. A man that loves none but who
are publikely affected, and he will not be wiser
then the rest of the Towne. That never ownes
a friend after an ill name, or some generall imputa-
tion though he knowes it most unworthy. That
opposes to reason, Thus men say, and thus most
doe, and thus the world goes, and thinkes this
enough to poyse the other. That worships men
in place, and those onely, and thinkes all a great
man speakes Oracles. Much taken with my Lords
Jest, and repeats you it all to a sillable. One that
justifies nothing out of fashion, nor any opinion
out of the applauded way. That thinkes certainly
all Spaniards and Jesuites very villaines, and is still
cursing the Pope and *Spynola*. One that thinkes
the gravest Cassocke the best Scholler: and the
best Clothes the finest man. That is taken onely
with broad and obscœne wit, and hisses anything
too deepe for him. That cries *Chaucer* for his
Money above all our English Poets, because the
voice ha's gone so, and hee ha's read none. That
is much ravisht with such a Noble man's courtesie,
and would venture his life for him, because he put
off his Hat. One that is formost still to kisse the
Kings hand, and cries *God blesse his Majestie*

loudest. That rayles on all men condemn'd and out of favour, and the first that sayes away with the Traytors: yet struck with much ruth at Executions, and for pittie to see a man die, could kill the Hang-man. That comes to London to see it, and the pretty things in it, and the chiefe cause of his journey the Beares: That measures the happinesse of the Kingdome, by the cheapnesse of corne; and conceives no harme of State, but il trading. Within this compasse too, come those that are too much wedg'd into the world, and have no lifting thoughts above those things that call to thrive, to doe well, and Preferment onely the grace of God. That ayme all Studies at this marke, & shew you poore Schollers as an example to take heed by. That thinke the Prison and want, a Judgement for some sin, and never like well hereafter of a Jaylebird. That know no other Content but wealth, bravery, and the Towne-Pleasures; that thinke all else but idle speculation, and the Philosophers, mad-men: In short, men that are carried away with all outwardnesses, shews, appearances, the streame, the people; for there is no man of worth but has a piece of singularity, and scornes something.

A Plodding Student

Is a kind of Alchymist or Persecuter of Nature, that would change the dull lead of his Brain into finer mettle, with successe many times as unprosperous, or at least not quitting the cost, to wit, of his owne Oyle and Candles. He ha's a strange forc't appetite to Learning, and to atchieve it brings nothing but patience and a body. His Studie is not great but continuall, and consists much in the sitting up till after Midnight in a rug-gowne, and a Night cap to the vanquishing per-haps of some sixe lines: yet what hee ha's, he ha's perfect, for he reads it so long to understand it till he gets it withoute Booke. Hee may with much industry make a breach into Logicke, and arive at some ability in an Argument: but for politer Studies hee dare not skirmish with them, and for Poetry accounts it impregnable. His Invention is no more then the finding out of his Papers, and his few gleanings there, and his dis-position of them is as just as the Bookbinders, a setting or glewing of them together. Hee is a great discomforter of young Students, by telling them what travell it ha's cost him, and how often his braine turn'd at Philosophy, and makes others feare Studying as a cause of Duncery. Hee is a man much given to Apothegms which serve him for wit, and seldome breakes any Jest, but which belong'd to some Lacedemonian or Romane in *Lycosthenes*. He is like a dull Cariers horse, that will go a whole weeke together but never out of a foot-pace: and hee that sets forth on the Satur-day shall overtake him.

Pauls Walke

Is the Lands Epitome, or you may call it the lesser Ile of Great Brittaine. It is more then this, the whole worlds Map, which you may here discerne in it's perfect'st motion justling and turning. It is a heape of stones and men, with a vast confusion of Languages and were the Steeple not sanctified nothing liker Babel. The noyse in it is like that of Bees, a strange humming or buzze, mixt of

walking, tongues and feet: It is a kind of still
roare or loud whisper. It is the great Exchange
of all discourse, & no busines whatsoever but is
here stirring and afoot. It is the Synod of all
pates politicke, joynted and laid together in most
serious posture, and they are not halfe so busie at
the Parliament. It is the Anticke of tailes to tailes,
and backes to backes, and for vizards you need goe
no further then faces. It is the Market of young
Lecturers, whom you may cheapen here at all rates
and sizes. It is the generall Mint of all famous
lies, which are here like the legends of Popery, first
coyn'd & stampt in the Church. All inventions
are emptyed here, and not few pockets. The best
signe of a Temple in it is, that it is the Theeves
Sanctuary, which robbe more safely in the Croud,
then a wildernesse, whilst every searcher is a bush
to hide them. It is the other expence of the day,
after Playes, Taverne, and a Baudy-House, and
men have still some Oathes left to sweare here.
It is the eares Brothell, and satisfies their lust, and
ytch. The Visitants are all men without exceptions, but the principall Inhabitants and possessors
are stale Knights, and Captaines out of Service,
men of long Rapiers, and Breeches, which after all
turne Merchants here, and trafficke for Newes.
Some make it a Preface to their Dinner, and
Travell for a Stomacke: but thriftier men make it
their Ordinarie: and Boord here verie cheape. Of
all such places it is least haunted with Hobgoblins,
for if a Ghost would walke more, hee could not.

A stayed Man

Is a man. One that ha's taken order with himselfe, and set a rule to those lawlesnesses within
him. Whose life is distinct and in Method, and his
Actions as it were cast up before. Not loos'd into
the Worlds vanities, but gathered up and contracted in his station. Not scatter'd into many
pieces of businesses, but that one course he takes,
goes thorough with. A man firme and standing in
his purposes, nor heav'd off with each wind and
passion. That squares his expence to his Coffers,
and makes the Totall first, and then the Items.
One that thinkes what hee does, and does what he
sayes, and forsees what he may doe, before he purposes. One whose (if I can) is more then anothers
assurance, and his doubtfull tale before some mens
protestations. That is confident of nothing in
futurity, yet his conjectures oft true Prophecies.
That makes a pause still betwixt his eare and
beleefe, and is not too hasty to say after others:
One whose Tongue is strung up like a Clocke till
the time, and then strikes, and sayes much when
hee talkes little. That can see the Truth betwixt
two wranglers, and sees them agree even in that
they fall out upon. That speakes no Rebellion in
a bravery, or talkes bigge from the spirit of Sacke.
A man coole and temperate in his passions, not
easily betraid by his choller: That vies not oath
with oath, nor heat with heat: but replies calmly
to an angry man, and is too hard for him too. That
can come fairely off from Captaines companies, and
neither drink nor quarrell. One whom no ill
hunting sends home discontented, and makes him

sweare at his dogs and family. One not hastie to
pursue the new Fashion, nor yet affectedly true to
his old round Breeches. But gravely handsome, &
to his place, which suites him better then his
Tailor. Active in the world without disquiet, and
carefull without miserie : yet neither ingulft in his
pleasures, nor a seeker of businesse, but ha's his
houres for both. A man that seldome laughes
violently, but his mirth is a cheerefull looke. Of
a compos'd and setled countenance, not set, nor
much alterable with sadnesse or joy. He affects
nothing so wholy, that hee must bee a miserable man
when he loses it : but forethinks what will come
hereafter, and spares Fortune his thanks and curses.
One that loves his Credit, not this word Reputation : yet can save both without a Duell : whose
entertainments to greater men are respectfull not
complementary, and to his friends plaine not rude.
A good Husband, Father, Master : that is without
doting, pampring, familiarity. A man well poys'd
in all humours, in whom Nature shewd most Geo-
metry, and hee ha's not spoyl'd the worke. A man
of more wisedome then wittinesse, and braine then
fancy; and abler to any thing then to make Verses.

A Modest Man

Is a far finer man then he knowes of, one that
shewes better to all men then himselfe, and so
much the better to al men, as lesse to himselfe : for
no quality sets a man off like this, and commends
him more against his will : And he can put up any
injury sooner then this (as he cals it) your Ironie.
You shall heare him confute his commenders, and
giving reasons how much they are mistaken, and

is angry almost, if they do not beleeve him. Nothing threatens him so much as great expectation, which he thinks more prejudiciall, then your under-opinion, because it is easier to make that false; then this true. Hee is one that sneaks from a good action, as one that had pilferd, and dare not justifie it, and is more blushingly deprehended in this, then others in sin. That counts al publike declarings of himselfe, but so many penances before the people, and the more you applaud him, the more you abash him, and he recovers not his face a moneth after. One that is easie to like any thing, of another mans : and thinkes all hee knowes not of him better, then that he knowes. He excuses that to you, which another would impute, and if you pardon him, is satisfied. One that stands in no opinion because it is his owne, but suspects it rather, because it is his own, and is confuted, and thankes you. Hee sees nothing more willingly then his errors; and it is his error sometimes to be too soone perswaded. He is content to be an Auditor, where he only can speake, and content to goe away, and thinke himselfe instructed. No man is so weake that he is ashamed to learne of, and is lesse ashamed to confesse it : and he finds many times even in the dust, what others over-looke, and lose. Every mans presence is a kinde of bridle to him, to stop the roving of his tongue and passions : & even impudent men looke for their reverence from him, and distaste that in him, which they suffer in themselves, as one in whom vice is ill-favoured, and shewes more scurvily then another. A bawdy jest shall shame him more then a bastard another man, and he that got it, shall

censure him among the rest. And hee is coward
to nothing more then an ill tongue, and whosoever
dare lye on him hath power over him, and if you
take him by his looke, he is guilty. The maine
ambition of his life is not to be discredited: and
for other things, his desires are more limited then
his fortunes, which he thinkes preferment though
never so meane, and that he is to doe something
to deserve this: Hee is too tender to venter on
great places, and would not hurt a dignity to helpe
himselfe. If he doe, it was the violence of his
friends constraind him, and how hardly soever hee
obtaine it, he was harder perswaded to seeke it.

A Prison

Is the grave of the living, where they are shut up
from the world, and their friends: and the wormes
that gnaw upon them, their owne thoughts, and
the Jaylor. A house of meager lookes, and ill
smells: for lice, drink, Tobacco are the compound:
Pluto's Court was express't from this fancy. And
the persons are much about the same parity that
is there. You may aske as *Menippus* in *Lucian*,
which is *Nireus*, which *Thersites*, which the begger,
which the Knight: for they all suited in the same
forme of a kinde of nastie poverty. Onely to be
out at elbowes is in fashion here, and a great
Indecorum, not to be thred-bare. Every man
shewes here like so many wracks upon the Sea,
here the ribs of a thousand pound, here the relicke
of so many Mannours a doublet without buttons.
And tis a spectacle of more pitty then executions
are. The company one with other, is but a vying
of complaints, and the causes they have, to rayle

on fortune, and foole themselves, and there is a great deale of good fellowship in this. They are commonly, next their Creditors, most bitter against the Lawyers, as men that have had a great stroke in assisting them hither. Mirth here is stupidity or hardhartednes, yet they faine it sometimes to slip Melancholy & keep off themselves from themselves, and the torment of thinking what they have beene. Men muddle up their life here as a thing of no use, and weare it out like an old suite, the faster the better: and hee that deceives the time best, best spends it. It is the place where new commers are most welcom'd, and next them ill newes, as that which extends their fellowship in misery, & leaves fewer to insult: And they breathe their discontents more securely here, and have their tongues at more liberty then abroad. Men see here much sin & much calamity: and where the last does not mortifie, the other hardens, & those that are worse here, are desperately worse, as those from whom the horror of sinne is taken off, and the punishment familiar. And commonly a hard thought passes on all, that come from this Schoole: which though it teach much wisedome, it is too late, and with danger: and it is better bee a foole, then come here to learne it.

A poore Fiddler

Is a man and a fiddle out of case: and he in worse case then his fiddle. One that rubs two sticks together (as the Indians strike fire) and rubs a poore living out of it: Partly from this, and partly from your charity, which is more in the hearing, then giving him, for he sells nothing dearer then

to be gone : He is just so many strings above a
begger, though he have but two : and yet hee begs
too, onely not in the downe-right *for Gods sake*,
but with a shrugging God blesse you, and his face
is more pyn'd then the blind mans. Hunger is
the greatest paine he takes, except a broken head
sometimes, and the labouring *John Dorry*. Otherwise his life is so many fits of mirth, and 'tis some
mirth to see him. A good feast shall draw him
five miles by the nose, and you shall track him
againe by the sent. His other Pilgrimages are
Faires, and good Houses, where his devotion is
great to the Christmas : and no man loves good
times better. Hee is in league with the Tapsters
for the worshipfull of the Inne, whom hee torments
next morning with his art, and ha's their names
more perfit then their men. A new song is better
to him then a new Jacket : especially if bawdie,
which hee calls merry, and hates naturally the
Puritan, as an enemy to this mirth. A countrey
wedding, & Whitson ale are the two maine places
he dominiers in, where he goes for a Musician,
and overlookes the Bag-pipe. The rest of him is
drunke, and in the stocks.

A good old Man

Is the best Antiquitie, and which we may with
least vanitie admire. One whom Time hath beene
thus long a working, and like winter fruit ripen'd,
when others are shaken downe. He hath taken
out as many lessons of the world, as dayes, and
learn't the best thing in it, the vanitie of it. He
lookes o're his former life as a danger well past,

and would not hazard himselfe to begin againe. His lust was long broken before his bodie, yet he is glad this temptation is broke too, and that hee is fortified from it by this weakenesse. The next doore of death sads him not, but hee expects it calmely as his turne in Nature: and feares more his recoyling backe to childishnes then dust. All men looke on him as a common father, and on old age for his sake, as a reverent thing. His very presence, and face puts vice out of countenance, and makes it an indecorum in a vicious man. Hee practises his experience on youth without the harshnesse of reproofe, and in his counsell is good companie. Hee ha's some old stories still of his owne seeing to confirme what he sayes, and makes them better in the telling: yet is not troublesome neither with the same tale againe, but remembers with them, how oft he ha's told them. His old sayings and moralls seeme proper to his beard: and the poetrie of *Cato* do's well out of his mouth, and he speakes it as if he were the Author. Hee is not apt to put the boy on a yonger man, nor the foole on a boy, but can distinguish gravity from a sowre looke, and the lesse testie he is, the more regarded. You must pardon him if he like his owne times better then these, because those things are follies to him now that were wisedome then: yet he makes us of that opinion too, when we see him, and conjecture those times by so good a Relicke. He is a man capable of a dearnesse with the yongest men; yet he not youthfuller for them, but they older for him, and no man credits more his acquaintance. He goes away at least too soone whensoever, with all mens sorrow but his owne, and his memory is fresh, when it is twice as old.

A Flatterer

Is the picture of a friend, and as pictures flatter manie times, so hee oft shewes fairer then the true substance: His looke, conversation, companie, and all the outwardnes of friendshippe more pleasing by odds, for a true friend dare take the liberty to bee sometimes offensive, wheras he is a great deal more cowardly, and will not let the least hold goe, for feare of losing you. Your meere sowre looke affrights him, and makes him doubt his casheering. And this is one sure marke of him, that he is never first angry, but ready, though upon his owne wrong, to make satisfaction. Therefore hee is never yok't with a poore man or any that stands on the lower ground, but whose fortunes may tempt his pains to deceive him. Him hee learnes first, and learnes well, and growes perfitter in his humours, then himselfe, and by this doore enters upon his Soule: of which hee is able at last to take the very print and marke, and fashion his own by it like a false key to open all your secrets. All his affections jumpe even with yours: hee is before-hand with your thoughts, and able to suggest them unto you. He will commend to you first, what hee knowes you like, and has alwayes some absurd story or other of your enemie, and then wonders how your two opinions should jumpe in that man. Hee will aske your counsell sometimes as a man of deepe judgement, and has a secret of purpose to disclose you, and whatsoever you say, is perswaded. Hee listens to your words with great attention, and sometimes will object that you may confute him, and then protests hee never heard so much before. A piece of witte bursts him with an overflowing laughter, and hee remembers it for you to all companies, and laughs againe in the telling. He is one never chides you but for your vertues, as, *You are too good, too honest, too religious;* when his chiding may seeme but the earnester commendation, and yet would faine chide you out of them too : for your vice is the thing hee has use of, and wherein you may best use him, and hee is never more active then in the worst diligences. Thus at last he possesses you from your selfe, and then expects but his hire to betray you. And it is a happinesse not to discover him : for as long as you are happy, you shall not.

A high spirited Man

Is one that lookes like a proud man, but is not: you may forgive him his lookes for his worth sake, for they are only too proud to be base. One whom no rate can buy off from the least piece of his freedome, and makes him disgest an unworthy thought an houre. Hee cannot crouch to a great man to possesse him, nor fall low to the earth, to rebound never so high againe. Hee stands taller on his owne bottome, then others on the advantage ground of fortune, as having sollidly that honour, of which Title is but the pompe. Hee does homage to no man for his Great styles sake, but is strictly just in the exaction of respect againe, and will not bate you a Complement. He is more sensible of a neglect then an undoing, and scornes no man so much as his surly threatner. A man quickly fired,

and quickly laid downe with satisfaction, but remits
any injury sooner then words. Onely to himselfe
he is irreconcileable, whom he never forgives a
disgrace, but is still stabbing himselfe with the
thought of it, and no disease that he dyes of
sooner. Hee is one had rather pinch, then bee
beholding for his life, and strives more to be quitte
with his friend then his enemy. Fortune may kill
him, but not deject him, nor make him fall into a
humbler key then before, but he is now loftier then
ever in his owne defence, you shall heare him talke
still after thousands; and he becomes it better, then
those that have it. One that is above the world
and its drudgery, and cannot pull downe his
thoughts to the pelting businesses of it. He would
sooner accept the Gallowes then a meane trade, or
any thing that might disparage the height of man
in him, and yet thinkes no death comparably base
to hanging neither. One that will doe nothing
upon commaund, though hee would do it otherwise : and if ever hee doe evill, it is when hee is
dar'd to it. Hee is one that if fortune equal his
worth, puts a luster in all preferment, but if otherwise hee be too much crost, turnes desperately
melancholy, and scornes mankind.

An affected Man

Is an extraordinary man, in ordinary things. One
that would goe a straine beyond himselfe, and is
taken in it. A man that overdoes all things with
great solemnity of circumstance : and whereas with
more negligence he might passe better, makes himselfe, with a great deale of endevour, ridiculous.
The fancy of some odde quaintnesses have put him

cleane beside his Nature, hee cannot bee that hee would, and hath lost what he was. He is one must be point-blank in every trifle, as if his credit, and opinion hung upon it: the very space of his armes in an embrace studied before, and premeditated: and the figure of his countenance, of a fortnights contriving. Hee will not curse you without booke, and *extempore*, but in some choise way, and perhaps as some Great man curses. Every action of his, cryes, *doe yee marke mee?* and men doe marke him, how absurd he is. For affectation is the most betraying humour: and nothing that puzzles a man lesse to find out then this. All the actions of his life are like so many things bodg'd in without any naturall cadence, or connexion at all. You shall track him all thorow like a schooleboyes Theame, one piece from one author, and this from another, and joyne all in this generall, that they are none of his owne: You shall observe his mouth not made for that tone, nor his face for that simper: And it is his lucke that his finest things most mis-become him. If hee affect the Gentleman, as the humour most commonly lyes that way: not the least *puntilio* of a fine man, but hee is strict in to a haire, even to their very negligences, which he cons as rules: He will not carry a knife with him to wound reputation, and pay double a reckoning rather then ignobly question it. And he is full of this *Ignobly* and *Nobly* and *Gentilely*, and this meer feare to trespasse against the *Gentill* way, puts him out most of al. It is a humor runs thorow many things besides, but is an ill-favour'd ostentation in all, and thrives not. And the best use of such men is, they are good parts in a play.

R. M.

Micrologia. Characters, or Essayes, Of Persons, Trades, and Places, offered to the City and Country. By R. M. . . . Printed at London by T. C. for Michael Sparke, dwelling at the blue Bible in Greene Arbor. 1629. 8vo.

[Bodleian Library. ? Unique copy.]

16 characters.

I can discover nothing about 'R. M.' He writes a long 'caveatory Epistle to the understanding Reader,' explaining that by tossing off his 'meane' characters lightly, they will become more effective than if he had followed the custom in the 'Presse' where is 'every one striving to distill the dewie Quintessence of his braine, thro' the Limbecke of invention,' and thereby oppressing the world. R. M. is not quite free from the 'eare-hony' he is decrying, but he has a pleasant directness which makes some of his home truths tell to-day. Not alone the 'country' shoe-maker is now 'the crooked Toes Jaylor, and oft keepes Chambermaids so fine in their feete, they halt downe-right.'

The Tooth-drawer altered his ways as little as the Quack-doctor. R. M. might, in 1629, have been describing Hans Sebald Beham's brilliant woodcut, made in 1535, when he notes the ragged teeth that 'dignifie his Banner,' or the Cut-purse who 'becomes a great sharer in the worke,' employing 'his limetwig-fingers to draw a Purse, as himselfe a Tooth.'

The banner is inscribed 'Hi guten Ti | riact vnd | Wurmsam.' The illustration is from one of the groups in *The Village Fair*, and the cut is described by Mr. Campbell Dodgson as a 'fine impression of the first state.' [Catalogue of Early German and Flemish Woodcuts . . . in the British Museum. London, 1903, i. p. 478, No. 146.]

A Country Shoo-maker

Is one, that seemes to have some insight in Mens dispositions, especially of his ordinary Customers; for he will soone have the length of your foote to an haire. Hee is not much unlike some carelesse Prelates; for he sets a smooth face on the upper Leather, but regards not the Soles flitting. His knowledge is merely superficial, and dives much into the Art of excoriation. The Butcher is the Prologue, or first branch of his profit: The Currier the intermedium or Chorus: Himselfe with the helpe of his cutting-knife, makes up the Cata- strophe, in Boots, Shooes, Pantofles, &c. Hee is an inveterate enemy to the lives of divers dumb beasts, not caring how many are put to slaughter, so their Hides come cheaply to him. His Fox-furre pre- tending ease by drawing on; is the truest Embleme of his fraud and subtilty, intending rather to draw in for his owne profit; and if you watch narrowly his insteps in a darke shop; you may characterize him uttering (if not changing) Calfe for Neate. He is a great tormenter of improfitable Cornes in a Commonwealth; yet if you intreat him faire, he is mercifull enough, and will at Last give you ease. Hee is the crooked Toes Jaylor, and oft keepes Chambermaids so fine in their feete they halt downe- right. In the Country he alway caries the Reliques of S. *Hugh's* Bones, till the hot Sun-shine, con- verts him to Hay-making, or Harvest-worke. In winter season you shall by 8 of the clocke, rather finde his nose steeled with a black pot, then his Aule with a Bristle. He is a spruce fellow at a Faire, & uses Truncke Hose at a Wake. He

pinches more at five groats then any other Trade
at two-pence. His skill is very raw in the Mathe-
maticks; yet ha's taught many, being a while in his
Leather prison, to prove weather-wise; and by
pricking and shooting of their Cornes perfectly
sensible of stormes ensuing. His greatest enemie
is a Rich man with the goute, who never weares
ought but slippers in all companies. Hee tels you
the onely Court fashion is to walke in Bootes, and
sweares they are the compleatest ornament of legge
or foote. His maine feare is a Parliament, lest
there might proceed some new addition to the last
Act, to thwart his designes, That as Butchers were
forbad to sell meat on Sundayes, so he should
shooes, which if it happen, he vowes neither King
nor Begger, shall passe his pinching jurisdiction
so long as he upholds the Trade. Briefly, he is
one uses least conscience on Sundayes, when if
your necessities bring you to his shop doore, hee
will bee sure to racke two pence or a groat more
on the price for comming so unseasonably. He
sings all the Rounds and Catches that *Robin-hood*
had; and the Pinder of *Wakefield* is commonly the
fore-horse of his Tenor. He deemes good-Ale the
onely up-holder of a cleare voyce, and wishes, that
he which loves it not may never sing more.

A Tooth-drawer

Is a man highly fam'd for his Art; for he got it
beyond the Seas, as by Labels at his doore may
appeare. As thus: Know all gentlemen, that
I Signior or Mounsieur such a one, after long
travaile, and great experience in forraigne parts,

A Tooth-Drawer

beyond the Seas, have industriously attained many rare secrets, viz. To draw Teeth, set in New, mundifie or make blacke Teeth white, rid the gummes, or take away the paine without drawing; nor doth hee rest heere, but if need require professes the Cure of many other diseases, as Cramp, Convulsions, Gouts, Palsies, Catars, &c. And can tell them at first sight, if they be curable or not. Howbeit, this superficiall view must bring him some feeling, else he is not well pleased. His businesse is never perform'd in so much State, as when he is mounted upon his Palfrey or Irish Hobby, riding through the high streets of the City, like *Caesar* in his Triumph, his Clyents following him laying their hands on their mouthes, as though they would keepe silence, till paine makes them roare out, which his horse or he perceiving, reflects backe on them an eye of ruthfull pitie, straight playes the Constables part to bid them come after him; and having felt their pulses, lookes next into their mouthes, to know their age, thrusts in his hand or fingers, and seemes in this posture a *Richard Corde-Lyon*, diving to the heart or stump of hollow Teeth. Yet have I heard he ha's a tricke to convey an iron punch in a hand-kerchiefe, which oft prove the jeopardy of a jaw to some of his Patients. He is a fellow very captious; for hee is apt to twit you in the Teeth on the least occasion; exceeding desperate, for if you take distaste or finde your selfe agreev'd, though it bee but a Tooth-aking, hee is straight ready to draw. He is the mouths Gardiner, that prunes the hedge-rowes of the Teeth, and like a Sergeant military set them in their due Rankes and Files. Those rotten,

ragged and corrupt Teeth he ha's drawne from
others have beene the onely meanes to draw in
him customers; and hee preserves them as Trophes
of Triumph to dignifie his Banner. At spreading
forth his Flags of affiance, streamers, Pendants, &c.
multitudes of people commonly assemble; when
the Cut-purse spying his best advantage, becomes
a great sharer in the worke, and can as nimbly
imploy his limetwig-fingers to draw a Purse, as
himselfe a Tooth. Of all Trades in the City, he
is most beholding to the Comfitmaker; for hee
and his Confections have been a great bane to
the Teeth, helpt him to much worke, and brought
sowre sawce to their sweete meats. To conclude
hee is a man onely us'd at a pinch; and the use
of his pincers ha's drawne his Patients out of
patience. Those that have once tride him, hope
they shall never have occasion to use him more.
So I leave him, till paine pricks me to employ him,
but desire no further acquaintance of him.

RICHARD BRATHWAITE
(? 1588-1673)

Whimzies : Or, A New Cast of Characters. . . . London,
. . . 1631. 12mo.

Edited by J. O. Halliwell, . . . London : . . . 1859. 4to.

24 characters, arranged to form an A. B. C.

Brathwaite's style is as various as the long list of his
writings, ranging from the solemn dulness of the *English
Gentleman* or the whimsicality of his *Spiritual Spicerie*,
to the jollity of *Barnaby's Journal* or the picturesque
appeal of *Whimzies*. The style in *Whimzies* is attractive
in its love of life and wit.

It might have been expected that the precision of the
character-form, which helped many writers to be definite,
would have curbed Brathwaite too, but he never learned
fully to control his pen. Perhaps he found his alphabet-
scheme difficult. Certainly some of the characters are
prosy enough to make the reader suppose their subjects
were not the author's choice. And yet the rewards for
reading them are not infrequent. Passages marked by a
felicitous rhythm may be found throughout his work.
The *Captive-Captain* (1665) is attributed to him, and its
unusual sketch of ' The fat Prisoner ' contains : ' This
May-bird can sing as sweetly in a *Cage*, as if he were in a
Forrest. He accounts his imprisonment the Embleme of
his life : and his life neither unhappier nor shorter by
being a Prisoner. He findes freedom in his greatest
restraint ; and that *inward liberty* which many Libertines
who have the wide world to walk in, could never purchase.'

An Almanack-maker

Is an *annuall Author*, no lesse constant in his
Method then *matter;* enlarging his yeerely Edition
with a *figure* or *cipher*. He cites as familiarly, as

if they were his *familiars*, *Euclid*, *Ptolomie*, *Ticho-Brache*, etc. But beleeve it, many have spoke of *Robin Hood*, that never shot in his bow. Hee scrapes acquaintance of a fortunate gentleman, one *Euphumemismus*, whom he erroneously takes for brother of that feigned knight *Parismus;* Whose name hee interprets to bee, *Boni ominis captatio*, whereof he himselfe for his part, was never capable. Horizons, Hemisphaeres, Horoscopes, Apogaeum's, Hypogaeums, Perigaeum's, Astrolabes, Cycles, Epicycles are his usuall dialect; yet I am perswaded they may bee something to *eate*, for ought he knowes. His frequent repetition of *Mazzaroth*, *Arcturus*, *Orion*, and the *Pleiades*, proclaime him highly versed in the astrologicall observations of *Job*, whom he resembles in a *Paralell line* of *Poverty*, rather than *patience*. Hee ha's the true situation and just proportion of the principall Angles or houses of the Heaven or Firmament : yet can hardly pay *house rent* for his owne. Forty shillings is his yeerely pension upon every impression : but his *vailes* are meaner, unlesse he have the Art for stolen goods to cast a figure : wherein, trust me, hee ha's a pretty smattering. He walks in the *Clouds*, and prates as familiarly of the influence of the *Moone*, as if hee had beene the *man* that was in her. Hee would make you beleeve hee had a smacke of Poetry, by the verses which hee fixeth above every moneth, but doe not credit him, hee is guiltlesse of that art : only some stolen threads he hath raked out from the kennell of other Authors, which most pedantically hee assumes to himselfe, and makes an additament to his Labours. Whole Summer nights long hee lyes on his backe, as if hee were mell-dew'd or Planet-strucke, gazing on the starrie gallerie: and would make you believe that hee knew the names and markes of all the Oxen that draw *Charles waine*. Hee talkes much of the 12 *Signes*, yet I am confident, that one might perswade him that the *Cardinals hat*, or *Sarazens head* were one of them. He keepes a terrible *quarter* with his *Jacobs staffe*, which he conjectures was first found at *Jacobs Well*: as his erring *Erra pater* informes him: for other *Cabals* hee disclaimes them. The Memorable work of conveying the *New River* from *Ware* to *London* was the issue of his braine, if you may believe him: yea, he will tell you, the *state* is much engaged to his notions. He ha's some small scruple of *Physitian* in him, and can most *Empyrically* discourse of the state of your Body: but had he store of *Patients*, hee would slaughter more than a *Pestilence*. He ha's a little judgement in your *Chrisis:* and which is best season for *Phlebotomie:* yet hee knowes not, whether *Phlebotomie* bee a man or a woman. Not a *highway man* in Europe can direct you better in the *Roade:* all which he ha's by *inspiration*, for he scarce ever travaild out of smoke o' th Citie. He ha's excellent observations for planting, plowing, setting, sowing, with other experimentall rules of husbandrie, yet never was Master of a Plough in all his time. Certaine (but most uncertaine) generall Notions hee ha's of the seasons of weathers, which hee expresseth in such strange and unbaptized language, as like the *Delphian sword*, it may cut either way. About four a clock at night (saith he) which may as soone fall out at

foure a clocke i' th morning for aught he know's,
there will fall some mizling, drizling drops, with
some whistling, rustling windes, &c, all which he
findes out of the depth of Art.   He professeth
some skill in *palmistry;* wherein trust me, the
Gipsies do farre out-strippe him : poring on the
table of your hand, hee fetcheth a deepe sigh,
thinking of his owne unfurnish'd *Table* at home,
than which none can bee barer.   And examining
the *lines* of your *Table*, he alwayes findes his owne
to be most ominous.   Hee shewes himselfe deeply
read in *antiquitie*, by the artlesse draught of his
threed-bare *Chronologie;* and imps his illiterate
worke, for want of better stuffe, with a trite discourse of *weights* and *measures:* most ponderously
dividing them into *Troy* and *Averdepois:* where
hee findes his owne gold too light by many graines
for either scale. His *Cage* (or *Studie* if you please)
is hung about with Moath-eaten *Mappes*, *Orbes*,
Globes, *Perspectives;* with which hee can worke
wonders. His shelves for want of authors, are
subtilly inter-woven with Spiders Caules, which hee
makes the stupid vulgar beleeve, are pure Elixirs
extracted from the influence of the *Moone*.   It is
the height of his ambition to aspire to the credit
of a *Blanke Almanack;* upon which election hee
holds himselfe a *Classicke Author*. If famous, he
seldome dies : for some inferiour Artist will assume
to himselfe his name. But if he die, an other
Phœnix-like, will bee forthwith raked out of his
ashes.   His death makes him in this infinitely
happy; It is not *bitter* to him in respect of his *substance:* And in *this* onely hee expresseth himselfe
a *Scholer; He dyes poore*. In a word, this may

be his comfort, he leaves his kindred in a settled
and composed peace: for they neede not fall by
the eares together for his goods.   That which he
long discoursed of but understood not (I meane
his Clymactericall yeare) ha's now attach'd him:
And so ends his perpetuall *Almanack*.

An Exchange-man

Is the peremptorie branch of an Intergatorie;
What do ye lacke? He would make you beleeve,
that hee will furnish you *gratis;* but such profuse
bounty will not pay *Scot* and *lot;* your mony must
therefore be your pledge, before you have his
trinket.   It is a wonder to see what variety of
Knick-knacks he ha's in so small a Compasse.   His
quest of *inquiry* is, what is most in *request:* so as,
his Shoppe consists as much of *fashion* as *substance; forme* as *matter.*   It would make one muse
how ever so many *Gew-gaws* should finde vent in
a wise state;And yet the labouring invention of the
Braine is ever teeming and producing some eye-
tempting Babie or other, to allure the Newfangle
passenger.   The hurriing of a Coach is as pleasing
melody to usher in his expectance, as the last sound
before a New-play is to an itching audience.   When
the Simple goe to market, then the Craftie get
mony.   By this my Lady with her Diapred traine,
having as many *poakes* as *heads,* are mounted the
staires; and entring now the long *Peripatetick* gallery; they are encountred with volleyes of more
questions, then they know how to *resolve.*   Gladly
would this *Salique* traine buy all they see, if their
revenues would mount to the price.   But they
must in civill curtsy leave some few Commodities

for others. Meane time they buy more then they know how to employ. "That is a pretty conceited toy (sayes my Ladies gentlewoman) I will buy it whatsoever it cost me": which discreete speech delivered in the hearing of our *Exchange-man*, it must want no praise, and consequently no price. Hee will usually demand the three times value for any commodity; but farre be it from me to imagine him to have the conscience to take it if they would give it. It is his onely drift without any other policy to make triall of their judgement: his equall and conscionable moderation is such (at least hee will pretend so much) in these triviall subjects of gaine, as hee hates to work on any ones weaknesse, being the expressivest argument of mercinarie basenesse. But were all that traffick with him as well-lin'd in pate as purse, wee should finde many emptie shoops before the next *vacation*. By this, a new troope of ruffling plum'd *Myrmidons* are arrived; and these will swoope up all before them; Not so much as a phantastick tyre, be it never so ougly, shall escape their encounter. Now out with your lures, baites, and lime-twiggs, my nimble *Didapper*. Your harvest is not all the yeare. See how hee shruggs; and with what downe-right reverence hee entertaines them! If oaths, civill complements, demure lookes have any hope to pre-vaile with raw and unexperienc'd credulity, he is in a notable thriving way: for he ha's set his *Partridge* already; there is no doubt of *springing* them till his *Net* be spread over them: By which meanes he ha's a tricke to catch the *Old One*. Silence, and you shall heare his project. The *Ancient Matron* which strikes the stroake, and

directs her *young charge* in their merchandize, is
by this time as firmly retained by our *Exchange-
man*, as ever was *Lawyer* by his *Client*. What
great matter is it, though it cost him a Muffe, a
wrought Wastcoate, or some curious Border? Hee
may pay himselfe in his price: for they are too
generous (so their *Directresse* approve it) to stand
upon tearmes. Let this suffice; it is a good market,
where all are pleased, fed, and so are these. They
joy no lesse in his Commodity, than hee in their
money. Yet are the *Savages*, in my opinion, much
more to be approved in their Commerce than these.
Indeed they *exchange* pretious stuffe for trifles:
Bevers and *Ermins* for knives, hatchets, kettle-
drums and hobby-horses. But this they doe out
of their Superfluity; whereas our nicer Dames
bestow that upon trifles, which might support a
needfull family. But the Age labours of this Epi-
demicall Error; too universall therefore is the Crime
to admit of Censure. Now you must suppose that
Invention is the *Exchange-mans* most usefull
Artizan. Therefore, for his better returne, he
keepes his weekely Synodall with his Girdler, Per-
fumer, Tyre-woman and Sempster: who bray their
braines in a mortar, to produce some usefull renew,
some gainefull issue for their thriving Master.
Never was poore Jade more troubled with *fashions*
than these are. By this time, imagine something
invented; which, whilst it is now in his *Embrio*,
receives admittance to his shoppe, and to take the
curious passenger, appears in his full shape. He
needs not use any *Exchange-Rhetoricke* to set it
forward; Novelties will vend themselves. A *vacation* is his *vexation;* and a *Michaelmas tearme* the

sole hope of his *reparation*. Hee ha's by this time,
serv'd all *offices* in his *Ward;* and now draws home-
ward. That portion hee had of the World, hee
ha's bequeathed to his Executors, Administrators,
and Assignes. The *Birds* are flowne; his *Customers* gone; It is high time to shut up shop.

An Ostler

Is a *bottleman;* not a Barber in *Europe* can set a
better edge on his razor, than hee can set on horses
teeth, to save his provender. The proverbe is;
The masters eye feedes his horse; but the *Ostlers*
starves him. Now, if you desire to have your
Palfrey make quicke dispatch of his provender,
make your *Ostler* his *Supervisor*, and by nimble
conveyance he will quickly make an empty
Manger. What a rubbing and scrubbing hee will
make in hope of a small reward at cloze of a
reckoning? What humble Obeysance may you
expect at his hand, when he prostrates himselfe in
such low service to the heeles of your Horse?
Thus labours he by currying your beast, to curry
favour with your selfe. Hee ha's no *Litterature*,
though hee trade something *neare* it. Hee profits
out of *measure;* his *Ostrie* must not betide
to *Winchester*. If Oates seeme deare, hee will
tell you how much their price quickned at every
quarter last Market day: and hee ha's one close at
his elbow that will second him. Hee will justifie
it, that no *Hoast* on all the *Road* got his hay so
sweetly or seasonably as his Master. Though there
bee *Ostlers* of all Countreys, yet generally are they
Northerne men; and those you shall finde the
simplest, but *diligent'st*, and consequently the

honestest; for *industry* and *simplicitie* are antidotes
against *knavery*. But it is twenty to one, hee will
be as neere your *Countreyman* as hee can informe
himselfe, purposely to procure your better respect,
and purchase the larger reward. Hee will tell you,
if hee find you *credulous*, that your horse hurts at
Withers, or hee is *hoofe-bound;* but referre all unto
him, and you shall bee sure to pay both *Sadler* and
Farrier for nothing. Hee can direct you to a pot
of the nappiest Ale in all the streete, and conduct
you too, so the *Tapster* know not. Hee ha's
sundry *petty-officers* as *Under-Ostlers*, *Litter-
strowers*, *Boot-catchers*, to whom little accrues after
his deductions. He professeth some skill in horses,
and knows how to cure divers maladies with Oyle
of Oates; but hee will never cure so many as he ha's
diseas'd, nor fat so many as he ha's starv'd. To a
bare stranger that promiseth but small profit to the
Stable, hee will bee as peremptorie as a *Beadle*. He
will feede his horse with delayes and demurres, and
cause him stay greater guests leasure. But how
officious the *Snake* will bee, where hee smels
benefit? He speakes in his *Ostrie* (the chiefe seate
of his *Hypparchie*) like a *Frog* in a *Well*, or a
Cricket in a *Wall*. When Guests horses stand at
Livery, he sleepes very little, fearing lest they
should eate too much; but at *bottle*, hee is more
secure; howsoever, he ha's a dainty *Dentifrice*
that will charme them. Hee is a constant *stable*
man; and herein only commendable; *constancy* in
respect of his *place*, and *humilitie* in respect of his
person, makes him both *knowne* and *knavish*. He
ha's a notable glib *veine* in vaine discourse : no
Countrey can you name, but it is in his *verge;* his

long acquaintance with people of all conditions and
Countries, is become so *Mathematically* usefull
unto him, as he ha's the *Geographicall Mappe* of
the whole Continent (so farre as this Iland extends)
in his illiterate *pericranium;* which he vents by way
of description upon every occasion; and this he
makes his weekely Stable-Lecture. He is at very
little charge with his *Laundresse* but for his false
shirt and night-cap; which he weares as Ornaments
to his profession, and in them acts his daily
penance : for it is his use to encounter your Palfry
in a *shirt* of *male*, be he *male* or *female*. If he rise
to any preferment, he may say, *Gramercy horse;*
yet wil he hardly confess so much. He aspires
sometimes to *Tapster*, holding it the more bene-
ficiall place; but howsoever, better for him, for hee
may now drinke of free cost. Long-winter nights
watching, and early rising (for hee must bee either
the Guests Cocke, or they his) have much fore-
slow'd his diligence : for now hee will endure a
call or two before hee rise. But this is no fault of
his, but the diversitie of his occasions : for his
desire is naturally to rise early, and to be officious
to his guests before they bee stirring, in giving
their horses provender, which they may dispatch in
a trice, before ever their Masters come out of their
chambers. When hee finds convenient time and
leasure, hee will tosse a pot sociably with his Neighbour. But none are so familiar with him as the
Smith and *Sadler*, whom hee is bound to present
(upon some private composition) to any Gentleman
or other, that shall have occasion to use them. If
hee may make so much bold with you, hee will
send his commends sweetned with a Nutmeg, by

you to the *Ostler* of your next Inne; & this begets reciprocall courtesies betwixt them, with *titles* too, which they are wholly guiltlesse off; as *honest Boy; true Blade,* &c. But these *stiles* are but given them by their fellow *Ostlers,* whose desertlesse commendations exact as much at their hands. If hee be but indifferently honest (as I would have no superlative degrees of honesty in that profession) hee improves the benefit of the *Inne* above comparison : All desire to harbour where there is an honest *Ostler.* Which opinion once purchased, hee retaines for ever; and by it strengthens him with his Masters favour. Hee begins now to bee a Landed man by meanes of his *honesty* and *usury.* If hee have the grace to stay the good houre, hee may succeed his Master, and by matching with his Mistresse rise to *Inne-keeper.* But this is very rare, for hee is not by halfe so neate a youth as the *Chamberlaine.* Long and sore did he labour in the *Spring* of his youth, before hee came to reape any crop in the *Autumne* of his age. Hee is now grown *resty.* Profit is an alluring baite, but it cannot make him doe that which hee did. Now hee loves to snort under the Manger, and sleepe out his time before his departure : yet he cannot endure that any should succeed him in his place, though hee cannot supply it himself. Well, suppose him now drawing on to his last Quarter; some graspes or gripes of mortality hee feeles, which makes him conclude in his owne Element; *Grasse and Hay, we are all mortall.* Hee could for all this, finde in his heart to live one yeare longer; to compare his last yeares vailes and this together; and perchance, redeeme his arrerages too with

M.A. O

better measure. But his *Ostrie* is shut up; the *Guests* gone; their *reckoning* paid; onely a poore *Guest* of his owne stayes yet in her *Inne*, and ha's not discharged. But now I see the *Inne* dissolved; the *Signe* of her *being* fallen to *Earth*, and defaced; and his *Inmate* lodged, where the great *Inne-keeper* ha's appointed.

FRANCIS LENTON (fl. 1630-? 1650)

Characters : Or, Wit and the World in Their proper
    Colours. . . . London : . . . 1663. 12mo.
Characterismi : Or, Lentons Leasures. . . . By F. L.
    Gent. . . . London, . . . 1631. 12mo. [Bodl.
    First edition.]
  41 characters.

Lenton held the honorary distinction of 'Queene's
Poet,' and dedicated some of his books to Queen
Henrietta Maria, but otherwise little is known of him.
An edition of his characters was published in 1653 con-
taining a dedication with an ambiguous reference to his
recent death. For ' J. C.' writes : ' The Authour of these
Characters dying suddenly, left them in my Custody ; . . .
If they live, his Memory may live with them. . . . if
otherwise, their Fate cannot be so disastrous as his was.'

Some of Lenton's characters are dull, but some are
observant and neatly written. The sincerity of ' A true
Friend ' and the light touch of ' A Prodigall ' should not
be forgotten.

A Prodigall

Is a profuse fellow puft up with affectation, and
nusled [1] in the same by vaineglory (the finall end
his smaller wit and thinner skull aymes at) towards
which all his untoward actions tend. Hee deemes
all his equals, his inferiours, especially those he
most accompanies, amongst which hee thinkes himselfe the best man for paying all the reckoning,
which they incontinently without grudging grant
him, lest their very offer should provoke him to
indignation, at least to oaths, to which he is very
apt. He is never in love with mony but when he

  [1] brought up. See O.E.D.

wants it, and when he hath it, he sleights it. He is one of a very yeelding nature, insomuch, that if you praise ought of his that he affects, he presently bestowes it on you, scorning to be so base as to stand a begging. Nothing troubles his soule so much as to be last in a new fashion, or the least in company when hee is so accoutred. His carriage is very courteous, yet somewhat quilted with singularity (the secret pride of Prodigals,) fooles are his admirers, and knaves his soothers, whilst hee forgets himselfe to remember them, and never thinks of shutting the stable-doore till the steed be stolne. His greatest bragge is, hee hates covetousnesse, not dreaming how in the meane time he imbraceth the contrary extreame vice. Hee spends with such confusion, that his supposed friends and associates doe willingly forget his Courtesies, and is of such sublimity of spirit, that he never lookes so low as hogs, til he eats husks with them, and then the Trough proves his Touchstone. All men behold him with an (alas! tis pitty) whilst few or none supply his poverty which pursues him like an armed man. He is at last o'retane like a Butterfly in a storme, and left by all those that seem'd to love, and (methinks) in anguish of Spirit I heare him crosse the Proverb and say, Better is a penny in one's purse, than a Courtly friend.

A true Friend

Is a Fountaine that cannot be drawne dry, but alwayes affords some fresh and sweet waters to him, whose necessities and extremities enforce him to fetch it. He is a mans second selfe, as deare as a good wife, more deare than a brother, else the wisest King had been mistaken : but our times justifie his Proverbe true, which hee knew before. He is *Solamen in miseriis,* a Copartner in distresses with you, and inwardly (not fainedly) beareth halfe the burthen. Love and amity hath so knit him to you, that 'tis a question whether you be two or one, reciprocally answering each other in affection, and are equally sensible of each others defects or disturbances. Hee is no Meteor or Comet, no nine dayes wonder, or wandring Planet, but a fixed starre, by whose operative influences, his needy is nourished. For he is not compos'd of words, but actions, alwayes ready at a dead lift, to draw Dun out of the myre. Not onely a bare Counsellor to goodnesse, and so leave you without meanes of prosecution (the niggardly wisedome of these times) but an assister in the way, and goes on the first mile with you for company, and lookes after you in the rest of your journey, if he doth not travell throughout the same. Hee never aymes at any of his owne ends in doing courtesies, but doth them freely and quickly; not drownding his good deeds in the dull performance; for, *Qui citò dat, bis dat;* He that gives timely, gives twice. He's a certaine perpetuity, that cannot bee lost by non-payment of Rent, and ought to bee loved above fee-simple. He is the pillar of constancy, & the very touch-stone of Truth. One that lookes upon men with the eye of Religion, and is not rounded in the eare with worldly applause for it. Hypocrisie and vain-glory are as farre from his heart, as the con-trary Poles are from each other, for his right hand shall not know what his left hand doth. Hee is, (in these iron dayes) *Rara avis in terra;* a blacke Swan, or a white Crow, as rare as the Phoenix, and such a precious Jewell as the Indies cannot afford his parallel. He is most happy that hath him, and I advise him to make much of him, for he hath great fortune indeed, if he findes a second.

WYE SALTONSTALL (fl. 1630-1640)

Picturae Loquentes. Or Pictures Drawne forth in Characters. . . . By Wye Saltonstall. . . . London, . . . 1631. 12mo.

The second Edition . . . London, . . . 1635. ['A Merry Man' and 'A Scrivener' from this.] 38 characters. 26 in the first edition.

The treatment of the thirty-eight characters in this little book varies nearly as much as their subjects. For while these range from 'The World' or 'A Jealous Man' to 'An Usurer' or 'A Countrey Alehouse,' the method and ideas are at times hackneyed; but happily, in a fair number, the sketches are marked by acute observation and a pleasant style.

The account of the 'Faire' is picturesque, and the affectations of speech in its 'Gentlewomen' visitors are again amusingly recorded in 'A Fine Dame,' whose 'mouth is drawne into so narrow a compasse that she will not speake a broad word, but calls her husband, hisband.'

The 'Melancholy man' may have been well known to Milton.

We know little of Saltonstall's story : an Oxford man, of Queen's College, he wrote and tutored, but 'fell into misery,' and his stern sketch of a 'Scrivener' (or notary) may be related to this part of his life.

A Merry Man

His heart is so light that it leapes in his breast, and daunces to the tune of his owne conceits. He is the musicke in all companies, and you cannot please him better then to laugh at his Jest, which proves like an Egge in the breking, for as the one is ful of meate, so the other is full of wit. He was fram'd by nature for mirth, for when he tells some merry story, it is doubtfull whether his words or action doe best become him, and it is his Art to hide what followes, that the conclusion may make them laugh, till they cry out of their sides, and are even pain'd with pleasure. Young maides doate upon him, for he tells them stories of love with such a sensible feeling of the passion, that his words are so many arrowes to strike them in love. He is good to comfort sickemen, for if he finde them too indulgent to their disease, he will make them ashamed of their humour, while his jesting reprehension shall prevaile more than the counsell of friends. In this merry vaine, he observes both the time, place, and persons, for to laugh when others weepe is an unseasonable folly. His conceits are not raked out of the dunghill of obscene language, but are season'd with the salt of judgement, so that the severest *Cato*, cannot chuse but delight in them. He can apply himselfe to all humors, but cannot endure a melancholy man, for when they meete together, they are sure to have a bout at the weapons of wit, and though the merry man give more hits, yet the melancholy man wounds deeper. He brings himselfe into company with a Jest for his first Induction, and hee takes his leave with this complement, *hilares sedete*, sit yee merry. Lastly, he is the glew of good company, a harmlesse consumer of time, that makes it passe away undiscerned, and shortens the winter evenings with merry Tales; and as his life made his friends laugh, so his death makes them weepe for the losse of his merry conversation.

A Melancholy Man

Is a full vessell which makes not so great a sound, as those that are more empty and answer to every knocke. His wise parsimony of words shewes more wisedome, than their many, which are often-times more than wise. Hee can be merry without expressing it by an ignorant laughter. And if his company screw themselves up to an excessive straine of mirth; he proves amongst them but like a jarring string to a consort of musicke, and cannot raise himselfe to so high a note of jollity. When other men strive to seeme what they are not, hee alone is what he seemes not, being content in the knowledge of himselfe, and not waying his owne worth in the ballance of other mens opinions. If he walke and see you not, 'tis because his mind being busied in some serious contemplation, the common sense has no time to judge of any sensuall object. Hee's hardly with much invitation drawne to a feast, where every man sits an observer of another mans action, and had rather with *Diogenes* wash his owne Roots at home, than with *Aristippus* frequent the Court of Kings. His actions shew no temerity, having beene long before Intentions, and are at last produc'd as the ripe issue of a serious, and deliberate resolution. His speech shewes more matter in't than words, and like your gold coyne contaynes much worth in a little, when other mens is but like brass-farthings, and expresses little in much. As his apprehensions so his passions, are violent and strong, not enduring on the suddaine any opposition of good counsell, but like a torrent beares downe all before it. If he fall in love, he wooes more by letter than his owne presence, and is not hasty in the desire of fruition. His apparell is playne like himselfe, and shewes the riches of his mind, which contemnes a gaudy outside as the badge of fooles. He goes therefore commonly in blacke, his Hat unbrusht, a hasty gate with a looke fixt on the ground, as though he were looking pins there, when yet his mind is then soaring in some high contemplation; and is then alwayes most busy, when hee seemes most idle.

A Scholar in the University

MAY be knowne by a harmelesse innocent looke; his nose seemes to be raw for want of fyres in winter, and yet has such a quicke sent, that he quickly smells out his chopt mutton commons a farre off. In his freshmanship hee's full of humility, but afterward ascends the steps of ambition by degrees. He studies so long words of Art, that all his learning at last is but an Art of words. His discourse is always grounded out of *Aristotle*, in whose αὐτὸς ἔφα hee puts as much confidence as in his Creede. In his letters hee's often ready to shake the whole frame of the sense to let in some great word, affecting a nonsensicall eloquence before propriety of phrase; if hee were compeld to salute a Gentlewoman, he would tremble more than ever he did in pronouncing his first declamation. Hee often frequents Booke binders shops, for his unconstant humour of tumbling over many bookes, is like a sicke mans pallat, which desires to taste of every dish but fixes on none. The University Library is his magazine of learning, where hee'le be sure to be seene in his formalityes assoone as hees graduated; for the liberty thereof expresses him a Batchelour. He earnestly enquires after the weekely Currantoes, and swallowes downe any newes with great confidence. His cheefest curtesy to strangers, is to shew you his Colledge Buttery, and to skonce himselfe a halfepeny farthing for your entertainement. If you seeme to admire the names of their small divisions, as halfepeny, farthing, and the like, out of a selfe simplicity he straight laughes at your ignorance. And if you contend for priority in going forth, puts you downe with a stale complement. *Egressus est Peregrini.* When he makes a journey 'tis in the vacation, and then hee canvises a fortnight aforehand amongst his friends for Bootes and Spurres. His purse like the Sea is governd by the Moone, for he has his severall ebbes and tides, according as hee receives his severall exhibitions from his friends. Lastly, hee weares out a great deale of time there to know what kind of Animal hee is, contemns every man that is not a Graduate if himselfe be one, and because he professes himselfe a Scholler, goes commonly in blacke, and many times 'tis all he has to shew for't.

A Horse Race

Is a way to let money run away full speed. Amongst the Romanes 'twas an Olimpick exercise, and the prize was a Garland, but now they beare the Bell away. 'Tis the prodigality of countrey Gentlemen, and the gullery of Londoners; the one dyets his horse till his purse growes lanck, and the other payes for rash betting. The former would give any thing for a horse of *Pegasus* Race, or one begot of the wind while the mare turn'd her backe-side in *Boreas* mouth. They lay wagers here on their horse heeles, and hope to win it by their running heads. The Riders speake northern howsoever, and though they want many graynes of honest men, yet when they are put into the Scale, they are made weight. The horses are brought hither in their night clothes, and from thence walke downe to the starting post, whence grew the Latine proverbe, *a carceribus ad metam*. The countrey people have time now to commend white-mayne and Pepper-corne, while the Gentlemen ride up and downe with Bets in their mouthes, crying three to one, till the word Done make it a wager. By this time they are comming up, and the forerunner is receiv'd ovant, with great acclamations of joy, and the hinder man though hee rid booty, yet he shewes that he favour'd nether side by the spur-galling. It being now done, they drop away into the villages, where their tongues runne over the race againe, which for that night fils Alehouses with noyse and discourse.

A Scrivener

Is a Christian Canniball that devoures men alive. He sits behinde a deske like a Spider in a Cobweb to watch what flies will fall into his net. He abuses money by using it, and so contrary to the nature thereof puts it to generation, while like a common whore, hee lets her out to trading. He lookes so thinne that a man may picke a good stomacke out of his face, and he wishes his belly

were a lether bagge that so being once full it might
never be empty. He will lend money upon good
security, and then you must pay for procuring and
ensealing of writings, and the utmost extremity is
his friendship. Besides this he is so impudent in
his Art of undoing others, that hee begins with
Noverint universi, let all men know it. He is a
Scribe by profession, for he devoures widdowes
houses, and a Pharisee in his religion, for though
he doe no good, yet he loves good deedes in Parchment. Hee has no signe but a few tottering
Labells, which are hang'd there to shew their
masters desert. Country fellowes admire him, and
his pen is better to him than their Plough; while
the parchment is the soyle, money is the seede,
and usury the harvest which he reapes, and brings
dry into his Coffer which is his Barne. He workes
upon the occasions of other men, and his Bonds
are like flyes in winter, which lye dead for a time,
but afterward recover life, and contrary to other
things, they have most force when they are ready
to expire. He is no scholler yet is a great writer,
and is never confuted, but in the Chancery or Star-
chamber and there his fallacies are discern'd, and
he punished. He will feede you with hope of
money till your necessity is growne so urgent, that
you are willing to yeeld to any conditions, and then
he will worke you like waxe, and make you buy
your owne undoing. He has blanckes ready to
insert names, and in drawing of writings hee will
leave out some materiall clause, that so it may
occasion a suite in Law. Discord is his delight,
and hee cares for no musicke but telling of money.
He loves Almanackes because they shew him the

day of the moneth, and the yeare of our Lord, and he is alwayes in the future tense, hoping for time to come. To conclude his life is so blacke that no Inke can paint it forth, he is one of the Devils engines to ruine others, he is a paper worme, or a racke for honest men, and his *Ultimum vale* is a deceitfull breaking.

A Gentlemans House in the Countrey

Is the prime house of some village, and carryes gentility in the front of it. The Tennants round about travell thither in Pilgrimage with their pigge and goose offrings, and their duty increases with the neere expiring of their leases. The Serving-men are like quarter wayters; for while some give attendance at home, the rest are disperst in the Ale-houses. Their master alowes them to make men drinke for his credit, while they sound forth his fame of hospitallity upon the Trumpets of blacke Jackes. They envye most their owne coate, for if a Gentleman bring halfe a dozen men with him, they'le not suffer a man to come off alive, and that expresses their Masters welcome. At meales you shall have a scattered troup of dishes, led in by some blacke puddings, and in the Reare some demolish'd pastyes, which are not fallen yet to the Servingmen. Betweene meales there's bread and Beere for all commers, and for a stranger a napkin, and colde meat in the buttery may be obtained. All the Roomes smell of Doggs and Haukes, and the Halls beares armes, though it be but a muskitt and two Corsletts. The maides have their severall sweet-hearts, which they get by befriending men in their severall offices: As the dayry mayde by a dish of Creame: The Chambermayd by her landry; and for this the Serving men do them as good a turne. After which if she knot and prove, she obtaines of her Mistresse a poore Coppihold, and they both turne Tennants to the family; and are called retayners. The Master of the house is ador'd as a Relique of gentilitye, and if his wife come by some home-match, he dares not let her see London or the Court, for feare she should make his woods pay for't. Hee observes all times and seasons of the yeare, and his Christmas is the butlers Jubile. To conclude, his house is the seat of hospitality, the poore mans Court of Justice, the Curates Sunday ordinary, and the onely exchequer of Charity, where the poore goe away relieved, and cry, God blesse the founder.

A Lawyers Clearke

His father thought it too chargable to keep him at Schoole till he could read *Harry Stottle*, and therefore preferd him to a man of Law. His Master is his genius, and dictates to him before he sets pen to paper. If he be to make a Bond or Bill, for feare of writing false Latin, he abbreviates the ending and termination of his word with a dash, and so leaves it doubtfull. He sits nigh the dore to give accesse to strangers, and at their going forth gives them a legge in expectation. His master is a cunning jugler of lands and knowes how to convey them underhand, hee onely coppyes them over againe, and lookes for a fee for expedition. His utmost knowledge is the names of the Courts and their severall offices, and begins after a while like a Pie that has his tongue slit, to chatter out some tearmes of Law, with more audacity than knowledge. At a new play hee'le be sure to be seene in the threepeny Roome, and buyes his pippins before he goes in, because hee can have more for mony. When hee heares some stale jest (which he best apprehends) he fils the house with an ignorant laughter. He weares cut fingered dog-skin gloves, for his ease, or the desire of bribes makes his hands grow itchy. In the vacation his master goes into the Countrey to keepe Courts, and then hee's tide to a Cloakebagge and rides after him. He cals himselfe the hand of the Law, and commends the wisedome thereof, in having so many words goe to a bargaine, for that both lengthens them, and makes his fees the larger. Hee would faine read *Littleton* if hee might have a comment on him, otherwise hee's too obscure, and dotes much on *Wests* Symboliography for teaching him the forme of an acquittance. In his freshman-ship hee hunts after cheape venerye, and is in debt to the Cooke, for Eele pyes on fasting dayes, and friday nights. The corruption of him is a weake Atturney, then he trafiques with countrymens businesses, and brings them downe a bill of charges, worse than a Taylers for a suite in the last fashion, and here we leave him, for now hee's at the highest.

A Petty Countrey Faire

Is the publication of some few Pedlers packs dis-tinguisht into Boothes, which is yet fild with a great confluence of countrey people, who flocke thither to buy some triviall necessaries. Afarre off it seemes a tumult of white staves, and red petticoates and muflers, but when you come nearer they make a fayre shew. The men buy hobnayles and plough-irons, and the women houshold trifles, yet such as are for use more than ornament. Your countrey Gentlewomen come thither to buy bone-lace, and London gloves, & are only knowne by a Maske hanging on their cheeke and an Anticke plume of feathers in a Faire, and 'twould doe you good to heare them bargaine in their owne dialect. The Inns are this day fild, every man meets his friend, and unlesse they crush a pot, they thinke it a dry complement. Heere the yong Lads give their Lasses Fairings, which if she take with a simpring consent, the next Sunday their banes are bidden. A Ballet-singer may be sooner heard heere than seene, for instead of the violl hee sings to the croud. If his Ballet bee of love, the countrey wenches buy it, to get by heart at home, and after sing it over their milkepayles. Gipsies flocke thither, who tell men of losses, and the next time they looke for their purses, they find their words true. At last after much sweate and trampling too and froe, each one carryes home a peece of the Faire, and so it ends.

DONALD LUPTON (d. 1676)

London and the Country Carbonadoed and Quartred into
 severall Characters. By D. Lupton. . . . London.
 . . . 1632. 8vo. Reprinted in the Harleian Mis-
 cellany. . . .

36 characters.

Lupton claims that his subject is ' new and merry.'
It is true that the extent to which he wrote characters of
places and institutions—26 of his 36 pieces—was new,
but the idea itself had been used by the other English
character-writers from the first. These twenty-six pieces
are essays rather than characters. The geographical
' characters ' written towards the end of the Common-
wealth by the traveller and exile were a natural development
from such work as Lupton's ; but they were pamphlets
and, as a rule, characters only in name.

Lupton's ten ' characters ' of occupations can be fairly
so described. He is fond of word-play, but his style
remains clear and is frequently agreeable.

The Bridge

IT is almost Arts wonder, for strength, length,
beauty, widenesse, height : It may be sayd to be
Polypus, because it is so well furnished with
legges : Every Mouth is foure times filled in eight
and forty houres, and then as a Child it is still, but
as soone as they be empty, like a Lyon it roares,
and is wondrous Impatient : It is made of Iron,
Wood, and Stone, and therefore it is a wondrous
hardy Fellow. It hath changd the forme, but as
few doe now a dayes, from worse to better : cer-
tainely it is full of Patience, because it beares so
much, and continually : It's no Prison, for any

one goes through it: It is something addicted to pride, for many a Great man goes under it; and yet it seemes something humble too, for the poorest Peasant treads upon it: It hath more Wonders then Arches, the houses here built are wondrous strong, yet they neyther stand on Land or Water: It is some praejudice to the Watermans gaines; many goe over here, which otherwise should row or sayle: It helpes many a Pennilesse Purse to passe the water without danger or charges: nothing afrights it more, then Springtides or violent inundations: It is chargeable to keep, for it must be continually Repayred: it is the onely chief crosser of the water, his Arches out-face the water, and like Judges in the Parliament are plac'd upon woolesackes: one that lives heere neede not buy strong Water, for heere is enough for nothing: it seemes to hinder the Water-bearers profit, for the Inhabitants easily supply their Wants by Buckets: He is a setled fellow, and a maine upholder of houses; hee is meanely plac'd, for there are diverse above him, and many under him, & his houses may wel bee called *None-such*, for there is none like them, and to conclude, he pertakes of two Elements, his nether parts are all for Water, his upper for Land; in a word, it is without Compare, being a dainty streete, and a strong and most stately Bridge.

Hospitality

THIS true noble hearted fellow is to be dignified and honor'd, wheresoever he keeps house: It's thought that pride, puritans, coaches and covetousnesse hath caused him to leave our Land: there are sixe upstart tricks come up in great Houses of late which he cannot brook. Peeping windowes for the Ladies to view what doings there are in the Hall, a Buttry hatch that's kept lockt, cleane Tables, & a French Cooke in the Kitching, a Porter that lockes the gates in dinner time, the decay of Blacke-jackes in the Cellar, and blew coates in the Hall: he alwayes kept his greatnesse by his Charity: he loved three things, an open Cellar, a full Hall, and a sweating Cooke: he alwayes provided for three dinners, one for himselfe, another for his Servants, the third for the poore: any one may know where hee kept house, either by the Chimnies smoak, by the freedom at gate, by want of whirligige Jackes in the Kitchin, by the fire in the Hall, or by the full furnish'd tables: he affects not *London*, Lent, Lackaies or Bailifes, there are foure sorts that pray for him, the poore, the passenger, his Tenants, and Servants: hee is one that will not hourd up all, nor lavishly spend all, he neyther rackes or rakes his Neighbours, they are sure of his Company at Church as wel as at home, and gives his bounty as wel to the Preacher, as to others whom hee loves for his good life and doctrine: hee had his wine came to him by full Buts, but this Age keepes her Wine-Celler in little bottles. Lusty able men well maintayned were his delight, with whom he would be familiar: his Tenants knew when they saw him, for he kept the olde fashion, good, com-mendable, plaine: the poore about him wore him uppon their backes; but now since his death, Land-lords weare and wast their Tenants uppon their backes in French, or *Spanish* fashions. Well, wee can say that once such a charitable Practitioner

there was, but now hee's dead, to the griefe of all
England: And tis shroudly suspected that hee will
never rise againe in our Climate.

Fisher-women

THESE Crying, Wandring, and Travailing
Creatures carry their shops on their heads, and
their Store-house is ordinarily *Bilings gate* or the
Bridge-foote, and their habitation *Turnagaine-
lane*, they set up every morning their Trade afresh.
They are easily set up and furnish't, get something, and spend it Jovially and merrily : Five
shillings a Basket, and a good cry, is a large stocke
for one of them.   They are merriest when all their
Ware is gone : in the morning they delight to have
their shop ful, at Even they desire to have it
empty : their Shoppe's but little, some two yards
compasse, yet it holds all sorts of Fish, or Hearbs,
or Roots, Strawberries, Apples or Plums, Cow-
cumbers, and such like ware : Nay, it is not destitute some times of Nutts, and Orenges, and
Lemmons.   They are free in all places, and pay
nothing for shop-rent, but onely find repaires to it.
If they drinke out their whole Stocke, it's but
pawning a Petticoate in *Long-lane*, or themselves
in *Turnebull-streete* for to set up againe.   They
change every day almost, for Shee that was this day
for Fish, may bee to morrow for Fruit; next day
for Hearbs, another for Roots : so that you must
heare them cry before you know what they are
furnisht withall, when they have done their Faire,
they meet in mirth, singing, dancing, & in the
middle as a *Parenthesis*, they use scolding, but they
doe use to take & put up words, & end not till

either their money or wit, or credit bee cleane
spent out. Well, when in an evening they are
not merry in a drinking-house, it is suspected
they have had bad returne, or else have payd some
old score, or else they are banke-rupts: they are
creatures soone up, & soone downe.

ANONYMOUS

A Strange Metamorphosis of Man, transformed into a
  Wildernesse. Deciphered in Characters. London,
  ... 1634. 12mo.

In the 'Epistle to the Reader' we are told, 'To finde
man we must leave the Citte, and seeke him in the Wildernesse,' but there is no attempt to satisfy our hopes of
finding new analogies for human types. The 40 brief
sketches, chiefly of animals and plants, confine themselves
to fanciful observations and to quaint imaginings about
their subjects. In a fashion that time has made attractive
we are told 'The hedgehog is a right Urchin and a
peevish Elfe.' Or the dream is suggested : ' As wee have
our Utopia, the Dogs have an Ile likewise, but not set
downe in *Mercator ;* ' The brief references to nature
are placid and rather formal, as of primroses : 'They make
a dainty shew with them, when they sit familiarly together
with their handmaids the leaves : But when they take
their sister Violets into their company, then they make an
admirable enamell.'

The Snayle

Is a Gentleman every inch of him; as ancient
surely as *Adams* time; while for Armes, hee hath
had a house for Coat ever since, which he bears
to this day. He seemes very stately in the manner
of his gate, but hee is not proud. He is cold of
complexion, because flegmaticke, which makes him
so slow of his pace. Hee is a Scholler, for he keepes
his study, though he have no bookes. He is no
Accademicke, though a Philosopher, because not
sociable, but rather a Peripateticke, because a
walker; but especially a Stoicke, because he carries

all whatsoeuer hee hath on his backe. If hee were confined to his five miles according to the statute, it would trouble him nothing, while hee would travaile where hee list, yet not incurre the forfeiture, or the penalty of the law. He hath indeed a certaine house of his owne, but no setled one, and a faire porch to it, but no doore. Hee is a freeholder, and no tenant at will, or for any terme that is lesse then his life. There is no covenant servants amongst them, but are housholders every one. They have no constant Cities of their owne, while their houses joyne not one to another, as others doe. Though they wander much, and gad abroad, yet they are not included in the Statute of rogues. The Snayle and the Periwincle are much alike, with this difference, that the Snayle with paines carries his house on his backe, and the Periwincle, house and all, is carried with the waves with ease, as held up by the chinne. In fine, they are at peace with all the world, and have no enimies at all; and so like the Hamburgers, trade and travaile where they please; unlesse in a time of famine, when perhaps for better food, they come to be snapt up and made good prize.

The Swallow

Is the little spirit of the ayre, who will bee here, and there, and every where, in the twinckling of an eye. Hee loves to dwell in the City for societies sake. His house is built in the manner of the Antipodes, in the vulgar opinion; for as their feet are opposite to ours, of consequence their houses must needs bee turned up-side downe; and so are theirs. They have no windowes, or posterns behind

their houses, but all their light, egresse, and re-
gresse, is at the porch only, where they keep watch
with their bils, both night and day, for feare of
forreigne invasion. Their fare is light and easie
of digestion, which makes them so active and
nimble as they are; not of worms, for that they
hold too grosse and earthly: not of corn, not to
put the world to so much cost: nor of flesh, for
they cannot indure the flesh pots of Egypt. They
hawke, hunt, and fish where they list, as being the
Rangers of the Forrests, allowed by nature through
the privilege of their wing. Hee must needs fly
well, that feeds on flyes, who is so fleet, that hee
will stay by the way for no mans pleasure, for hee
is alwayes set on the spurre, and, as it were, the
Post of the Eagles Court. The difficulty is, he
can hardly stay so long in a place, as to take his
message ere hee goeth, so tickle he is. They are
notable Physitians, or Chirurgians, which you will,
for they will cure you the blinde, as readily with
the herb Chelidonia, as cause it with their dung.
In fine, they are welcome ghests when they come
first, because they bring in the Summer with them;
and never depart without teares when Winter
comes.

RICHARD CRASHAW (?1612-1650)

Hygiasticon : Or, The right course of preserving Life and
    Health unto extream old Age : . . . Written in
    Latine by Leonard Lessius, And now done into
    English. . . . Cambridge. 1634. 12mo.

[On the verso of the title] : . . . ' 2. Cornaro's Treatise
    of Temperance, translated by Master George
    Herbert.'

This must be one of the loveliest addresses ' To the
Reader' that has been written. Crashaw, at Pembroke
College since March 1632, wrote it for the second edition
of Lessius's *Hygiasticon*, which included Herbert's translation of Cornaro. It were pleasing to fancy that the
young Crashaw wrote this poem with the saintly George
Herbert in his mind, though the whole piece could not be
intended for him, since the age of 40, when Herbert
died (in 1633) could hardly, even then, be described as
' December.' The poem was reprinted in Crashaw's
first collection of poems *The Steps to the Temple. With
other Delights of the Muses* (1646), when twelve lines were
prefixed, out of harmony with the poem, and reading
as if they were written to order to fit the title. The
original ' Heark hither, Reader—' remained as line 13,
a witness to an unhappy addition and a careless join.
Can Crashaw be responsible ? The title was finally
changed in 1652 to ' Temperance. Of The Cheap
Physitian Upon The Translation of Lessius.'

A Man

HEARK hither, Reader : wouldst thou see
Nature her own Physician be ?

Wouldst see a man all his own wealth,
His own physick,[1] his own health?
A man, whose sober soul can tell
How to wear her garments well;
Her garments that upon her sit
(As garments should do) close and fit?
A well-cloth'd soul, that's not opprest
Nor choakt with what she should be drest?
Whose soul's sheath'd in a crystal shrine,
Through which all her bright features shine?
As when a piece of wanton lawn,
A thinne aëriall vail, is drawn
O're Beauties face; seeming to hide,
More sweetly shows the blushing bride?
A soul, whose intellectual beams
No mists do mask, no lazie steams?
A happie soul, that all the way
To heav'n rides in a summers day?
Wouldst see a man, whose well-warm'd bloud
Bathes him in a genuine floud?
A man whose tuned humours be
A set of rarest harmonie?
Wouldst see blithe looks, fresh cheeks beguile
Age? wouldst see December smile?
Wouldst see a nest of roses grow
In a bed of reverend snow?
Warm thoughts, free spirits, flattering
Winters self into a spring?
In summe, wouldst see a man that can
Live to be old, and still a man;
Whose latest and most leaden houres
Fall with soft wings, stuck with soft flowres?

[1] sic 1646, 'musick' in 1634.

And when lifes sweet fable ends,
His soul and bodie part like friends:
No quarrels, murmures, no delay;
A kisse, a sigh, and so away?
This rare one, Reader, wouldst thou see?
Heark hither, and thy self be he.

R. Crashaw, Pemb.

DUDLEY, THIRD LORD NORTH
(1581-1666)

A Forest of Varieties. . . . London, . . . 1645. fol.

A Forest Promiscuous . . . London, . . . 1659. fol.

This book is pre-eminently a personal document. Its essays, letters, verses and characters are one and all the meditations of a thoughtful man afflicted with melancholia. He writes one morning : ' I have been forced to live so far under my natural rate and faculties of soul, that I wanted spirits to counterlook a cat.' This experience was not rare, for the theme of the whole book is ' me miserum.'

The ten characters were ' written about the yeare 1625.' They lengthily record the introspection rather than the observation of the writer, for they are theoretical accounts of what his various subjects should be and do. The most definite is the one most closely based on experience : ' A Physitian ' must have been continually in the neurasthenic's mind.

A Physitian

A GOOD Physitian (if any such there be) for bad enough is the best, in respect of the Arts uncertainty, will more affect the life and health of his Patient, then his own gain and living, and will not minister Physick to him to do good to himselfe. He will be sorry that by a surprize of his over-deeming election, he findes himself imbarqued in a profession, where it is hard to thrive and be honest, in giving Physick only where there is reall need, and a good confidence in himself, that it shall doe good to his Patient; for he will have discovered that his title is but as a Mountaine from not moving, and that nature is the true Physitian placed by God in every man for his preservation, and himself but a Professor of a most conjecturall Art: so that who commits himself from nature to him, takes himself from a seeing to a blind guide. Though it be incident to his Colledge to be over peremptory, as being used to the authority of pre-scriptions, and prostrate sick Patients, yet he will avoid it; for a discreet, plausible, and winning car-riage upon the Patients good opinion and affection is the one halfe of the cure. He will not contemn an honest Emperick, knowing that his own Art grew but from experience often casuall, and that Gods blessings are not restrained to their Colledge and old Books. He will not bee sparing of his inter-rogatories, nor of his attention to his Patients relation, who being sick, and paying, ought to bee born with and humoured; But an humorous Phy-sitian is a most intolerable disease, for all is but too little to effect a true information, and to doe well, he will often suspect, that the disease may grow from the minde. In case of which discovery he will no lesse industriously indeavour the Cure of the body by it, and his good precepts and instruc-tions thoroughly urged to that purpose, then by any other means, it being often the onely way of Cure, but nothing more ordinarily neglected by such as only affect to say something to draw a Fee, but wil be sure not to trouble their own mindes to cure their Patients: But from such God deliver me, who will as little admit them to the tryall of my disease and constitution, as the Law doth a Butcher to be a Juror. Purging Medicines shall bee his last refuge, after prescription of convenient exercise, order, and dyet, which by some of the best are affirmed to bee sufficient to cure any disease curable. Hee will affect chearefulnesse of countenance and fashion, for it is a Cordiall to the sick, but he will take heed of an unseasonable merriment, which is often as absurd as unwelcome to the seriousnesse of a sick man. . . .

THOMAS FORD (fl. 1647)

The Times Anatomiz'd, In severall Characters. By
   T. F. . . . London, . . . 1647.   12mo.

30 characters.

Ford assures his readers ' Certainly to play the Foole in
this age, when the whole World's distracted, is not only
tolerable, but necessary.' But he cannot free himself
from the shadow.

About ten of his pieces are written in the style of the
contemporary essay, to which they contribute a feeling
for rhythm that was still rare.

An inconstant Man

HE is a wandring Star, never fixed in any resolution. Whatsoever he meant or said, is presently
altered, for he meant it not long enough to take
impression, his strongest resolutions being rather
tack'd then fastned. He is always building and
pulling down, striving to out-vey time it selfe in
mutability: in the best things continuance is
quarrell sufficient, and novelty the highest style of
commendation in the meanest. His understanding
writes upon his wit, as men write on water, no
sooner written, but forgotten. He is a stranger
to himselfe, and all his actions so different from
another, that one would think it impossible they
should all come out of one the same shop. A piece
of clay, tempered with running water, which keeps
his wit in a perpetuall motion. He often resolves,
seldome Acts, being rul'd by passion, not reason.
He is the best enemy that can be, but the worst
friend, for 'tis a wonder if his love or hatred, last

so long as a wonder.   All his purposes are built
upon the floting Islands of his severall humours:
but Ile here cast anchor, and leave him to the winde
of his own will.

Rebellion

Is a poysonous weed growing up in a Common-
wealth, by the fatnesse of the soyle.   It may
flourish for a while, but the sword of justice doth
in the end cut it down, being whetted by time and
divine revenge.   It is a true Viper, for as the shee-
viper biteth off the head of the hee, and thereby
conceives with young, & those young prove her
own destruction, making their birth her death; and
thus doth Rebellion when it hath bitten off the
head of government, it proves its own destruction,
and will be the end of the beginners thereof; And
not seldom, it is made its owne scourge.   For
though Majesty may be eclipsed for a season, yet
will it at length breake out againe into its force
like the Sun in his greatest brightnesse, and dispell
those misty fogs and vapours that before had
clouded it.   Whilest the two petty combatants (in
the Fable) strove which should overcome the other,
they were both made a prey unto the royall Eagle:
ambition and discontent are the two main wheels
this Engine moves on, and because it is so ugly
in it selfe, that all men would detest it, it seldome
appears but with a borrowed face for the good of
the Common-wealth, and if it get hold on Religion,
it flies (too truly) like wilde-fire.

Of *War*

WAR is a Tragœdy, that most commonly destroyes the Scene whereon 'tis acted. An unwelcome guest that devoures his Host. The cursed off-spring of two blessed parents, Peace and Plenty, both which it destroyes and devoures, as *Pharoes* leane kine did the fat ones. Peace chains up al furies & mischiefs, which the sword of Warre lets loose. War is a Wolfe whose pestilent breath stops the mouth of the Laws, whose voyce cannot be heard for the cryes of oppressed people, the effect, and the roaring of Cannons, and clashing of Armes, the sadder causes. Wars griping hand squeezeth and scattereth what good husbandry had raked together in time of peace. Time of War is the true Iron Age, for it converts all into iron, which iron will be master of all mens gold. Warre never comes but attended with a train of devouring followers: Destruction and that usually goe hand in hand. This Generall Warre hath so universall a command, that no particular man can have any command of his now. But of all Wars, none so uncivill as civill War, other wars kill foes, but this friends, in this, one member rises up against another. If a Kingdom divided from others cannot stand, a Kingdom divided against it self must needs fall. But the uglinesse of War will appeare better, or rather worse, by viewing the beauty of Peace.

Death

DEATH is that universall winde to which all mortals, become wind-fals from the tree of life.

Sickenesses & sleep, are as pauses and parentheses, in the line of life, but Death the full point; the period, and *Ne plus ultra*, of the longest. The grisly *Atropos* that cuts in sunder the strongest cord of life, it is that unavoidable debt levied upon all mankind, by force of that Statute enacted by God in Paradise : and recorded by Saint *Paul*, *That all must dye*. As when one told *Anaxagoras*, the *Athenians* have condemn'd thee to dye, He answered, and Nature then. It is that black night, which over-takes, and over-spreads the brightest day of life. The grim Sergeant sent from the Almighty with an *Habeas Corpus*, to arrest every one for that unavoidable debt, due to Nature, ever since our first Parent broke and turn'd Bankerupt. The grave is his Prison wherein he keeps them, till the Resurrection, the time of their Gaol-delivery from it. But to the godly, it is a friendly-fo, which by robbing them of a mortall life, makes them capable of immortality; and by splitting the vessell of their bodies, upon the rock of death, engulphs their souls into Eternity : setting her free from the prison of the body, and endenizing her into Heaven. It is their *Exodus* out of the *Egypt* of the World, preparing them to enter into their promised Land of the heavenly *Canaan:* or new *Hierusalem*. At this Port must we all arrive : whatsoever our Voyage be. This is the totall summe of all mankinde. It is the bitter cup our father *Adam* begun, and wee must all pledge it : the Inheritance which he purchased, as his wages of sin, and is entayl'd to all his posterity. A Deluge which broke in by *Adams* breach of Gods Commandement that sooner or later will over-flow all mankind. By his rebelling against God, al are become subject to deaths command. What the Epigram sayth wittily on the Grammarian is true of every man, that being able to decline all other Nownes in every Case, could decline Death in no Case. All must fall down at deaths feet, as well the Prince as the Pesant He cannot be resisted, nor will he be flatterd. No Orator so eloquent, that could perswade Death to spare him, nor Monarch so mighty that could resist him. *Hezekiah*, indeed was repriev'd, by God himselfe, for fifteen yeares, but he came to it at last. When this wind blowes, and when this rain descends, it irresistably blowes down, and washeth away the clay tenements of our bodies. He is an Archer that shooteth, somtimes beyond us hitting our superiours, somtimes short of us, striking our inferiors, somtimes at our right hand, depriving us of our freinds, somtimes at our left hand, taking away our foes: and then at last hits the marke it selfe, and we must tread the same path, that all have, who are gon before us, and all must that shall come after.

ANONYMOUS

A fresh Whip For all Scandalous Lyers. Or, A true
description of the two eminent Pamphliteers, or
Squib-tellers of this Kingdome. With a plaine and
true Relation of their Tricks and Devices wherewith
they use to couzen and cheate the Common-wealth.
London printed. 1647. 4to.

This lively sketch takes us at once into the riotous
' Fleet-Street ' of 1647. The Royalist author begins by
referring to the diurnals with a scorn that is not unjustifiable ; for these periodicals, belonging almost entirely to
the Roundheads, which crowded into brief existence at
the outbreak of the Civil War to give accounts of the
proceedings of the Parliament, were in the main illiterate
and scurrilous.

He then gives a vigorous account of the most notorious
figure among these boggling journalists. ' Harry Walker '
[why ' Thomas ' here ?] the ironmonger turned journalist,
though dishonest and ignorant, was yet possessed of a
queer efficiency that made its mark. A character of him
as *Mercurious Morbicus* (1647) foretells the gallows for
him and provides the epitaph :

> ' Faithless, fruitlesse he was ever,
> Except in lyes, but loyall never.
> From hence h'as taken wing to be,
> Old *Belzebub's* chief *Mercury*.'

Cleveland's characters of ' A London Diurnall ' and
' Diurnall-Writer ' are well-known and in their own
time they caused a stir, but the anonymous writer's work
in ' A fresh Whip ' is closer to the character-form and is
of more general interest to-day.

Two eminent Pamphliteers

I must beginne with the *Diurnall-Writer* first, as
indeed order it selfe doth enjoyne me, by the con-

stant course of the dayes in the week; and whose
large volumne is issued out every Munday morning. I may not unfitly tearme him to be the chiefe
Dirt-raker, or Scafinger of the City; for what ever
any other book lets fall, he will be sure, by his
troting horse, and ambling Booke-selers have it
convey'd to his wharfe of rubbish, and then he will
as a many petty fogging scriveners do (I may not
exempt himselfe out of the profession) put out
here and there to alter the sence of the Relation;
and then he shelters it under the title of a new and
perfect Diurnall. This merchant when he hath
loaden his Sheet (or Dung-Cart) with his stale
informations, and mis-informations; then ye shall
have him strut up and down with his gingling
spurs, as if he had a paire of Aarons Bells at his
heeles, or that hee had done the state mighty good
service. He was once a Stationer, till he crept into
the little hole at Westminster-Hall, where indeed
he began his trade of inditing or framing; and so
rose at last to the stile of the *Diurnall-Writer*. I
must confesse at his first beginning to write, he
was very industrious, and would labour for the
best intelligence, as his large volumnes do testifie,
but when he found the sweetnesse of it, and how
easily he could come by his Intelligence, he fell to
his sports and pastimes, for you should hardly ever
finde him at home all the weeke, till Saturday-
morning, and then you should be sure to find him
abed, panting and puffing as if he had over-rid
himselfe, with riding too and agen from the Army,
when God-wot hee hath not been out of the Lynes
of Communication; (but a little too much within
the Lynes of *M.M.*). And so by this means making

the poor workmen stand still for their labour, and that which he should do on Saturday, he must do on Sunday. This merchant hath his two Printers to attend his worke, whereof one hath a man, that rather then it should be thought that he were not diligent enough for his Master, he will content himselfe with a peice of Thursdayes news for his Prayers, Fridayes Intelligence for the first Sermon, and Saturdayes for the afternoone Lecture, and if it do not hold them over-long, he will sit downe and sing a Psalme, or take a pipe of Tobacco, and think he hath done God good service. 'Tis a shame such a Conventicle (*I* can tearm it no otherwise) which tends to the dishonour of God, should be suffered.

Now I must doe as many false Prognosticators mistake, or skip 3. dayes in the change of the Moone: I must come to Friday, stiled the *Perfect Occurrence Writer*. He whose face is made of Brasse, his body of Iron, and his teeth are as long as tenpenny-nayles. I think he is a youth not unknown to most in the City, since the great preferment he had to stand in the Pillory. He is a great merchant in this way of writing, and very excellent for framing a Title for an old, or new lye. This is he that when our men lay of one side of Shotover-Hill against *Oxford*, he got the favour to discharge a peece of Ordnance against the City; when he had done, for London he came, with a greater report and execution then ever the piece did, that he had shot down one of the chiefest Colledges in the University, and that he could perceive the very Battlements to fall: and after this great victory of his, because he would be taken notice of, hee

causes his Printer to set downe the very place
where he lives, as for example, London printed for
Thomas Walker living at a great brick house and
balcony, as you turne up to St. *James's;* when
indeed the three cornerd house without a roofe,
turning up to *Padington* were more fitter. He was
an Ironmonger in St. *Martins* by his trade, where
having but little trading for his Tinkerly ware, fell
to this trade of mis-informing; and so by his
venomous pen framing, and with his chafing dishes
of Hell, hee hath bestrowd the whole City, nay
the whole Kingdome with unsavory languages,
and burning coales of contention. This merchant
I must needs confesse doth take a great deale more
pains then the other in compacting his relations
together, and it doth chiefly lye in running up
and down, he may well be called the Bellman of
the City, for he is up all houres in the night, running to and agen, from the Post-house; and when
he is questioned with who goes there; my name is
Walker, I am about the States service, pray do not
stop me : when he hath been at a Printing house,
laying his sower Leven of raylings and scandaliz-
ings against honest, and reverend men; or else
compacting his damnable lyes together. Witnesse
how many times hath he taken and killed Prince
Rupert, and Prince *Maurice*, and Sir *Ralph
Hopton:* he hath an excellent faculty to put a new
title to an old book, and he wil be sure to put
more in the Title page then is in all the booke
besides; how many victories, and sometimes small
losses hath he fram'd, and especially out of Ireland,
and many times strange sights in the ayre, appear-
ing like Champions ready to encounter. I wonder

he never met with the Divell, but indeed he was ever a favourer of Lyes, and I believe hath granted him a large Patten for his profession. Nay rather then he will be out of action, he will robbe *Hammon* of his Patten of one side, and draw out a list of halfe a side with Malignants names, or Horses, and frame an Order as from the House whereby they may sell; For his Fridayes *Occurrences* he doth take a great deale of paines to keep up the sale of them, he doth as many times Grocers use to do by their mouldy, musty ware, take and shake them together with a new glosse of Hony, and they will passe as if they came newly over. So when hee hath compacted all his Rubbish or Ribaldry together, he will set them off with an Order or Ordinance of Parliament. *I* could inlarge my selfe a great deale more, but I would keepe within the compasse of my sheete. And conclude with this, that *I* do think that his, and many other scurrillous Pamphlets, have done more mischief in the kingdome then ever all my Lord of *Essex's*, or Sir *Thomas Fairefaxes* whole traine of Artillery ever did. Finis.

THOMAS HEYWOOD (d. ? 1650)

Machiavel. As He lately appeared to his deare Sons,
    the Moderne Projectors. . . . London : . . . 1641.
    4to.

1 long character, 9 brief sketches.

Heywood devoted his few and well-written characters
to satirising the ' Innovators ' of his time. In 1609, in
his heroic poem *Great Britaines Troy*, he suspended his
discussion of Saturn and the origin of the Mediterranean
Sea to give us a clear cameo of a Puritan. And he began
a short tract against the Puritans in 1636, the *Discourse of
the Two infamous upstart Prophets*, with a lively sketch of
one of these ' Innovators in Religion.'

The ' Projector in generall ' was reprinted by itself in
1642 as ' Hogs Character of a Projector.'

The illustration enlivened John Taylor's broadside.
*The complaint of M. Tenter-hooke the Projector, and Sir
Thomas Dodger the Patentee* (1641). This was an
amusing comment on a matter of great topical interest.
Charles I's efforts to raise money by monopolies had
failed. For as Clarendon tells us, these projects ' Many
ridiculous, Many scandalous, All very grievous,' brought
' Envy, and Reproach to the King, the Profit to other
men.'[1] Charles's propitiatory proclamation in 1639 against
the greater number of them had not produced its effect,
and the Long Parliament tackled the problem before
proceeding to other business. Certain monopolist members were expelled, and most of the monopolies still
outstanding were called in. Taylor neatly summarises
the situation. His Projector laments both the failure of
his own efforts ' to cheat the Common-weale,' and of his
accomplice's, the Patentee's, ' tricks . . . to passe the Seale.'
For you, he says, I made my *Fingers fish-hookes* to catch
at all *Trades*, . . . I wore ' *Asses eares*, To listen unto all

[1] *The History of the Rebellion*, Oxford, 1702, vol. i. p. 53.

I heard, Wherein your worships profit was prefer'd,'
I put on a Swine's face to taste all things,

> *Soape*, *Starch*, *Tobacco*, *Pipes*, *Pins*, *Butter*, *Haye*,
> *Wine*, *Coales*, *Cards*, *Dice*, and all came in my way.

But you screwed me up too high. The Patentee can only
regretfully run over their joint accomplishments, and he
has to conclude that his Patent which lately had power
'strange things to do,' has now

> Brought us to ruine by a Parliament : . . .
> I'le shift for one, doe thou shift for thy selfe.

A Projector in generall

. . . He is a Mongrill by birth : His Father was
an *Hittite*, and his Mother an *Amorite*. His Education in his youth was with a Poet, and by him
infected with strange raptures, and whimsies, which
hee strives to put in practice, and calls them Projects : his riper yeares were corrupted with the
abominable termes of Lawyers Lattin, and Pedlers
French. His actions at the first view speake him
honest, and politicke; but the end he aimes at
proves him the cleane contrary way. Hee is in his
discourse a Gymnosophist, by Religion a *Bannian*,
and in his Faith an Alchymist.

He is the winter Fowle that know their seasons,
and you may find as many Projectors in Parliament
time, as Woodcocks in Summer : of all Professions,
a Baud, a Pimpe, a pander, and a Projector, hate
to be called by their proper names, although they
love their Trades.

Hee is one that hath alwayes more money in
his mouth, than in his purse, and feedes as heartily
upon his Aiery hopes, as the newes Mongers in
Pauls upon Duke *Humphreyes* Cates.

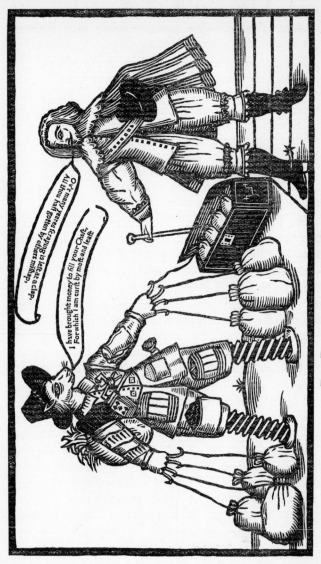

Hee is one that is wiser in his owne conceit than the Privie Councell, can reforme a Common-wealth better than a Parliament: you may read all the penall Statutes, if his tongue chance to peepe out of his mouth: onely he makes a *quaere*, and demurres upon *primo Hen*. 8. where his predecessors *Empson* and *Dudley* were honoured with a Hempen Garland, and conclude, that Session to bee Apocrypha, yet makes his bragges in the vulgar, how they suffered for the Common-wealth, and deserve to bee stiled Martyrs.

Hee is made all of Cringes and Complements, as if he dropt out of the Docke of a Courtier, and can change himselfe into as many shapes as Painters doe colours, either a decayed Merchant, a broken Citizen, a silent Minister, an old maym'd Captaine, a forejudged Atturney, a busie Soliciter, a crop-ear'd Informer, a pick-thanke Pettyfogger, or a nimble pac'd Northerne Tike, that hath more wit than honestie.

These are the men that make the bravest Projectors, who in short time may bee dignified with the title of Knight of the Post, or Canker Generall of the Common-wealth.

He will pinguifie all manner of Pullen, with Carrots and Turnips, fatten all foure footed beasts without Hay, or Grasse, or any manner of Graine, make bread of Pumpions, and Cucumbers, and will finde the Guard Beefe and Brues for God a mercy, till their bellies crack; and victuall the King an Army without meat, and take all the *Scots* in a pursuit, if they Rebell.

Hee is an excellent Architecture, hee will pull downe *White-hall*, and build the King a new

Palace, to which the banqueting house shall bee but halfe the Porters lodge, and at his owne cost, if the King will not give him leave, hee would turne an hospitall into a Court, and annexe the Savoy to Sommerset house, if the Dutchy were not betweene them, and then all the poore people may be admitted in *Forma Pauperis* to seek their lodgings without certificate of the Parish. Hee is the onely imitator of *Guido Vaux* his darke Lanthorne, and by it, hath made a device to convey people above ground that shall see every body, and no man see them, with the helpe of two-footed beasts, and hath jugled into credit with a strange name and call it a Sedan.

He will turne all Waggons, Carts, and Coaches into the nature of Wind-mills, to saile to the Stages for the benefit of the Kingdome in sparing horse-flesh in the warres, and to that intent hath got a Patent to make wooden horses, fit for Brewers, Butchers, Maulters, and Carriers that shall doe as good service, as if they were alive, carry burthens, and fast much longer.

Hee is one that scrapes up a living in this world, though hee be put out of possession in the next; and hath crept neatly into the favour of the Clergie, by advancing the returne of the whole Kingdome a third part, whereby their tythes are increased more than ever.

Hee can saile thorow *London* Bridge against wind and Tide, cleare the Thames from Sands and Shelves; weigh up all Wracks, though in the bottome of the Sea, and fifty fathome under water, blow up the enemy with fire: if you seeme to doubt any of these Projects, hee hugges himselfe

with conceit of your ignorance, and his owne wit:
if you question him, his answer is; This age is a
cherisher of Arts, and new Inventions, the former
dull and heavie, that these times are active, as may
appear by the draining of the Fens, building of
Townes, and Churches, repairing of *Pauls*, his
Majesties expedition to *Yorke*, and concludes,
Nihil est quod non Solertia vincat.

To say truth, he is a man of knowledge, very
great in knavery; hee is well read in deceit of all
Trades; hee knowes how to dye silke to make it
weigh heavy: hee knowes, that divers sorts of
wooll mixt together, will never cotten well, to make
good Demicasters: he knowes those Malsters are
knaves that make a Bushell of Barly pute above
nine in Mault; and I protest in good earnest, he
doth deserve wel, if he can cast out the beames of
his owne eye, that he may see the clearer to make
themselves honest men. . . .

He is one that thinks he can cozen the Devill,
for hee will Wire-draw the Covetous, and worme
the Usurer of their estates for hope of gaine; they
will drop all three into a hangmans budget, if my
Art doe not cousen me: Hee is a rare extracter
of the quintessences of Beere, Ale, Wine, Tobacco,
Mault, Bricke-tiles, Sope, Starch, Allome, Cards,
Dice, and Tapsters, *cum multis aliis;* the pure
Spirit gat by imposing a fine, and an annuall rent
upon those that take Patents to sell them, and
suffer others to sell them for nothing. . .
. . . you shall heare his Epitaph.

> *Reader, here intomb'd doth lye*
> *One, who thought he could not dye,*

Yet Death to shew no flesh can be
Compos'd of Immortalitie,
Trembling did let flie a Dart,
Which kild him midst of all his Art:
For had he longer drawne his breath,
'Tis thought 'twould have infected death:
So many hot contagions flew
From his braine, each threatned new
Infections: blasting where they came,
The tree and fruit, nay even the name
Of honesty: But now hee's gone,
Like a Comet by his owne
Fire consum'd: The wormes doe feare,
Now hee's in earth that he should there
Practise on them: for in his grave,
Hee dead still lives toth' world a Knave.

ANONYMOUS

Two Essays of Love And Marriage. . . . Together with
some Characters and other Passages of Wit. Written
by Private Gentlemen for recreation. . . . London,
. . . 1657. 12mo.

13 characters.

There is some good writing and plenty of wit, though
both are second-rate, in this collection. Of a ' Hum-
ourist' for instance, whose 'principall humour . . . is,'
inconstancy. . . . He is no stranger to *Poetry*, which is
Musick in words ; nor to Musick, which is Poetry in
sound ; yet rather makes them his Sauce then Meat.'
Of the ' self-conceited Fellow,' ' he writes like the
Egyptian darkness, wherein he shews cunning ; for when
men laugh at his Verses, he may say they laugh at they
know not what ; and can boast of more then any Modern
Poet, that he writes above humane apprehension.'

A politick Citizen

Is a lump of *combustible ignorance*, whom the
least spark of newes fires into a *blaze* of unlikely
conjectures; he measures all the designs of Foraign
News by the line of *Stow's Chronicle;* which he
never hears read, but out flies a piece of *nonsense*,
which he miscalls State-policy, able to confound
Machiavel. He much haunts the *Pothouse* to note
into what forms men concoct their faces at the
reading of Letters; he frequents the *Exchange* in
the *Postmeridian* hours, because then men empty
themselves of intelligence; his only factorage is
news; viewing a Bill of *Exchange*, he swears 'tis
a *Libell.* Tell him of a *Curranto* and he's in

Heaven; he takes an *Almanack* of foul weather for one of *Merlin's* Prophesies. Upon hearing of a Victory, or loss of a *Sconce*, he is enraged, and blames the State that he was not a *Generall;* he extolls the *Low-Countreys* Government above any *Monarchy*, because the fat *Citizens* rule the roast; he holds it impossible for the State ever to be ruined, because it swims in *Butter*. His face is a piece of *Stenography*, where all *Richeliews* designs are writ in *short-hand*. He keeps a common *place-book* of hard State-words, which though nor he nor his *English Dictionary* understand, he after an *Aldermans* Plumb-broth Feast *spews* out among the learned Fraternity; and is therefore slander'd with the name of a *Politician*, and he turns *Heretick* and believes it; for they had rather ignorantly admire his speeches, then go to the price of *understanding* them. All the passages he hears are *Stratagems;* if he hear but a Ballad, he smells *Treason* in it; he cannot endure *Plays*, because there are *Plots* in them; ask him a question, you *undermine* him; answer him with silence, he takes you for a *State Informer;* he tells you news by *tale*, not by *weight*. There is no way to strike him dumb but drawing out your *Table-Book;* every man is a *fool* that is not of his *opinion:* but he takes him for an undoubted wise man that applauds his *conjectures;* he seldome approves any thing that he understands, and yet he approves most things; he meditates on an old *Manuscript* more then the *Pentateuch;* he wonders why the *Apocalyps* is put in the end of the Bible, and thinks it a disgrace; he takes *Brightman* for a better Interpreter then *Daniel;* he cuts the *Apocrypha* out of his Bible, for fear of infection; yet cannot tell why he hates it, but because 'tis *Apocrypha;* and thinks *Solomon* but a fool in suffering his wisdom to be put there. *Monarchy* he cannot abide, but says 'tis against *Christian Liberty;* but thinks *Anarchy* is as old as the *Chaos.* He takes *Malchus's* Servant to be a Saint, because he had his ear cut; yet thinks him not right of his opinion, because he had one left. He takes *Peter* for a Popish *Bishop,* because he cut off that eare. Where'ere the Scripture says *strive,* he takes it for *fighting;* that makes him so in love with *Civill War.* Among his Superiours he is *dumb;* to his inferiours *deaf;* the one he offends by *silence,* the other by *prating;* to both he is *ridiculous.* In a word, he is the State *Incendiary,* the Cities *bane,* and Kings *evil.*

RICHARD FLECKNOE (d. 1678)

Enigmaticall Characters, All Taken to the Life, from severall Persons, Humours, & Dispositions. By Rich. Fleckno. Anno Dom. 1658. 8vo.

Rich. Flecknoe's Ænigmatical Characters. . . . London, . . . 1665.

Characters Made at Several Times. London, . . . 1673.

The first and last pieces are taken from the 1658 edition, the seventh from that of 1673, and the rest from the edition of 1665.

In 8 character-books Flecknoe wrote 135 characters.

So far as Flecknoe is remembered it is as the titular anti-hero of Dryden's satire, though it is not plain that he earned this position by being eminently bad even in his verse. Dryden is certainly too sweeping in linking the prose with the verse, for a fair number of Flecknoe's characters are agreeable to read. In various small ways he is continually revealing his personality, so that his readers are tantalised by the vain wish that some of his greater contemporaries had been similarly moved. In a friendly manner, with no self-consciousness, he talks of his aims and methods : in one dedication (*Ænigmatical Characters*, 1665) he describes his characters as the ' perfectest of all my Works ' : in the ' Postscript ' to his 1673 volume, he tells us ' I pass then my Thoughts through finer and finer Sieves of first Writing, then Printing, and lastly Reprinting them before I have done with them.' This is true. He likes re-writing his characters in each edition. Their brevity is one of their positive merits. And it is well to remember that the titles are often more tempting than the piece itself proves to be.

Said to be a Roman Catholic priest, Flecknoe was abroad during the years of the Civil War, and his characters reflect his travels in France and the East. His ' Portrait ' of himself, an account of 'body and mind,' depicts, more seriously than is his wont, a shy spirit, whose youthful desires have been quenched, and now he 'only paints his hopes in water colours.' Not all his attitudes are changed, ' He loves all things chearful, splendious, and noble, and hates *Sectaries* most of all, because they are otherwise.' This must have applied with special point to his ' troublous times,' but it suggests a haven still remote and still attractive.

Of an irresolute Person

HE hovers in his choice, like an empty Ballance with no waight of Judgement to incline him to either scale; he dodges with those he meets, nor he can ever resolve which way to let them passe: every thing he thinks on, is matter of deliberation, and he does nothing readily, but what he thinks not on: discourse that helps others out of *laborinths*, is a *laborinth* to him; and he of all creatures would be far wiser, if he had none at all: he begins nothing without deliberation; and when he begins to deliberate, never makes an end. Has some dull *demon* cryes, *do not, do not* still, when hee's on point of doing any thing, which he obeys as a divine Revelation; He plays at *shall I, shall I?* so long, till oppertunity be past, and then as he did the fault, repents at leisure. He is enemy to Resolution, or rather as Resolution were enemy to him, his heart fails him; and like a coward he turns back presently, at sight of it: He still misliking the present choice of things as *Scoggan* did his Tree to hang on: He could never Bet at Cocking nor Horse-race yet, because the battaile or race was alwayes done ere he could deliberate which side to take, & he is only happy in this, that his irresolution hinders him from marrying and entring into Bonds: Nor ist (perhaps) the least part of his happinesse to be as long in choosing his Religion now, amongst so many new Sects, that sprout up every day; though tis thought he is a *Quaker;* and if he be superstitious withall, he is in for his wits, and next news you hear from him will be from *Bedlam.*

Of a Chymerical Poet | Made in Africk

WITH his monstrous *Simile's* and *Hyperbole's* he is like a *Painter*, who makes onely *Chimera's* and *Grotesque* work, whilst others Figures are natural, and to the life; by seeking out new wayes, he mistakes the way to *Helicon*, and loses himself by going out of the common *Road.* He is like *Statius* on his great Horse, now on the top, now on the bottom of *Parnassus*, and ha's not art enough to keep him to a constant pace. His Conceits come *across* from him, and stick by the way; and his many *Parenthesis's* are but like the boggling of resty Jades, when they can't or won't advance. His *Muse* is none of the *Nine*, but a *Mungril* or *By-Blow* of *Parnassus;* and her Beauty, is rather Sophistical then natural. He offers at *Learning* and *Philosophy*, as *Pullen* and *Stubble-Geese* offer to flye, and presently come fluttering down agen. His high-sounding Words and Verses are but like empty Tunns or Hogs-heads, which make the greater sound the emptier they are. A long while some admir'd him, because they understood him not; and for the same reason he admir'd himself: But now they have found out the *Cheat*, 'tis thought *Icarus* fate will be his, who for flying too high, came to be drowned at last; and he had sunk long since, had not some like bladders buoyd him up; which support now failing him, he will sink faster then heavy bodies fall into the Center.

Of an Excellent Actor

He is a delightful *Proteus*, changing and transforming himself into what shapes he please. He puts off himself with his clothes, and never assumes himself agen (not so much as in the Tyring-house) till the Play be done. There is as much difference betwixt him and a common Actor, as betwixt a Ballad-singer and an excellent Musician; t'one onely mouthing it, whilst t'other artfully varies and modulates his voice; knowing all his graces even to how much breath he is to give to every syllable. He has all the parts of an excellent Orator, (animating his words with speaking, and speech with action) his Auditors being never more delighted then when he speaks; nor more sorry then when he holds his peace. Yet even thên he is an excellent Actor still, not falling in his part when he has done his speech, but with his looks and gesture maintaining it still unto the heighth: imagining *age quod agis* onely spoke to him; so as whosoever calls him a Player does him wrong, no man being less idle, nor more imploy'd then he; his whole life being nothing else but Action, with onely this difference from other men; that as what is a play to them is his business, so what is their business is but a play to him.

Of *An Excellent Companion*

He is the life and spirit of the Company, and sparkling liquor, whilst others are but dregs and lees. He is never dry nor pumping, but alwayes full and flowing; every thing affording him matter of merriment; and for a need he can extract it out of nothing too. He differs from the *Buffoon*, as an excellent *Comedy* does from the *Farse;* and is all wit, t'other onely foolery. He is neither scurrulous nor prophane, but a good man as well as a good companion; and so far a good fellow, to take a chearful cup or two, (for wine's a good whetter of a fine edg'd wit, so with too much they whet it not quite away) and though to men of business he seems to confer but little to the seriouser part of life; yet he whets the knife of the serious man, and makes them more apt for business afterwards, (as Musick makes them apter for Devotion) and those who are displeas'd with his mirth, are just like *Saul* displeas'd with *Davids* musick, possest with some melancholly devil, or other, which onely such as he can cast out; for which they send for him farther, then they did for Dr. *Butler,* and every one loves and cherishes him, he being the Darling of all the nobler sort, the Favourite of Kings, and Companion for any Prince.

Of *troublesome Kindness*

When he meets you, he asks you with a great deal of joy, *whether you be there or no?* and though you have never so much business, makes you stay. He shakes you by the hand, till h'as

shak't it out of joynt, and tells you twenty times,
he's *glad to see you well;* and if he embrace you,
and get you in the hug, y'ad as good fall into the
hands of a *Cornish Wrestler.* He is troublesome
at Table, with bidding you *heartily welcome,* and
often drinking unto you, whilst he winks upon
you without knowing wherefore himself, and
carves you, and makes you eat whether you will
or no.   He asks you so often *how you do?* as he
makes you doubt whether you be well or no; and
when you are not indeed, he is more troublesome
yet, with his *how d'ye's?* and *pray be well,* &c.
He ha's a Receipt for every Disease, and twenty
at least for an *Ague,* all one as good as another;
and so pesters you with them, as you would give
as much to be rid of his visits, as y'are forc't to
give the Physician for his.   In fine, he is so troublesome, as y'are forc't to put it in your *Letanies,*
to be *deliver'd from him,* and all will scarcely do.

Of a Suspicious Person

SHE torments her self and others, by putting
every thing on the Rack of doubt, and wresting
all unto suspicion; mean time she makes them
rather confess what she'd have them, then what
is true indeed.   As all things seem yellow to those
infected with the *Jaundies,* so all things seem of
the colour of her suspicions.   She affixes an ill
sense still unto your words, and an ill meaning
to all your actions, and like *French* Poast Horses,
goes on with her suspicions, who when they
stumble once, never leave till they be down.   Like
Snow-balls; she revolves slight offences in her
minde, till sh' as made mighty injuries of them at

last, and her Surmizes are alwayes wiser then the *Truth*, when both for her own sake and theirs, her friends could wish they were but as wise at least. She explicates others words and actions, as *Hereticks* do Scripture, in the dark and mystick sense, when the literal is obvious and clear enough; and there's as little hopes of converting t'one as t'other from their erroneous opinions. So whilst her minde is just like the Winters Sun, that exhales more vapours then it can dissipate agen; she both loses her self in the mists she makes, and loses her Friends, by mistaking them for her Enemies.

Of a Common Newsmonger

His word is, *What news! What news!* And he may well be added to the Cryes of *London*, with that word in his Mouth; he is an excellent *Embrotherer of Lies*, for any ground serves him to work on; and for a need he can do it, without any ground at all. He deals more with *Conjectures* than *Almanack Makers*, and will venture the repute of a *Lier* twenty times, for that of a *Prophet* once. He wishes more for ill news, than *ingrossers* of *Corn* do for dear years, and is sorry with *Caligula*, when none happens in his time. He runs faster away with a Rumor, than a Pack of Hounds do with a full Scent, and warrants it for true, though it be never so great a lye for his publick news; the *Gazette* with some comments of his own, are his *Pourlieus;* and the *Coffee-House*, the place where he vents it afterwards: But for his *Avisi secreti*, or secret Advice, he has some other *Authors* who deserve to be whipt for their pains, and he too for divulging it, it being commonly the defaming some Noble Persons, taxing of the State, or Rumors tending to Sedition.

Of the Author's Idea, or of a Character

IT gives you the hint of discourse, but discourses not; and is that in *mass* and *ingot*, you may *coyn* and *wyer-draw* to infinitie; tis more *Seneca* than *Cicero*, and speaks rather the language of *Oracles* than *Orators:* every line a *sentence*, & every two a *period*. It says not all, but all it sayes is good, and like an Aire in Musick is either full of *clozes*, or still driving towards a *close:* tis no long-winded exercise of spirit, but a forcible one, and therefore soonest out of breath; tis all *matter*, and to the *matter*, and has nothing of *superfluity*, nothing of *circumlocution;* so little comporting with *mediocrity*, as it or extols to *Heaven*, or depresses unto *Hell;* having no mid'place for *Purgatory* left. Tis that in every sort of writing delighteth most, and tho' the *Treatise* be gold, it is the Jewell still, which the Authour of *Characters*, like your *Lapidary*, produces single, whilest others *Goldsmith*-like inchass them in their works. Tis a *Portraiture*, not onely oth' *Body*, but the *soul* and minde; whence it not onely delights but teaches and moves withall, and is a *Sermon* as well as a *Picture* to every one. In fine, 'tis a *short* voiage, the *Writer* holds out with equall force, still comming fresh unto his journeys end, whilest in *long* ones, they commonly tire and falter on their way: And to the *Reader* 'tis a *garden*, not *journey*, or a *feast*, where by reason of the subject's variety, he is never cloyed, but at each *Character*, as at a new service, falls too with fresh Appetite.

JOHN CLEVELAND (1613-1658)

J. Cleaveland Revived : Poems, Orations, Epistles, And
other of his Genuine Incomparable Pieces, never
before publisht. . . . London, . . . 1659. 8vo.

This is one of the many satirical sketches of the puritan,
a subject as a rule better suited to prose.

Cleveland must have enjoyed using his vigorous pen
against a type he had good reason for disliking. It
seemed preferable to represent the ' Cavalier poet ' by a
piece in his natural medium, rather than to give any
of his prose characters, such as *A London Diurnal* or *A
Country Committeeman*, for though these are also written
with force, they have suffered somewhat from the fate
that overtakes most work written as propaganda. The
' Puritan ' is saved by its form, which acted here as a
useful restraint.

The Puritan

WITH face and fashion to be known,
For one of sure election,
With eyes all white, and many a grone,
With neck aside to draw in tone,
With harp in's nose, or he is none.
See a new Teacher of the town,
O the town, O the towns new Teacher.

With pate cut shorter than the brow,
With little ruff starch'd you know how,
With cloake like *Paul*, no cape I trow,
With Surplice none; but lately now,
With hands to thump, no knees to bow.
See a new Teacher, &c.

With coz'ning cough, and hollow cheek,
To get new gatherings every week,
With paltry change of *and* to *eke*,
With some small Hebrew, and no Greek,
To finde out words when stuffe's to seek.
    See a new Teacher, &c.

With shop-board breeding, and intrusion,
With some Outlandish Institution,
With *Ursines* Catechism to muse on,
With *Systems* method for confusion,
With grounds strong laid of meer illusion.
    See a new Teacher, &c.

With Rites indifferent all damned,
And made unlawfull, if commanded,
Good works of Popery down banded,
And Morall Laws from him estranged,
Except the Sabbath still unchanged.
    See a new Teacher, &c.

With speech unthought, quick revelation,
With boldness in predestination,
With threats of absolute damnation,
Yet *yea* and *nay* hath some salvation,
For his own Tribe, not every Nation.
    See a new Teacher, &c.

With after licence cost a crown,
When Bishop new had put him down,
With tricks call'd repetition,
And doctrine newly brought to town,
Of teaching men to hang and drown,
    See a new Teacher, &c.

With flesh-provision to keep Lent,
With shelves of sweet-meats often spent,
Which new Maid bought, old Lady sent;
Though to be sav'd a poor present;
Yet legacies assure the event.
    See a new Teacher, &c.

With troops expecting him at th' door,
That would hear Sermons, and no more;
With noting tools, and sighs great store,
With Bibles great to turn them o're,
While he wrests places by the score.
    See a new Teacher, &c.

With running text, the nam'd forsaken,
With *For* and *But*, both by sense shaken,
Cheap doctrines forc'd, wilde Uses taken,
Both sometimes one by mark mistaken,
With any thing to any shapen.
    See a new Teacher, &c.

With new wrought caps, against the Canon,
For taking cold, though sure he have none;
A Sermons end, where he began one,
A new hour long, when's glass had run one,
New Use, new Points, new Notes to stand on.
    See a new Teacher, &c.

ANONYMOUS

The Character of a Phanatique. London,. . 1660. fol.
single leaf.

This vigorous and well-written sketch is an exception
to the general rule that the controversial character is
unliterary. In La Bruyère's fashion we might well
supply for it to-day one name or another. Will the time
ever come when it will not be true ?

A Phanatique

A *Phanatique* is the Mushrom of distemper, a
false Conception gotten by the Air upon the sick
womb of a confused phancy, a meer changeling,
who devours greedily all doctrines, but receives
nourishment from none; the dishonour of his
reputed father, the plague and ruine of his miserable mother; he is a reasonable creature uncapable
of the right use of reason. He is a certain thing
that would puzzle *Plato* or *Aristotle* to define, and
indeed no man knowes well what he is, but himself least of all. You may better expresse him in
the Negative than the Affirmative; for he is neither
Pagan, Turk, Jew, nor true Christian. But to
come as close to him as we can, he is a confused
lump of earth not refined, still retaining the habit
of that *Chaos* from whence he first proceeded, and
is like a beggars bag fill'd with scraps of all sorts
of food, or like a Botchers cushion made up of
the various kinds of Shreds and patches, which he
hath filched from several garments. He is of a
sceptical humour, and you may sooner pick all

Religions out of him than one : and is somewhat
a kin to all professions different from his own, but
varies most from the Orthodox Protestant. So
that a right phanatique is a phantastick fellow,
pleasing himself with new fangles, and continually
gaping after Novelties, and the discovery of New
lights. He forsakes the true fire, and runs over
bogs and moorish places to light his torch at an
ignis fatuus, and (ten to one but) he sinks in the
pursuit of it, and is never able to return again.
He is fit for neither Heaven, Earth, nor yet Hell,
because he is against all order and government,
which is not only exercised in Heaven and Earth,
but practised by the Devils themselves. He pretends much to a good conscience, yet thinks it
lawful to murder all that dissent from him in
opinion, although he changes from himself more
often than the Moon. If you talk with him to-day
you are never the nearer to know him to morrow,
for you shall finde him perfectly metamorphosed.
He rayls much against the Pope of *Rome*, and the
Whore of *Babylon*, when none so much resemble
the beast as himself, whose mark he bears in his
fore-head, but wants the Looking-glass of reason
to discern it. He writes all men in the black book
of Reprobation, but his own fraternity, and concludes all his Fore-fathers damned. He thinks
himself wiser than all others, although he be a
verier fool than a meer Naturalist. He will prate
two hours together, and after all you may sooner
resolve a *Delphian* Oracle, than unfold his meaning, only he is dexterous in blaspheming those two
great Ordinances of God, Magistracy and Minis-
try. He is naturally an arrand Coward, yet his

Chymerical opinions infuse into him a kinde of
frenetique valour. He is a perfect *Saint* in his own
conceit, and would not change places in *H*eaven
with any of the Apostles, whom he calls nothing
but bare *Paul*, *Peter*, *John*, *&*c. and dare not add
the title of *Saint* for fear of sinning. *H*e hath but
a mean respect to the Scripture, and could wish
some things expunged out of the Bible, having
blotted them out of his minde and opinion, which
is all one as to curtel the Scripture. And for
Tradition he cannot abide it, esteeming of the
writings of antient Fathers as Winter tales, or old
Womens fables. If he be not an enemy to
Government in the abstract, he is rarely reconcile-
able to present powers, (in case they do not showre
preferments upon him) for that he thirsts after
innovation as well in things Civil as *E*cclesias-
ticall. And loathes Antiquity as a French-man
does his fashions of the last year. He is by nature
covetous, yet will not grudge to squander away
his whole estate to maintain Conventicles, and is
charitable to none but his own tribe. The Proverbs of *Solomon* are a great eye-sore to him, but
especially that Text, *My son, fear God and the
King, and meddle not with them that are given
to change*. To conclude, He is a bubble or
bladder tossed to and fro with every winde, which
at length breaks, and vanisheth to nothing.

MARGARET CAVENDISH, DUCHESS OF NEWCASTLE (? 1625-1674)

CCXI. Sociable Letters, . . . London, . . . 1664.   fol.

The character-form suited the rather wandering ideas of Lamb's Duchess so well that it is curious how little she used it.   There are but a few sketches in these letters, and only hints of the form elsewhere.

In ' Mode-Minds ' her good sense and power of satirical observation are happily illustrated.

On Mode-Minds

MOST men and Women in this Age, in most Nations in *Europe*, are nothing but Mode, as mode-Minds, mode-Bodyes, mode-Appetites, mode-Behaviours, mode-Cloaths, mode-Pastimes or Vices, mode-Speeches and Conversations, which is strange to have Minds according to the Mode, as to have a mode-Judgment, for all will give their Judgments and Opinions according to the Mode, and they Love and Hate according to the Mode, they are Couragious or Cowardly according to the Mode, Approve or Dislike according to the Mode, nay, their Wits are according to the Mode, as to Rallery, Clinch, Buffonly Jest, and the like, for Better Wit is not usually the Mode, as being alwayes out of Fashion amongst mode-Gallants, but True and Good Wit lives with the Seniors of the Time, such as Regard not the Mode, but Chuse or Prefer what is Best, and not what is Most in Fashion, unless that which is Best be in Fashion, which is very seldom if ever Known . . .

and for Wise men, they Speak not with Mode-
Phrases, but such Words as are most Plain to be
Understood, and the Best to Deliver or Declare
Sense and Reason, and their Behaviours are those
which are Most Manly and Least Apish, Fan-
tastical or Constrain'd; and their Clothes are such
as are most Useful, Easie and Becoming; neither
do their Appetites Relish Mode-Meats or Sauces,
because they have the Mode Haut Goust, but
they Relish Best what is most Pleasing or Savoury
to their Taste; and so for Drinks Compounded,
as Chocolata, Limmonada, and the like, they will
not Drink them because of the Mode; neither do
they Affect Mode-Songs or Sounds, because they
are in Fashion to be Sung or Play'd, but because
they are Well-Set Tunes, or Well-Compos'd
Musick, or Witty Songs, and Well Sung by Good
Voices, or Well Plaid on Instruments; neither do
they follow Mode-Vices or Vanities for Fashion,
but for Pleasure, or their own Humour or Fancy;
nor do they use those Exercises that are in Mode,
but those they like Best.   Thus a Wise Man
Follows not the Mode, but his own Humour,
for if it be the Mode to Play at Tennis, or Paille-
maille, or the like, if he like better to Ride or
Fence, he will let alone the mode-Exercises and
Use his Own; if it be the mode-Pastime to Play
at Cards or Dice, if he like better to Write or
Read, he will leave the mode-Pastime and Follow
his Own; and if it be the mode-Custom to Dine
and Sup, and Meet at Ordinaries or Taverns, if
he like better to Sup and Dine at Home alone,
he will not go to Ordinaries or Taverns; if it be
the Mode to make General Courtships, if he Like,

or is better pleased with a Particular Mistress, he will not follow the Mode; neither will he Ride Post because it is the Mode, but because his Affairs Require it; neither will he Journey from Place to Place to no Purpose, because it is the Mode, but will Wisely Sit Still or Rest at his own Home, because it is Easie, Peaceable, Quiet, and Prudent, as not so Chargeable.

RICHARD HEAD (? 1637-? 1686)

The English Rogue . . . London, . . . 1665.   8vo.
  3 characters.

Proteus Redivivus : Or The Art of Wheedling. . . .
    London, . . . 1675.   8vo.
  17 characters.

The three witty characters in the *English Rogue* are
given as set-pieces, almost as ' extra-illustrations,' but in
Proteus the characters form part of the ordinary text,
which is almost a character-book in its discussion of the
various types of wheedlers.

Head frequently borrows, and usually without acknowledgement, from preceding character-writers.   He is indebted to Earle for nearly one-third of his ' Wheedle of
the Shop-Keeper.'

The Character of A Bottle of Canary

HE is a Gentleman I assure you well extracted,
which once lived like a Salamander in the midst
of the flames, and had he not been burnt, he had
never proved sound.   He seems a Prodigy : For
that which we live by, decays him; hating Air,
as *Bacchus* hates small Beer.   He will lie still if
you smother him, and is never so well, as when
his breath is stopt.   Bury him, and you make him
quicker.   As for his habit, it is ever plain, yet
neat : Though Nobly born, he scorns not to wear
a Green Coat, with a badge on it; and you cannot
injure him worse than to pick a hole in his Coat.
Though he wears for the most part one sort of
Garb, yet he is never out of fashion, acceptable
to the best of company, not regarding his out-

ward dress, but valuing his inward worth: However, his Suit is made of admirable Stuff, for his outside never grows barer, and his Linings are the fresher for wearing. So choice he is in his Cloathing, that he rather chuseth to have his brains knockt out, then to have a rent in his Garment. He wears an *à la mode* Hat, as light (and almost as little) as a Shittle-cock, which he puts off to none; but like the Quaker when brought before a Magistrate, hath it taken off for him.

As for his Pedegree, I know not how to derive it; for he hath had in him, the best and purest of the *French* Blood, but will now acknowledge his race onely from the *Spaniard*, whom he imitates, being stately, and standing always upright; treads for the most part on Carpets, and never stirs abroad but when he is carried; yet full of activity. If he runs fast and long, the more wind he gets. If he chance to fall, which is seldom, for many look to him; he will be extreamly moved, yet (contrary to all men) the fuller his belly is, the less hurt he receives. His credit is large, never paying for what he wears, running on the score perpetually; his conditions are a riddle; there is in him pure vertue, and notorious vice; the quintescence of love, and the venome of hatred. He is the beginning and the end of a thousand quarrels in an year. Yet a very Coward, for he suffers any to take him by the ear, and never broke any ones pate, but when company was by. He is very facetious in society, and will spend himself freely to the last drop, if a Ladies soft and warm hand will raise him. He is a brisk Spark, and therefore Courtiers adore him; he is smooth in his expression, and therefore Ladies delight in him; he is fill'd with nimble fancies, therefore the Wits frequent him, exhausting his radical moysture to distil it into Poetical Raptures; for conceits never run faster from the Limbick of their brain, then when this Gentleman adds fewel to the Furnace: he whets wit, yet dulls it; creates new fancies, and stupifies. Gives the Orator a fluent tongue, and mutes him speechless: gives a Poet feet till he cannot go. And as he helps *Ministers* to Preach, so he likewise silenceth more then the Bishops. He hath a great many tricks in him: He will make a Falkner fly high within doors: *Make* a Huntsman catch a Fox by the fire side. Whatever he holds, is made good; and unless you mind him well, much good matter that falls from him, may be lost: for he is often fluent beyond measure. All Tongues Court him, and those that look narrowly unto him, shall find him no dry Fellow. The truth is, he is too profound for shallow brains to meddle with him: He will pour out quaint expressions and hard words so thick, that the best Scholars are glad at last to give him something to stop his mouth: yet hold him up fairly, and you may get all he hath out of him. He is excessively belov'd, and relishes all Company, being pleasant, and full of admirable humours. He is inwardly acquainted with the Lord *Mayor* and Aldermen, and incorporateth with their Wives daily. His kisses are so sweet, that they lick their lips after him; and though his breath be strong, yet tis not offensive. He is a true *Good-Fellow*, drinking till he hath no eyes to see with: Good Liquor is his Life and Soul, and he is never musty but for want of it. He will drink till he be fill'd up to the very throat, and gape whilest others put it in. He will bear as much Sack as any man in *England* of his bulk, yet he will be soon drunk in Company: but if you will give him leave to vomit, he will take his *L*iquor, and drink fresh, till all the Company be forc'd to leaue him. Drinking is his hourly exercise, seldom lying out of a Tavern. He is the main Upholder of Club-Meeting, without fear of being broke. He picks mens Pockets, yet is never made more reckoning of then by such persons. As for his Estate, I can onely say this, That all he hath he carries about him; yet generally he is reputed rich: What he hath, he holds upon courtesie; but what he gives others, it is held *in Capite*. What he possesseth, is commonly upon Sale; yet more for plenty, then for want; and if you can purchase him, you purchase all.

The Wheedle of the Shop-keeper

METHINKS I see him standing at his Shopdoor this cold Weather, either blowing his fingers, eagerly waiting (if he be a young Man) for one kick at the Ball, or basting his sides with his own hand, and so makes every cold day a *Good-Friday* to chastise him for the sins he hath committed. If any person pass by him, and but looks into his shop, he fondly imagins him a Customer, and intreats for his own necessities by asking others *what they lack;* if any chance to step in, he hath *Hocus tricks* enough to delude them, and rarely shall they stir out, like sheep engaged in Bryers, but they shall leave some Fleece behind them.

Some have dark shops, with false lights, which wonderfully set off a commodity: others for want of that make use of their tongues, arrogantly commending their own things and protesting whatever they exhibit to view is best in the Town, though the worst in his shop; his words are like his wares, twenty of one sort, and he goes over them alike to all Comers; and when he hath done with his yard, he invites you to the Tavern, to oblige you for the future; you may there soon measure his understanding, which extends no further than the Longitude of his shop, but for the latitude of his Conscience it is as little known as the *North-west-passage:* Others say that he has no such thing now as Conscience; for finding it a thing that was likely to lye upon his hands, he was forced to put it off, and in its stead took upon him the pretence of Religion, that by the profession thereof he might take the greater liberty of Lying, which he does by rote, having spent most of his time in learning that Art, and the language, and crafty phrase of selling dear, and that to his friends, and acquaintance, rather than other persons, knowing he can make more bold to cheat them, than Strangers; from hence you may gather that he never speaks more truly than when he says *he will use you as his own Brother*, you may believe him, for he will not stick to abuse the nearest Relation he hath in this kind, and in his Shop thinks it lawful. He is commonly of that Religion which brings him in most Customers, and is never more angry at others tenets, than when they bring him in no profit, and so by a mis-interpreted sense of Scripture, *to him Godliness is great gain*. How obsequious, and full of cringes he is to him that pays ready money, but where he does befriend a man, he is a Tyrant, and by his frequent duns makes a man weary of his native Country. One thing I like in him very well, he takes special care of not letting Conyes burrough in his Shop-book, knowing 'twill be hard ferretting them out again.

SAMUEL BUTLER (? 1612-1680)

The Genuine Remains in Verse and Prose of Mr. Samuel
   Butler. [ed.] R. Thyer. London : ... 1759. 8vo.
121 characters.

Satyr upon the ... Abuse of human Learning. [Pedants.]
   [The illustration is preserved in Harl. 5931. 12, without
trace of origin or date.]

Characters and Passages from Note-Books. Edited by
   A. R. Waller. Cambridge : ... 1908. 8vo.
121 characters from 1759 edition, and 66 characters
from Brit. Mus. MSS.

Of the characters published in the seventeenth century
Butler's are second only to Earle's. Not many could have
made this judgment then, for the collection was not
published until 1759. One imagines that this was unfortunate, since their strength of idea and of wit might
have been a stimulating force in literature as well as a
pungent criticism of the hypocrisy that was an unpleasant
feature ' when godliness became profitable.'
   The ' Characters ' are closely connected in theme and
method with ' Hudibras.' Parallels from these works can
be readily collected, and they would be equally illuminating
to both. Butler's ' controversial-characters ' are almost
alone in being of permanent interest, since they are generic
as well as particular in reference. The ' Zealot ' was not
peculiar to the seventeenth century, he still

> ' Compounds for Sins he is inclined to
> By damning those he has no Mind to.'

Pedants

THE *Pedants* are a mungrel Breed, that sojourn
Among the ancient Writers and the modern;
And, while their Studies are between the one
And th' other spent, have nothing of their own;

Like Spunges, are both Plants and Animals,
And equally to both their natures false.
For whether 'tis their want of Conversation
Inclines them to all Sorts of Affectation,
Their sedentary Life and Melancholy,
The everlasting Nursery of Folly;
Their poring upon black and white too subt'ly
Has turn'd the Insides of their Brains to motly;
Or squand'ring of their Wits and Time upon
Too many Things has made them fit for none;
Their constant overstraining of the Mind
Distorts the Brain, as Horses break their Wind;
Or rude Confusions of the Things they read
Get up, like noxious Vapours, in the Head,
Until they have their constant *Wanes* and *Fulls*,
And *Changes* in the Insides of their Skulls:
Or venturing beyond the Reach of Wit
Has render'd them for all Things else unfit;
But never bring the World and Books together,
And therefore never rightly judge of either;
Whence Multitudes of reverend Men and *Critics*
Have got a kind of intellectual Rickets,
And by th' immoderate Excess of Study
Have found the sickly Head t' outgrow the Body.

A Huffing Courtier

Is a Cypher, that has no Value himself, but
from the Place he stands in. All his Happiness
consists in the Opinion he believes others have of
it. This is his Faith, but as it is heretical and
erroneous, though he suffer much Tribulation for
it, he continues obstinate, and not to be convinced.
He flutters up and down like a Butterfly in a Garden; and while he is pruning of his Peruke takes

Occasion to contemplate his Legs, and the Symmetry of his Britches. He is part of the Furniture of the Rooms, and serves for a walking Picture, a moving Piece of Arras. His Business is only to be seen, and he performs it with admirable Industry, placing himself always in the best Light, looking wonderfully Politic, and cautious whom he mixes withal. His Occupation is to show his Cloaths, and if they could but walk themselves, they would save him the Labour, and do his Work as well as himself. His immunity from Varlets is his Freehold, and he were a lost man without it. His Cloaths are but his Taylor's Livery, which he gives him, for 'tis ten to one he never pays for them. He is very careful to discover the Lining of his Coat, that you may not suspect any Want of Integrity or Flaw in him from the Skin outwards. His Taylor is his Creator, and makes him of nothing; and though he lives by Faith in him, he is perpetually committing Iniquities against him. His Soul dwells in the Outside of him, like that of a hollow Tree; and if you do but pill the Bark off him he deceases immediately. His Carriage of himself is the wearing of his Cloaths, and, like the Cinamon Tree, his Bark is better than his Body. His looking big is rather a Tumor, than Greatness. He is an Idol, that has just so much Value, as other Men give him that believe in him, but none of his own. He makes his Ignorance pass for Reserve, and, like a Hunting-nag, leaps over what he cannot get through. He has just so much of Politics, as Hostlers in the University have *Latin*. He is as humble as a Jesuit to his Superior; but repays himself again in Insolence over those, that are below him; and with a generous Scorn despises those, that can neither do him good, nor hurt. He adores those, that may do him good, though he knows they never will; and despises those, that would not hurt him, if they could. The Court is his Church, and he believes as that believes, and cries up and down every Thing, as he finds it pass there. It is a great Comfort to him to think, that some who do not know him may perhaps take him for a Lord; and while that Thought lasts he looks bigger than usual, and forgets his Acquaintance; and that's the Reason why he will sometimes know you, and sometimes not. Nothing but want of Money or Credit puts him in mind that he is mortal; but then he trusts Providence that somebody will trust him; and in Expectation of that hopes for a better Life, and that his Debts will never rise up in Judgment against him. To get in debt is to labour in his Vocation; but to pay is to forfeit his Protection; for what's that worth to one that owes Nothing? His Employment being only to wear his Cloaths, the whole Account of his Life and Actions is recorded in Shopkeepers Books, that are his faithful Historiographers to their own Posterity; and he believes he loses so much Reputation, as he pays off his Debts; and that no Man wears his Cloaths in Fashion, that pays for them, for nothing is further from the Mode. He believes that he that runs in Debt is beforehand with those that trust him, and only those, that pay, are behind. His Brains are turned giddy, like one that walks on the Top of a House; and that's the Reason it is so troublesome to him to look downwards. He is a Kind of Spectrum, and his Cloaths are the Shape he takes to appear and walk in; and when he puts them off he vanishes. He runs as busily out of one Room into another, as a great Practiser does in *Westminster*-Hall from one Court to another. When he accosts a Lady he puts both Ends of his Microcosm in Motion, by making Legs at one End, and combing his Peruque at the other. His Garniture is the Sauce to his Cloaths, and he walks in his Portcannons[1] like one, that stalks in long Grass. Every Motion of him crys *Vanity of Vanities, all is Vanity*, quoth the Preacher. He rides himself like a well-managed Horse, reins in his Neck, and walks *Terra Terra*. He carries his elbows backward, as if he were pinioned like a trust-up Fowl, and moves as stiff as if he was upon the Spit. His legs are stuck in his great voluminous Britches, like the Whistles in a Bagpipe, those abundant Britches, in which his nether parts are not cloathed, but packt up. His Hat has been long in a Consumption of the Fashion, and is now almost worn to Nothing; if it do not recover quickly it will grow too little for a Head of Garlick. He wears Garniture on the Toes of his Shoes to justify his Pretensions to the Gout, or such other Malady, that for the Time being is most in Fashion or Request. When he salutes a Friend he pulls off his Hat, as Women do their Vizard-Masques. His Ribbons are of the true Complexion of his Mind, a Kind of painted Cloud or gawdy Rainbow, that has no Colour of it self, but what it borrows from Reflection. He is as tender of his

---

[1] An ornamental roll around the legs of breeches.

Cloaths, as a Coward is of his Flesh, and as loth to have them disordered. His Bravery is all his Happiness; and like *Atlas* he carries his Heaven on his Back. He is like the golden Fleece, a fine Outside on a Sheep's Back. He is a Monster or an *Indian* Creature, that is good for nothing in the World but to be seen. He puts himself up into a Sedan, like a Fiddle in a Case, and is taken out again for the Ladies to play upon, who when they have done with him, let down his treble-String, till they are in the Humour again. His Cook and Valet de Chambre conspire to dress Dinner and him so punctually together, that the one may not be ready before the other. As Peacocks and Ostridges have the gaudiest and finest Feathers, yet cannot fly; so all his Bravery is to flutter only. The Beggars call him *my Lord*, and he takes them at their Words, and pays them for it. If you praise him, he is so true and faithful to the Mode, that he never fails to make you a Present of himself, and will not be refused, tho' you know not what to do with him when you have him.

An Antiquary

Is one that has his Being in this Age, but his Life and Conversation is in the Days of old. He despises the present Age as an Innovation, and slights the future; but has a great Value for that, which is past and gone, like the Madman, that fell in Love with *Cleopatra*. He is an old frippery-Philosopher, that has so strange a natural Affection to worm-eaten Speculation, that it is apparent he has a Worm in his Skull. He honours his Forefathers and Fore-mothers, but condemns his Parents as too modern, and no better than Upstarts. He neglects himself, because he was born in his own Time, and so far off Antiquity, which he so much admires; and repines, like a younger Brother, because he came so late into the World. He spends the one half of his Time in collecting old insignificant Trifles, and the other in shewing them, which he takes singular Delight in; because the oftener he does it, the further they are from being new to him. All his Curiosities take place of one another according to their Seniority, and he values them not by their Abilities, but their Standing. He has a great Veneration for Words that are stricken in Years, and are grown so aged, that they have out-lived their Employments—These he uses with a Respect agreeable to their Antiquity, and the good Services they have done. He throws away his Time in enquiring after that which is past and gone so many Ages since, like one that shoots away an Arrow, to find out another that was lost before. He fetches things out of Dust and Ruins, like the fable of the chymical Plant raised out of its own Ashes. He values one old Invention, that is lost and never to be recovered, before all the new ones in the World, tho' never so useful. The whole Business of his Life is the same with his, that shows the Tombs at *Westminster*, only the one does it for his Pleasure, and the other for Money. As every Man has but one Father, but two Grand-Fathers and a World of Ancestors; so he has a proportional Value for Things that are antient, and the further off the greater.

He is a great Time-server, but it is of Time out of Mind, to which he conforms exactly, but is wholly retired from the present. His Days were spent and gone long before he came into the World, and since his only Business is to collect what he can out of the Ruins of them. He has so strong a natural Affection to any Thing that is old, that he may truly *say to Dust and Worms you are my Father, and to Rottenness thou art my Mother.* He has no Providence nor Foresight; for all his Contemplations look backward upon the Days of old, and his Brains are turned with them, as if he walked backwards. He had rather interpret one obscure Word in any old senseless Discourse, than be Author of the most ingenious new one; and with *Scaliger* would sell the Empire of *Germany* (if it were in his Power) for an old Song. He devours an old Manuscript with greater Relish than Worms and Moths do, and, though there be nothing in it, values it above any Thing printed, which he accounts but a Novelty. When he happens to cure a small Botch in an old Author, he is as proud of it, as if he had got the Philosophers Stone, and could cure all the Diseases of Mankind. He values things wrongfully upon their Antiquity, forgetting that the most modern are really the most ancient of all Things in the World, like those that reckon their Pounds before their Shillings and Pence, of which they are made up. He esteems no Customs but such as have outlived themselves, and are long since out of Use; as the *Catholics* allow of no Saints, but such as are dead, and the *Fanatics*, in Opposition, of none but the Living.

An Astrologer

Is one that expounds upon the Planets, and teaches to construe the *Accidents* by the *due joining of Stars in Construction.* He talks with them by dumb Signs, and can tell what they mean by their twinckling, and squinting upon one another, as well as they themselves. He is a Spy upon the Stars, and can tell what they are doing, by the Company they keep, and the Houses they frequent. They have no Power to do any Thing alone, until so many meet, as will make a *Quorum.* He is Clerk of the Committee to them, and draws up all their Orders, that concern either public or private Affairs. He keeps all their Accompts for them, and sums them up, not by *Debtor,* but *Creditor* alone, a more compendious Way. They do ill to make them have so much Authority over the Earth, which, perhaps, has as much as any one of them but the Sun, and as much Right to sit and vote in their Councils, as any other: But because there are but seven Electors of the *German* Empire, they will allow of no more to dispose of all other; and most foolishly and unnaturally depose their own Parent of its Inheritance; rather than acknowledge a Defect in their own Rules. Those Rules are all they have to shew for their Title; and yet not one of them can tell whether those they had them from came honestly by them. *Virgil's* Description of *Fame,* that reaches from Earth to the Stars, *tam ficti pravique tenax,* to carry Lies and Knavery, will serve Astrologers without any sensible Variation. He is a Fortune-Seller, a Retailer of Destiny, and petty Chapman

AN ASTROLOGER

to the Planets. He casts Nativities as Gamesters do false Dice, and by slurring and palming *sextile*, *quartile*, and *trine*, like *size*, *quater*, *trois*, can throw what chance he pleases. He sets a Figure, as Cheats do a Main at Hazard; and Gulls throw away their Money at it. He fetches the Grounds of his Art so far off, as well from Reason, as the Stars, that, like a Traveller, he is allowed to lye by Authority. And as Beggars, that have no Money themselves, believe all others have, and beg of those, that have as little as themselves : So the ignorant Rabble believe in him, though he has no more Reason for what he professes, than they.

A Lawyer

Is a Retailer of Justice, that uses false Lights, false Weights, and false Measures—He measures Right and Wrong by his retaining Fee, and, like a *French* Duelist, engages on that Side that first bespeaks him, tho' it be against his own Brother, not because it is right, but merely upon a Punctilio of Profit, which is better than Honour to him, because Riches will buy Nobility, and Nobility nothing, as having no intrinsic Value. He sells his Opinion, and engages to maintain the Title against all that claim under him, but no further. He puts it off upon his Word, which he believes himself not bound to make good, because when he has parted with his Right to it, it is no longer his. He keeps no Justice for his own Use, as being a Commodity of his own Growth, which he never buys, but only sells to others : and as no Man goes worse shod than the Shoemaker; so no Man is more out of Justice than he that gets his Living by it. He draws Bills, as Children do Lots at a Lottery, and is paid as much for Blanks as Prizes. He undoes a Man with the same Privilege as a Doctor kills him, and is paid as well for it, as if he preserved him, in which he is very impartial, but in nothing else. He believes it no Fault in himself to err in Judgment, because that part of the *Law* belongs to the Judge, and not to him. His best Opinions and his worst are all of a Price, like good Wine and bad in a Tavern, in which he does not deal so fairly as those, who, if they know what you are willing to bestow, can tell how to fit you accordingly. When his Law lies upon his Hands, he will afford a good Penyworth, and rather pettyfog and turn common Barreter, than be out of Employment. His Opinion is one Thing while it is his own, and another when it is paid for; for the Property being altered, the Case alters also. When his Council is not for his Client's Turn, he will never take it back again, though it be never the worse, nor allow him any Thing for it, yet will sell the same over and over again to as many as come to him for it. His Pride encreases with his Practice, and the fuller of Business he is, like a Sack, the bigger he looks. He crouds to the Bar like a Pig through a Hedge; and his Gown is fortified with Flankers about the Shoulders, to guard his Ears from being galled with Elbows. He draws his Bills more extravagant and unconscionable than a Taylor; for if you cut off two thirds in the Beginning, Middle, or End, that which is left will be more reasonable and nearer to Sense than the whole, and yet he is paid for all: For when he draws up a Business,

like a Captain that makes false Musters, he produces as many loose and idle Words as he can
possibly come by, until he has received for them,
and then turns them off, and retains only those
that are to the Purpose—This he calls drawing of
Breviates. All that appears of his Studies is in
short Time converted into Waste-Paper, Taylor's
Measures, and Heads for Children's Drums. He
appears very violent against the other Side, and
rails to please his Client, as they do Children,
*give me a Blow and I'll strike him, ah naughty,
&c.*—This makes him seem very zealous for the
good of his Client, and, though the Cause go
against him, he loses no Credit by it, especially
if he fall foul on the Council of the other Side,
which goes for no more among them than it does
with those virtuous Persons, that quarrel and fight
in the Streets, to pick the Pockets of those that
look on. He hangs Men's Estates and Fortunes
on the slightest Curiosities and feeblest Niceties
imaginable, and undoes them like the Story of
breaking a Horse's Back with a Feather, or sinking a Ship with a single Drop of Water; as if
Right and Wrong were only notional, and had
no Relation at all to practice (which always requires more solid Foundations) or Reason and
Truth did wholly consist in the right Spelling of
Letters, when, as the subtler Things are, the
nearer they are to nothing; so the subtler
Words and Notions are, the nearer they are
to Nonsense. He overruns *Latin* and *French*
with greater Barbarism, than the *Goths* did
Italy and *France*, and makes as mad a Confusion
of Language by mixing both with *English*. Nor

does he use *English* much better, for he clogs it so with Words, that the Sense becomes as thick as Puddle, and is utterly lost to those, that have not the Trick of skipping over, where it is impertinent. He has but one Termination for all *Latin* Words, and that's a Dash. He is very just to the first Syllables of Words, but always bobtails the last, in which the Sense most of all consists, like a Cheat, that does a Man all Right at the first, that he may put a Trick upon him in the End. He is an *Apprentice* to the Law without a Master, is his own Pupil, and has no Tutor but himself, that is a Fool. He will screw and wrest Law as unmercifully as a Tumbler does his Body, to lick up Money with his Tongue. He is a *Swiss*, that professes mercenary Arms, will fight for him, that gives him best Pay, and, like an *Italian* Bravo, will fall foul on any Man's Reputation, that he receives a retaining Fee against. If he could but maintain his Opinions as well as they do him, he were a very just and righteous Man; but when he has made his most of it, he leaves it, like his Client, to shift for itself. He fetches Money out of his Throat, like a Jugler: and as the Rabble in the Country value Gentlemen by their Housekeeping and their Eating; so is he supposed to have so much Law as he has kept Commons, and the abler to deal with Clients by how much the more he has devoured of *Inns* o' *Court* Mutton; and it matters not, whether he keep his Study, so he has but kept Commons. He never ends a Suit, but prunes it, that it may grow the faster, and yield a greater Increase of Strife. The Wisdom of the Law is to admit of all the petty, mean, real Injustices in the World, to avoid imaginary possible great ones, that may perhaps fall out. His Client finds the Scripture fulfilled in him, that *it is better to part with a Coat too, than to go to Law for a Cloke;* for *as the best Laws are made of the worst Manners,* even so are the best Lawyers of the worst Men. He humms about *Westminster-Hall,* and returns Home with his Pockets, like a Bee with his Thighs laden; and that which *Horace* says of an Ant, *Ore trahit quodcunque potest, atque addit acervo,* is true of him; for he gathers all his Heap with the Labour of his Mouth, rather than his Brain and Hands. He values himself, as a Carman does his Horse, by the Money he gets, and looks down upon all that gain less as Scoundrels. The Law is like that double-formed ill-begotten Monster, that was kept in an intricate Labyrinth, and fed with Men's Flesh; for it devours all that come within the Mazes of it, and have not a Clue to find the Way out again. He has as little Kindness for the Statute Law, as *Catholics* have for the Scripture, but adores the common Law as they do Tradition, and both for the very same Reason : For the statute Law being certain, written and designed to reform and prevent Corruptions and Abuses in the Affairs of the World (as the Scriptures are in Matters of Religion) he finds it many Times a great Obstruction to the Advantage and Profit of his Practice; whereas the common Law being unwritten, or written in an unknown Language, which very few understand but himself, is the more pliable and easy to serve all his Purposes, being utterly exposed to what Interpretation and Construction his

Interest and Occasions shall at any Time incline
him to give it; and differs only from arbitrary
Power in this, that the one gives no Account of
itself at all, and the other such a one as is perhaps
worse than none, that is implicit, and not to be
understood, or subject to what Construction he
pleases to put upon it.

A Virtuoso

Is a Well-willer to the Mathematics—He pursues Knowledge rather out of Humour than
Ingenuity, and endeavours rather to seem, than
to be. He has nothing of Nature but an Inclination, which he strives to improve with Industry;
but as no Art can make a Fountain run higher
than its own Head; so nothing can raise him above
the Elevation of his own Pole. He seldom converses but with Men of his own Tendency, and
wheresoever he comes treats with all Men as such,
for as Country-Gentlemen use to talk of their
Dogs to those that hate Hunting, because they
love it themselves; so will he of his Arts and
Sciences to those that neither know, nor care to
know any Thing of them. His Industry were
admirable, if it did not attempt the greatest Difficulties with the feeblest Means: for he commonly
slights any Thing that is plain and easy, how
useful and ingenious soever, and bends all his
Forces against the hardest and most improbable,
tho' to no Purpose if attained to; for neither
knowing how to measure his own Abilities, nor
the Weight of what he attempts, he spends his
little Strength in vain, and grows only weaker by
it—And as Men use to blind Horses that draw

in a Mill, his Ignorance of himself and his
Undertakings makes him believe he has advanced,
when he is no nearer to his End than when he set
out first. The Bravery of Difficulties does so
dazzle his Eyes, that he prosecutes them with as
little Success, as the Taylor did his Amours to
Queen Elizabeth. He differs from a Pedant, as
Things do from *Words;* for he uses the same
Affectation in his Operations and Experiments, as
the other does in Language. He is a Haber-
dasher of small Arts and Sciences, and deals in as
many several Operations as a baby-Artificer does
in Engines. He will serve well enough for an
Index, to tell what is handled in the World, but
no further. He is wonderfully delighted with
Rarities, and they continue still so to him, though
he has shown them a Thousand Times; for every
new Admirer, that gapes upon them, sets him a
gaping too. Next these he loves strange natural
Histories; and as those, that read Romances,
though they know them to be Fictions, are as
much affected as if they were true, so is he, and
will make hard Shift to tempt himself to believe
them first to be possible, and then he's sure to
believe them to be true, forgetting that *Belief
upon Belief is false Heraldry*. He keeps a Catalogue of the Names of all famous Men in any
Profession, whom he often takes Occasion to mention as his very good Friends, and old Acquaint-
ances. Nothing is more pedantic than to seem
too much concerned about Wit or Knowledge, to
talk much of it, and appear too critical in it. All
he can possibly arrive to is but like the Monkies
dancing on the Rope, to make Men wonder, how

'tis possible for *Art* to put *Nature* so much out of her Play.

His Learning is like those Letters on a Coach, where many being writ together no one appears plain. When the King happens to be at the University, and Degrees run like Wine in Conduits at public Triumphs, he is sure to have his Share; and though he be as free to chuse his Learning as his Faculty, yet like St. *Austin's* Soul *creando infunditur, infundendo creatur.* *Nero* was the first Emperour of his Calling, tho' it be not much for his Credit. He is like an Elephant that, though he cannot swim, yet of all Creatures most delights to walk along a River's Side; and as in Law, *Things that appear not, and things that are not, are all one;* so he had rather not be than not appear. The Top of his Ambition is to have his Picture graved in Brass, and published upon Walls, if he has no Work of his own to face with it. His want of Judgment inclines him naturally to the most extravagant Undertakings, like that of *making old Dogs young, telling how many Persons there are in a Room by knocking at a Door, stopping up of Words in Bottles,* &c. He is like his Books, that contain much Knowledge, but know nothing themselves. He is but an Index of Things and Words, that can direct where they are to be spoken with, but no further. He appears a great Man among the ignorant, and like a Figure in Arithmetic, is so much the more, as it stands before Ciphers that are nothing of themselves. He calls himself an *Antisocordist* a Name unknown to former Ages, but spawned by the Pedantry of the present. He delights most in attempting Things beyond his Reach, and the greater Distance he shoots at, the further he is sure to be off his Mark. He shows his Parts, as Drawers do a Room at a Tavern, to entertain them at the Expence of their Time and Patience. He inverts the Moral of that Fable of him, that caressed his Dog for fawning and leaping up upon him, and beat his Ass for doing the same Thing; for it is all one to him, whether he be applauded by an Ass, or a wiser Creature, so he be but applauded.

An Intelligencer

WOULD give a Peny for any Statesman's Thought at any Time. He travels abroad to guess what Princes are designing by seeing them at Church or Dinner; and will undertake to un-riddle a Government at first Sight, and tell what Plots she goes with, male or female; and discover, like a Mountebank, only by seeing the public Face of Affairs, what private Marks there are in the most secret Parts of the Body politic. He is so ready at Reasons of State, that he has them, like a Lesson, by Rote: but as Charlatans make Dis-eases fit their Medicines, and not their Medicines Diseases; so he makes all public Affairs conform to his own established Reason of State, and not his Reason, though the Case alter ever so much, comply with them. He thinks to obtain a great Insight into State-Affairs by observing only the outside Pretences and Appearances of Things, which are seldom or never true; and may be re-solved several Ways all equally probable; and therefore his Penetrations into these Matters are like the Penetrations of Cold into natural Bodies, without any Sense of itself, or the Thing it works upon—For all his Discoveries in the End amount only to Entries and Equipages, Addresses, Audiences, and Visits, with other such politic Speculations, as the Rabble in the Streets is wont to entertain itself withal. Nevertheless he is very cautious not to omit his Cipher, though he writes nothing but what every one does, or may safely know; for otherwise it would appear to be no Secret. He endeavours to reduce all his Politics into Maxims, as being most easily portable for a travelling Head, though, as they are for the most Part of slight Matters, they are but, like Spirits drawn out of Water, insipid and good for nothing. His Letters are a Kind of Bills of Exchange, in which he draws News and Politics upon all his Correspondents, who place it to Accompt, and draw it back again upon him; and though it be false, neither cheats the other, for it passes between both for good and sufficient Pay. If he drives an inland Trade, he is Factor to certain remote Country *Virtuosos*, who finding themselves unsatisfied with the Brevity of the *Gazette* desire to have Exceedings of News, besides their ordinary Commons. To furnish those he frequents Clubs and Coffee-Houses, the Markets of News, where he engrosses all he can light upon; and, if that do not prove sufficient, he is forced to add a Lye or two of his own making, which does him double Service; for it does not only supply his Occasions for the present, but furnishes him with Matter to fill up Gaps in the next Letter with retracting what he wrote before, and in the mean-time has served for as good News as the best; and, when the Novelty is over it is no Matter what becomes of it, for he is better paid for it than if it were true.

A Jugler

Is an artificial Magician, that with his Fingers casts a Mist before the eyes of the Rabble, and makes his Balls walk invisible which Way he pleases. He does his Feats behind a Table, like a *Presbyterian* in a Conventicle, but with much more Dexterity and Cleanliness, and therefore all Sorts of People are better pleased with him. Most Professions and Mysteries derive the Practice of all their Faculties from him, but use them with less Ingenuity and Candour; for the more he deceives those he has to do with, the better he deals with them, while those that imitate him in a lawful Calling are far more dishonest; for the more they impose the more they abuse. All his Cheats are primitive, and therefore more innocent and of greater Purity than those that are by Tradition from Hand to Hand derived to them: for he conveys Money out of one Man's Pocket into another's with much more Sincerity and Ingenuity than those, that do it in a *legal* Way, and for a less considerable, though more conscientious, Reward. He will fetch Money out of his own Throat with a great deal more of Delight and Satisfaction to those that pay him for it, than any Haranguer whatsoever, and make it chuck in his Throat better than a Lawyer, that has talked himself hoarse, and swallowed so many Fees, that he is almost choaked. He will spit Fire, and blow Smoke out of his Mouth, with less Harm and Inconvenience to the Government, than a seditious

Holder-forth; and yet all these disown and scorn him, even as Men, that are grown great and rich despise the Meanness of their Originals. He calls upon *Presto begone*, and the *Babylonian's Tooth*, to amuse and divert the Rabble from looking too narrowly into his Tricks; while a zealous Hypocrite, that calls Heaven and Earth to witness his, turns up the Eye, and shakes the Head at his Idolatry and Profanation. He goes the Circuit to all Country Fairs, where he meets with good strolling Practice, and comes up to *Bartholomew* Fair as his *Michaelmas* Term; after which he removes to some great Thorough-fare, where he hangs out himself in Effigie, like a *Dutch* Malefactor, that all those, that pass by, may for their Money have a Trial of his Skill. He endeavours to plant himself, as near as he can, to some Puppet-Play, Monster, or Mountebank, as the most convenient Situation, and, when Trading grows scant, they join all their Forces together, and make up one grand Shew, and admit the Cut-Purse and Ballad-Singer to trade under them, as Orange-Women do at a Playhouse.

A Romance Writer

PULLS down old Histories to build them up finer again, after a new Model of his own designing. He takes away all the Lights of Truth in History to make it the fitter Tutoress of Life; for *Truth* herself has little or nothing to do in the Affairs of the World, although all Matters of the greatest Weight and Moment are pretended and done in her Name; like a weak Princess, that has only the Title, and *Falshood* all the Power. He

observes one very fit Decorum in dating his Histories in the Days of old, and putting all his own
Inventions upon Ancient Times; for when the
World was younger, it might, perhaps, love, and
fight, and do generous Things at the Rate he
describes them; but since it is grown old, all these
heroic Feats are laid by and utterly given over, nor
ever like to come in Fashion again; and therefore
all his Images of those Virtues signify no more
than the Statues upon dead Men's Tombs, that
will never make them live again. He is like one
of *Homer's* Gods, that sets Men together by the
Ears, and fetches them off again how he pleases;
brings Armies into the Field like *Janello's* leaden
Soldiers; leads up both Sides himself, and gives
the Victory to which he pleases, according as he
finds it fit the Design of his Story; makes Love
and Lovers too, brings them acquainted, and appoints Meetings when and where he pleases, and
at the same Time betrays them in the Height of
all their Felicity to miserable Captivity, or some
other horrid Calamity; for which he makes them
rail at the Gods, and curse their own innocent
Stars, when he only has done them all the Injury
—Makes Men Villains, compells them to act all
barbarous Inhumanities by his own Directions, and
after inflicts the cruellest Punishments upon them
for it. He makes all his Knights fight in Fortifica-
tions, and storm one another's Armour, before
they can come to encounter Body for Body; and
always matches them so equally one with another,
that it is a whole Page before they can guess which
is likely to have the better; and he that has it is
so mangled, that it had been better for them both

to have parted fair at first; but when they encounter with those, that are no Knights, though ever so well armed and mounted, ten to one goes for nothing—As for the Ladies, they are every one the most beautiful in the whole World, and that's the Reason why no one of them, nor all together with all their Charms have Power to tempt away any Knight from another. He differs from a just Historian as a Joyner does from a Carpenter, the one does Things plainly and substantially for Use, and the other carves and polishes merely for Show and Ornament.

A Medicine-Taker

Has a sickly Mind, and believes the Infirmity is in his Body; like one, that draws the wrong Tooth, and fancies his Pain in the wrong Place. The less he understands the Reason of Physic, the stronger Faith he has in it, as it commonly fares in all other Affairs of the World. His Disease is only in his Judgment, which makes him believe a Doctor can fetch it out of his Stomach, or his Belly; and fright those Worms out of his Guts, that are bred in his Brain. He believes a Doctor is a Kind of Conjurer, that can do strange Things, and he is as willing to have him think so; for by that means he does not only get his Money, but finds himself in some Possibility, by complying with that Fancy, to do him good for it, which he could never expect to do any other Way; for like those that have been cured by drinking their own Water, his own Imagination is a better Medicine than any the Doctor knows how to prescribe, even as the Weapon-Salve cures a Wound by being

applied to that which made it. He is no sooner
well, but any Story or Lye of a new famous Doctor,
or strange Cure puts him into a Relapse, and he
falls sick of a Medicine instead of a Disease, and
catches Physic, like him that fell into a Looseness
at the Sight of a Purge. He never knows when
he is well, nor sick, but is always tampering with
his Health till he has spoiled it, like a foolish
Musician, that breaks his Strings with striving to
put them in Tune; for *Nature*, which is *Physic*,
understands better how to do her own Work than
those that take it from her at second hand. *Hippo-
crates* says—*Ars longa*, *Vita brevis*, and it is the
truest of all his Aphorisms,

> *For he that's giv'n much to the long Art,*
> *Does not prolong his Life, but cut it short.*

An Highwayman

Is a wild Arab, that lives by robbing of small
caravans, and has no *way* of living but the King's
high way. Aristotle held him to be but a kind
of huntsman; but our sages of the law account him
rather a beast of prey, and will not allow his game
to be legal by the forest law. His chief care is to
be well mounted, and, when he is taken, the law
takes care he should be so still while he lives. His
business is to break the laws of the land, for which
the hangman breaks his neck, and there's an end
of the controversie. He fears nothing, under the
gallows, more than his own face, and therefore
when he does his work conveys it out of sight,
that it may not rise up in judgment, and give evidence against him at the sessions. His trade is

to take purses and evil courses, and when he is taken himself the laws take as evil a course with him. He takes place of all other thieves as the most heroical, and one that comes nearest to the old Knights errant, though he is really one of the basest, that never ventures but upon surprizal, and where he is sure of the advantage. He lives like a Tartar always in motion, and the inns upon the road are his hoordes, where he reposes for a while, and spends his time and money, when he is out of action. These are his close confederates and allies, though the common interest of both will not permit it to be known. He is more destructive to a grasier than the murrain, and as terrible as the Huon-cry to himself. When he despatches his business between sun and sun he invades a whole county, and like the long Parliament robs by representa-tive. He receives orders from his superior officer the setter, that sets him on work and others to pay him for it. He calls concealing what he has taken from his comrades *sinking*, which they account a great want of integrity, and when he is discover'd he loses the reputation of an honest and just man with them for ever after. After he has rov'd up and down too long he is at last set himself, and convey'd to the jail, the only place of his residence, where he is provided of a hole to put his head in, and gather'd to his fathers in a faggot cart.

An Ignorant Man

HAS opinions contracted within a narrow com-pass, which renders them the more intense and violent. He is one half of all the vexations of mankind, which the knave and he divide equaly between them; and, though his ignorance be the mother of devotion (as the church of *Rome* very ingenuously confesses) all the rest of the kindred are the basest breed and generation in the whole world, and obstinacy is ever of the elder house and chief of the family. The extremity of his defects (as contraries do in nature) produces the same effects with other mens abundance; for he believes himself sufficiently qualified, because he does not understand his own wants. His understanding is hidebound and straitlac'd, which makes it more stiff and uneasy than those that are free and active. And as among beggars he that is most maim'd, and can shew most sores is esteem'd the ablest man in his calling: so he, that is most voluble in expressing and shewing his ignorance and confidence, is esteem'd by the rest of his own latitude for the most excellent and incomparable person. The less he understands of anything, the more confident he is of it; and because he knows no better him self believes nobody else does. His dull ignorance has the same operation with the wiser part of the world as lead has in the test of metals, that being apply'd to gold carries away all the baser metals that are mixt with it, and leaves only the pure behind. He makes more noise with his emptiness, like a tub, than others do that are full; and some late philosophers, that have found out a way by knocking at a door to find how many persons are in a room, may much more easily discover by his noise how little is in him. His dull temper, like lead, is easily melted with any passion, and as quickly cold again, whereas solider metals are the more difficult to be wrought upon.

ANONYMOUS

The Coffee House or News-Mongers Hall. . . . London, . . . 1672. fol.

[First edition] News from the Coffe-House ; . . . London, . . . 1667. fol. single leaf.

The Character of a Coffee-House, With the Symptomes of a Town-Wit. . . . London, . . . 1673. fol.

[The illustration, The Coffe Hous Mob, is the frontispiece of the Fourth Part of *Vulgus Britannicus*, 1710.]

Coffee was not altogether quietly introduced into this country. A good deal of humorous opposition to the novelty followed the opening of what seems to be the first London Coffee-house in 1652 :

' For men and Christians to turn Turks, and think
T''excuse the Crime because 'tis in their drink ! ' [1]

News from the Coffe-House is a brightly-written specimen of many contemporary accounts, generally in verse, of these new institutions. I have preferred the second edition for the sake of its title, *News-Mongers Hall*, which neatly satirises one of their chief functions during their prime. An example of the way these topical pieces are brought up to date is the substitution of 'our "Fleet"' for ' Monck ' in stanza 4.

The Character of a Coffee-House, for reasons more cogent than usual, remained anonymous. Its vigour is admirable. And it is crowded with such amusing ' things seen ' as the ' whole Roomful of Fops . . . searching the Map for Aristocracy and Democracy, not doubting but to have found them there, as well as Dalmatia and Croatia.'

[1] 'A Cup of Coffee : or, Coffee in its Colours,' 1663, quoted by Mr. H. C. Shelley.

The Coffee House or News-Mongers Hall

You that delight in Wit and Mirth,
   And long to hear such News,
As comes from all Parts of the *Earth*,
   Dutch, *Danes*, and *Turks*, and *Jews*,
I'le send yee to a Rendezvous,
   Where it is smoaking new;
Go hear it at a *Coffe-house*,
   It cannot but be true.

There Battles and Sea-Fights are Fought,
   And bloody Plots display'd;
They know more Things then ere was thought,
   Or ever was betray'd:
No Money in the Minting-house
   Is half so Bright and New;
And coming from a *Coffe-house*,
   It cannot but be true.

Before the *Navyes* fall to Work,
   They know who shall be Winner,
They there can tell ye what the *Turk*
   Last Sunday had to Dinner;
Who last did Cut *de Ruyters* Corns,
   Amongst his jovial Crew;
Or who first gave the *Devil* Horns,
   This sounds as if 'twere true.

A *Fisherman* did boldly tell,
   And strongly did avouch,
He Caught a Shoal of Mackarel,
   That Parley'd all in *Dutch*,
And cry'd out *Yaw, Yaw, Yaw myn Heer;*
   But as the Draught they drew,

THE COFFE HOUS MOB

They stunk for fear, our Fleet being near
Which cannot but be true.

There's nothing done in all the World,
   From *Monarch* to the *Mouse*,
But every Day or Night 'tis hurld
   Into the *Coffe-house.*
What *Lillie* or what *Booker* can
   By Art, not bring about,
At *Coffe-house* you'l find a Man,
   Can quickly find it out.

They'l tell ye there, what Lady-ware,
   Of late is grown too light;
What Wise-man shall from Favour fall,
   What Fool shall be a Knight;
They'l tell ye when our sayling Trade,
   Shall rise again, and Florish,
And when *Jack Adams* first was made
   Church-Warden of the Parish.

They know who shall in Times to come,
   Be either made, or undone,
From great St. *Peters-street* in *Rome*,
   To *Turnbul-street* in *London;*
And likewise tell, at *Clerkenwell*,
   What *Whore* hath greatest Gain;
And in that place, what Brazen-face
   Doth wear a Golden Chain.

At Sea their Knowledge is so much,
   They know all Rocks and Shelves,
They know all Councils of the *Dutch*,
   More then they know themselves;

Who 'tis shall get the best at last,
 They perfectly can shew
At *Coffe-house*, when they are plac'd,
 You'd scarce believe it true.

They know all that is Good, or Hurt,
 To Dam ye, or to Save ye;
There is the *Colledge*, and the *Court*,
 The *Countrey*, *Camp*, and *Navie;*
So great a *Universitie*,
 I think there ne're was any;
In which you may a Schoolar be
 For spending of a Penny.

A *Merchants Prentice* there shall show
 You all and every thing,
What hath been done, and is to do,
 'Twixt *Holland* and the *King;*
What *Articles* of *Peace* will bee,
 He can precizely show;
What will be good for *Them* or *Wee*,
 He perfectly doth know.

Here Men do talk of every Thing,
 With large and liberal Lungs,
Like Women at a Gossipping,
 With double tyre of Tongues;
They'l give a Broad-side presently,
 Soon as you are in view,
With Stories that, you'l wonder at,
 Which they will swear are true.

The Drinking there of *Chocalat*
 Can make a *Fool* a *Sophie:*
'Tis thought the *Turkish Mahomet*
 Was first Inspir'd with *Coffe*,

By which his Powers did Over-flow
   The land of *Palestine:*
Then let us to, the *Coffe-house* go,
   'Tis Cheaper far then Wine.

You shall know there, what Fashions are;
   How Perrywiggs are Curl'd;
And for a Penny you shall heare,
   All Novels in the World,
Both Old and Young, and Great and Small,
   And Rich, and Poor, you'l see:
Therefore let's to the *Coffe* All,
   Come All away with Mee.

A Coffee-House, &c.

A COFFEE-HOUSE is a *Lay-Conventicle*, Good-
fellowship turn'd *Puritan*, Ill-husbandry in *Mas-
querade*, whither people come, after *Toping* all day,
to purchase, at the expence of their last peny, the
repute of *sober Companions;* a *Rota*[1]-*Room* that
(like *Noahs* Ark) receives Animals of every sort,
from the precise *diminutive Band*, to the *Hectoring
Cravat* and Cuffs in *Folio;* a *Nursery* for training
up the smaller Fry of *Virtuosi* in confident Tat-
tling, or a Cabal of *Kittling Criticks* that have
only learn't to *Spit* and *Mew;* a Mint of *Intelligence*, that to make each man his *peny-worth*,
draws out into petty parcels, what the Merchant
receives in Bullion: He that comes often saves
two pence a week in *Gazets*, and has his News and
his Coffee for the same charge, as at a *three peny
Ordinary* they give in Broth to your Chop of

---

[1] The Rota (1659), a political club which advocated rotation
in the offices of Government.

Mutton; 'tis an *Exchange* where Haberdashers of *Political small wares* meet, and mutually abuse each other, and the Publique, with bottomless stories, and headless notions; the Rendezvous of *idle Pamphlets*, and persons more idly imployd to read them; a *High Court of Justice*, where every little Fellow in a *Chamlet-Cloak*[1] takes upon him to transpose Affairs both in Church and State, to shew reasons against *Acts* of Parliament, and condemn the Decrees of *General Councels;* . . .

The Room stinks of *Tobacco* worse than Hell of *Brimstone*, and is as full of *smoak* as their Heads that frequent it, whose humours are as various as those of *Bedlam*, and their discourse oft-times as *Heathenish* and *dull* as their Liquor; that Liquor, which by its looks and taste, you may reasonably guess to be *Pluto's Diet-drink;* that Witches tipple out of *dead mens Skulls*, when they ratifie to *Belzebub* their Sacramental Vows. . . .

As you have a *hodge-podge* of Drinks, such too is your Company, for each man seems a Leveller, and ranks and files himself as he lists, without regard to degrees or order; so that oft you may see a silly *Fop*, and a worshipful *Justice*, a griping *Rock*, and a grave *Citizen*, a worthy *Lawyer*, and an errant *Pickpocket*, a Reverend *Nonconformist*, and a Canting *Mountebank;* all blended together, to compose an *Oglio* of Impertinence.

If any *Pragmatick*, to shew himself witty or eloquent, begin to talk high, presently the further *Tables* are abandon'd, and all the rest flock round (like smaller birds to admire the gravity of *Madge-Howlet*). They listen to him a while with their

---

[1] Camlet, material made of the hair of the Angora goat.

mouths, and let their *Pipes* go out, and *Coffee* grow *cold*, for pure zeal of attention, but o' th' sudden fall all a yelping at once with more noise, but not half so much harmony as a *Pack* of *Beagles*, on the full Cry, to still this bawling, Upstarts

Captain *All-man-sir*, the man of mouth, with a face as blustring as that of *Eolus* and his four Sons in Painting, and a voice louder than the Speaking *Trumpet*, he begins you the story of a Sea-fight; and though he never were further by water than the *Bear-garden*, or *Cuckolds-Haven*, yet having pyrated the names of Ships and Captains, he per-swades you himself was present, and performed Miracles; that he waded *Knee-deep* in blood on the upper Deck, and never thought *serenade* to his Mistress, so pleasant as the Bullets *whistling;* how he stopt a *Vice-Admiral* of the Enemies under full sail, till she was boarded, with his *single arm* instead of *Grapling Irons*, and puft out with his breath a *Fire-ship* that fell foul on them. All this he relates sitting in a *Cloud* of Smoak, and belch-ing so many common *Oaths* to vouch it, you can scarce guess whether the real Engagement, or his Romancing account of it, be the more *dreadful:* However, he concludes with railing at the Con-duct of some *Eminent Officers*, (that perhaps he never saw) and protests, had they taken *his advice* at the Councel of War, not a *Sail* had escap'd us.

He is no sooner out of breath, but another begins a Lecture on the *Gazet*, where finding several *Prizes* taken, he gravely observes, if this Trade hold, we shall quickly rout the Dutch *Horse* and *Foot* by *Sea* : He nick-names the *Polish Gentlemen* where ever he meets them, and

enquires, whether *Gayland* and *Taffaletta* be
Lutherans or *Calvinists*: *Stilo Novo* he interprets
a vast new *Stile* or *Turn-pike* erected by his Elec-
toral Highness on the borders of *Westphalia* to
keep Mounsieur *Turenes* Cavalry from falling
on his retreating Troops; He takes words by the
sound without examining their sense : *Morea* he
believes to be the Country of the *Moors*, and
Hungary a place where famine alwayes keeps her
Court, nor is there any thing more certain, than
that he made a whole Roomful of Fops, as wise
as himself, spend above two hours in searching the
Map for *Aristocracy* and *Democracy*, not doubting
but to have found them there, as well as *Dalmatia*
and *Croatia*.

Next Seigniour *Poll* takes up the Cudgels, that
speaks nothing but *Designs*, *Projects*, *Intrigues*,
and *Experiments*, One of those in the old *Come-
dian*, *Plautus*, *Sciunt id quod in Aurem Rex
Reginæ dixerit, Quod* Juno *confabulata est cum*
Jove, *Sciunt quæ neque futura neque facta sunt,
tamen illi sciunt*, &c. All the Councels of the
German Dyet, the *Romish Conclave*, and *Turkish
Divan*, are as well known to him as his *Landresses
Smock*. He kens all the Cabals of the Court to
a hairs breadth, and (more then an hundred of us
do,) which Lady is not painted; you would take
his mouth for a *Limbeck*, it distills his words so
niggardly, as if he was loath to enrich you with
lies, of which he has yet more plenty than *Fox*,
Stowe, and *Hollingshead* bound up together; He
tels you of a Plot to let the *Lyons* loose in the
Tower, and then blow it up with *white-powder;*
of five hundred and fifty *Jesuits* all mounted on

Dromedaries seen by Moonshine on *Hampstead-heath*, and a terrible design hatch'd by the Colledge of *Doway*, to drain the narrow Seas and bring Popery over *dry shod;* besides he has a thousand inventions dancing in his brain-pan; an *Advice-boat* on the Stocks, that shall go to the East-Indies, and come back again in a *Fortnight*, a trick to march *under water*, and bore holes through the *Dutch-ships* Keele with Augurs, and *sincke* them, as they ride at Anchor, and a most excellent *pursuit to catch Sunbeams*, for making the Ladies new fashioned *Towrs*, that *Poets* may no more be damn'd for telling lies about their *Curls* and *Tresses*.

But these are puny *Pugs*, the *Arch-Devil*, where-with this *Smoke-hole* is haunted, is the *Town-wit*, one that playes *Rex* where ever he comes, and makes as much hurry as *Robin Goodfellow* of old amongst our *Granams Milk-bouls;* He is a kind of a *Squib* on a Rope; a *meteor* compos'd of Self-conceit and noise, that by *blazing and crackling* engages the wonder of the ignorant, till on a sudden he vanishes and leaves a *stench*, if not *infection* behind him; he is too often the *stain* of a good Family, and by his debaucht life blots the noble *Coat* of his Ancestors. A *wilde unback'd Colt*, whose *brains* are not half *codled*, indebted for his *cloaths* to his Tailor, and for his wit (such as it is) to his Company: The School had no sooner *'dued* him with a few superficial besprink-lings, but his *Mothers indulgence* posted him to Town for *Genteeler breeding*, where three or four wilde *Companions*, half a dozen bottles of *Bur-gundy*, two leaves of *Leviathan*, a brisk encounter

with his *Landlords Glasswindowes*, the charms of
a little *Miss*, and the sight of a new *Play* dub'd
him at once both a *Wit* and a *Hero*, ever since he
values himself mainly for *understanding the Town*,
and indeed *knows* most things in it, that are not
worth knowing: The two *Poles* whereon all his
discourses turn are *Atheism* and *Bawdry;* Bar him
from being profane or obscene, and you *cramp* his
Ingenuity, which forthwith *Flags* and becomes
useless, as a meer *Common Lawyer* when he has
cross'd the *Channel*. . . .

By means of some small *scraps of learning*
matcht with a far greater stock of Confidence, a
voluble Tongue, and bold delivery, he has the
ill-luck to be celebrated by the vulgar; for a man of
Parts, which opinion gains credit to his Insolences,
and sets him on further extravigances to maintain
his Title of a *Wit* by continuing his practice of
Fooling, whereas all his mighty parts are sum'd up
in this Inventory. "Imprimis, A *pedling way* of
Fancy, a *Lucky hit at Quibbling*, now and then
an *odd metaphor*, a conceited *Irony*, a ridiculous
Simile, a *wilde fetch*, an unexpected *Inference*, a
Mimick Gesture, a pleasing *Knack* in humouring
a Tale, and lastly an irresistable Resolution to speak
last, and never be *dasht* out of Countenance: . . ."

You would think he had got the *Lullian* Art,
for he speaks *Extempore* on all subjects, and ventures his words without the Relief of *Sense* to
second them, his thoughts start from his *imagination*, and he never troubles himself to Examine
their decency, or solidity by Judgement. To discourse him seriously is to read the *Ethicks to a
Monkey*, or make an Oration to *Caligula's Horse*,

whence you can only expect a *weehee* or *Jadish spurn;* after the most convincing Arguments, if he can but muster up one plausible *Joque* you are routed, For he that understood not your *Logick*, apprehends his droll, and though *Syllogysmes* may be answered, yet Jests and loud *laughter* can never be confuted, but have more sway to degrade things with the *unthinking croud*, than *demonstrations;* There being a Root of envy in too many Men, that invites them to applaud that which Exposes and villifies what they cannot comprehend. He pretends great skill in curing the *Tetters* and *Ringworms* of State, but blowes in the sores till they Rankle with his poisonous breath, he shoots *libels* with his forked tongue at his Superiors and abuses his dearest *Friends*, chusing to forfëit his neck to the *Gibbet*, or his shoulders to the *Batoon* rather than lose the driest of his idle *Quibbles;* In brief he is the *Jack-pudding of Society*, a *fleering Buffoon*, a better kind of *Ape* in the judgement of all *Wisemen*, but an incomparable *Wit* in his own. . . .

Thus have we led you from *Board to Board*, like the fellow in the Tower, to show you *strange Beasts* wherewith this place is sometimes frequented. To take now a *farewel view* of the House will be difficult, since 'tis always shifting Scenes and like *O Brazile* (the Inchanted Island) seldome appears twice in a posture; The *wax Candles* burning, and low devout whispers sometimes strike a kind of Religious Awe, whilst the modish Gallant swears so oft by *Jesu*, an ignorant Catholick would take it for a Chappel, and think he were saying our Ladies Psalter; In some places the *Organs* speak it a Musick Room, at others a pair of *Tables and draught board*, a smal gaming house, on a sudden it turns *Exchange*, or a Warehouse for all sorts of *Commodities*, where fools are drawn in by inch of Candle, as we betray and catch *Larks* with a Glass; The Bully-*Rook* makes it his *Bubbling* pond, where he angles for *Fops*, singles out his man, insinuates an *acquaintance*, offers the wine, and at next Tavern sets upon him with *high Fullums*,[1] and *plucks* him: The *Ingeniosi* use it for an after *Rehearsal*, where they bring *Plays* to Repetition, sift each *Scene*, examine every *uncorrected Line*, and *damn* beyond the fury of the *Rota*, whilst the *incognito Poet* out of an overweening affection to his *Infant Wit*, steals in *muffled* up in his Cloake, and sliely *Evesdrops* like a *mendicant Mother* to praise the *prettiness* of the *Babe* she has newly pawn'd on the Parish.

But 'tis time to be *gone*, who knows what *Magick* may be a working. For, behold! the *Coffee-Powder* settles at the bottome of our dish in form of a most terrible *Saracens Head*.

[1] A high fulham (-am, -om, -um), a die loaded so as to ensure a cast of 4, 5 or 6.

ANONYMOUS

A Character of London-Village. By a Countrey-Poet.
London, . . . 1684. fol. single leaf.

To a 'Countrey-Poet' living in an England whose
total population was not five and a half millions, the capital,
in which half a million were concentrated, was an im-
pressive sight.

[Macaulay, *History*, i. 3, gives these figures based on
Gregory King's estimate in 1696. *Vide D.N.B.* King.]

A Character of London-Village

A *Village!* Monstrous! 'Tis a mighty Beast,
Behemoth, or *Leviathan* at least;
Or like some Wilderness, or vast Meander,
Where to find Friends one long enough may
    wander.
The Towring Chimneys like a Forrest Show,
At whose low Branches do Balconies grow.
When I came there at first, I Gazed round,
And thought myself upon *Inchanted Ground;*
Or else that I (in Rapture being hurl'd)
Was lately Dead, and this was *th'other World.*
But was surpris'd with Doubts, and could not tell,
Which of the two 'twas, whether *Heav'n* or *Hell:*
The Noise and Shows my Eyes and Ears invade,
By Coaches, Cryes, and Glitt'ring Gallants made.
My reason was Convinced in a Trice
That it was neither, But *Fools Paradice;*
Ladies I saw, not Handsome one in ten;
Great store of Knights, and some few Gentlemen.
Fine Fellows Flanting up and down the Streets,
Where *Fop* and *Flutter* Each the Other Greets,

Each Mimick Posture does an Ape present,
While *Humble-Servant*, Ends the Complement.
For *Garb* and *Colour* there's no certain Rule,
Here is your *Red*, your *Blew*, your *Yellow-Fool*.
Most of these Gallants seem to view Refin'd;
The *Outside* wond'rous *Gay*, but *Poorly Lin'd*.
I saw some of them in the Playhouse-Pit,
Where they three hours in Conversation sit,
Laugh and *Talk Loud*, but scarce a *grain of Wit*.
The Ladies to Ensnare will something say,
Tending to show the Brisk Gallants their way,
But scorn as much to *Prattle Sence as they*.
Here comes a *Hero* Cover'd close from Air,
By Porters born in a Silk-Curtain'd-Chair.
Whose Sire in honest Russet *Trail'd a Plow*,
And with *Stout Flayl* Conquer'd the Haughty
     Mow.

.   .   .   .

There goes a *Brisk Young Lass* in a Gay Dress,
Here an *Old Crone* in Youthful Gawdyness.
Strange *Miracles* of Nature here are plac'd!
Ill-Favour'd Wenches, Cracks; some *Fair*, are
     chaste.
The Temp'rate, Sick: Great Drinkers live in
     Health.
Here *Usurers* have *Wit*, and *Poets Wealth*.
The *Coffee House*, the *Rendez-vouz of Wits*,
Is a Compound of *Gentlemen* and *Cits;*
And not all *Wise*, or else their Wits they Smother,
They sit as if *Afraid* of *One Another*.
So *Pickpocket* (when Deeper *Lifter*'s by)
Budging aloof, Disowns the Mystery.
In comes a Cockt-up *Bully*, Looking big,
With Deep-fring'd Elbow-Gloves, and Ruffl'd Wig,

He turns his Back to th' Chimney, with a Grace,
Singing and staring in each Strangers Face;
Talks Mighty things, his late Intrigues, and then
Sups off his Dish, and out he struts Agen.
And as I Rambled through this *Quondam-City*,
I look'd on Founding *Pauls* with Tears of Pity;

. . . .

Village, for now to you I tell my Tale;
You have Produc'd a *Mountain* from a *Dale:*
The Countrey thought the Fire had quite undone
    ye,
But now I find you have both *Zeal* and *Money.* . . .

ANONYMOUS

The Character and Qualifications of an Honest Loyal Merchant. . . . London : . . . 1686. 4to.

The ideal view of the merchant has found a favourable expression in our literature. Chaucer's ' marchant ' had the traditional skill in arranging that ' Ther wiste no wight that he was in dette ' ; but the poet's summary is kindly enough ' For sothe he was a worthy man with-alle.' ' An Honest Loyal Merchant ' might be considered an amplification of Breton's brief sketch of ' A Worthy Marchant.' Its new contribution is a tribute to the merchant at the end of the century that a small script of 2 or 3 lines only under our true-bred merchant's hand 'passes over the world for Thousands of Pounds.'

Fuller's sketch, ideal too, has a robust quality that is grateful to those who rarely meet ' The Good Merchant.' The dishonest ones, he tells us, ' rob a man of his purse, and never bid him stand.'

The first part of the sketch has been selected, though the second contains an interesting discussion of what should be the merchant's standing in the world and includes an account of his education in which there is a plea for ' *Latin* enough to understand an *Author*, or Discourse a *Stranger* ; and to serve as a Preparative and Ground-Work for the rest of his necessary Accomplishments ; ' a plea too for seemly penmanship, he ' writes a fair Genteel Hand, not crampt up to a *set Secretary* like a Scriveners Boy ; nor scrawling *Long-Tails*, like a Wench at a Boarding-School, but a neat charming *mixture of Roman and Italian* flowing with a kind of Artificial Negligence.'

An Honest Loyal Merchant

THE Loyal Honest MERCHANT is an Universal Tradesman, and all the World is his *Shop;* A diligent Bee, ever busie in bringing Honey to the *Publick Hive;* The Nations *Purveyor,* that improves its Superfluities, and supplies its Necessities; The same to the *Body Politick,* as the *Liver, Veins,* and *Arteries* are to the *Natural;* for he both raises and distributes *Treasure,* the *vital Blood* of the Common-Weal. He is the *Steward* of the Kingdoms *Stock,* which by his good or ill management, does proportionably increase or languish. One of the most useful members in a State, without whom it can never be *Opulent* in Peace, nor consequently *Formidable* in War.

FOR he fetches in the good things of the remotest Regions to Enrich his Countrey, and by the *honest Magick* of Industry, removes the *Mines of Peru,* and the Golden *Sands of Guinea* whither he pleases. He can make a *barren Heath,* or a contemptible *Bogg,* (that has not one *Tree* but what you must plant, nor one *Stone* but what you must bring thither, a place that has nothing of its own product worth speaking of) to be yet the richest City for its Bigness, and the greatest Storehouse and Empory for all sorts of Commodities in the World.

'Tis by his means,

> *The Taste of choice* Arabian Spice *we know,*
> *Without those scorching* Heats *that make it grow.*
> *In* Indian Gems, *and* Persian Silks *we shine;*
> *And without* Planting, *drink of every* Vine.

WITHOUT him the World would still be a kind of *Wilderness,* one part unknown and unbeholding to the other; and if ever its remote

Inhabitants *met*, it would be rather for mischief and *slaughter*, than mutual assistance; Whereas *his pains* unites divided Empires, and those that never beheld the *same Stars;* joins people separated by different Climates, Religions, and Policies, into one common Society; And by the Mediation of *Commerce*, makes the *Sun-burnt Ethiopian* contribute to the relief of the *Frozen Muscovite*.

HE is the true *Orpheus* that charms the *Savages*, and spreads Civility amongst *Barbarians;* he communicates *Arts* and Sciences, and all useful *Inventions* both for Necessity and Ornament: Unless he had advanced *Navigation*, Geography might have still lain muffled in *Strabo's Cloak*, and *Astronomy* been confin'd to *Ptolemy's* narrow *Horizon;* we might to this day have believed the Poets Fables of *Frigid* and *Torrid Zones* uninhabitable; That there was no living (forsooth) under the *Æquator*, or within the *Artick* and *Antartick* Circles; Each quick-sighted *Vergilius* might have been in danger of Deprivation, for holding the supposed Heresie of *Antipodes;* The *Art of Healing* it self had incurably languisht, our Apothecaries Shops been destitute of the best part of the *Materia Medica*, or choicest Rarities of the *Tripple Kingdom;* and an *English Herbal* might have bounded the studies of our most Learned *Colledg of Physicians*.

NAY further, there seems yet a more sublime and mysterious designment of *Providence* attending his pains; for by establishing an intercourse with *Infidels* for Civil Traffick, a door is not seldom open'd to advance the *Divine Interest;* so that he may propagate our most *Holy Faith*, as well as vend our Temporal Commodities; and by penetrating both *Indies*, and (like the Sun) compassing the World, administers opportunities to divulge the light of the *Gospel;* whilst our stupid Gallants think, he Voyages only to bring them Pearls to hang at the Ears of their *Mistresses*, *Mango's* to relish their *Mutton*, or Pepper to strew over their *Cucumbers*.

IN these remote Negotiations, he counts it next to denying his *Saviour*, to occasion by any dishonest or *immoral* Act, his Blessed Name to be *Blasphem'd amongst the Gentiles*. He would rather endure the *Rack* himself, than stretch a Piece of Cloath on the Tenters to make it three or four Yards longer, which when sold to a *Turk*, shall in the next shower, *Cockle* all up in a *Ruck*, causing the honest *Musulman* to revile both the cheating Christian and his Religion; Tho the later altogether undeservedly, since It most severely condemns Circumvention, and enjoyns not only strict *Fidelity* and *Justice* in our dealings, but *Charity* too, towards all Mankind, even our most professed Enemies.

THIS our *Merchant* is sensible of, and trembles at that WOE pronounced against those by whom such scandalous *Offences* come; Therefore keeps a *double Guard* on his Conversation abroad, as knowing that not only his own private Reputation, but the Honour of his *Religion* and *Nation*, in some measure depends thereon. His *Faith* is firmer than the *Needle* of his *Compass*, for it admits not of the least *Variation;* his Devotion is one and the *same*, in all Countries, and his *Zeal* as great beyond, as on this side *the Line;* For like the *Sun*, tho he traverse round the habitable Globe, yet still he keeps constant to the *Ecliptick* of *Truth*, and will not Barter away *the Pearl of Price*, for any worldly gains, but uses diligence in the first place to Ensure his *Soul*, dreading no *Shipwrack* so much as that *of a good Conscience*.

AND as Piety and *Loyalty* are inseparable; so next to *Sacriledg*, (which is a robbing of God) he abhors *Smuckling* and *Running of Goods*, or *Entring* one commodity for another that pays more, *&c.* (Which is a robbing of Gods Viceregent, the *King;*) His practice being a daily comment on that Text, *Render unto Cæsar the things that are Cæsars*, &c. He reckons all those that use any such unlawful Courses, far from being either good *Christians* or Loyal *Subjects;* Nay esteems it not only a simple *Cheat* or bare *Felony*, by any Pretensions, Concealments, Trick or Artifices to defraud his *Sovereign* of those Dues the *Law* has setled, But a kind of unfledg'd *Treason* against the Crown, since 'tis apparently a design to weaken and subvert the *Royal* Power, when we purloin the *Revenues* necessary for the support of the *Government*.

HE knows, That a Nation may be impoverisht and ruin'd by a *great Trade* ill manag'd, as well as by *too little;* and that the Kingdom may *get*, even when the Merchant *loses*, and the Merchant often get when the Kingdom *loses;* But for his own part is so passionate a Lover of his Country, as to postpone his private Advantages to the utility of the *Publick;* And therefore thinks himself obliged (whenever fit opportunity is offered) humbly to inform *his Sovereign*, or some of the Chief Ministers of State, (or Parliament, when conven'd), of

the *Over-ballance of Importations* from any
Country; and of all Exportations or Importations
of any sort of Goods that are notably *prejudicial*
or *profitable* to the Kingdom, to the end there may
be *wholsom Laws* made to prevent the One, and
encourage the Other;

FOR not only the increase or decay of *Sea-men*
and *shipping*, (the Walls of our *British* Empire)
The encouragement or discouragement of *Manu-
facturers*, and consequently the *Encrease of People*,
(which if duly employed can never be too many,
their multitudes being always the first *Riches* as
well as *Strength* of any Nation) but also the Value
of every Country-Gentlemans *Lands*, Rents, Corn,
Cattel, *&c.* does all ultimately depend upon, and
are Influenced by It, and must either *Rise* or *Fall*
in equal proportion as Forreign Traffick is well or
ill manag'd, clog'd, or Encouraged.

JUSTICE, square Dealing, and a *punctual
Honesty*, are Essential Qualities in our true-bred
Merchant. Hence his *Books* are allow'd *Evidence*,
and lookt upon as a kind of *Records;* and a small
Script of two or three Lines only under his hand,
without either *Witness* or *Seal*, passes over the
world for Thousands of Pounds, as Authentick as
Twenty *Noverint universi's*, or other long-winded
Instruments, Sealed and Delivered in the Presence
of *John Doe*, and *Richard Roe*, and half the Parish
besides.

H. C.

The Character of an Honest Lawyer. By H. C.
. . . London, . . . 1676. fol.

This, like Overbury's ' Reverend Judge,' is an idealised
presentation of the law. The other side of the picture,
so brilliantly depicted by Butler, is usually turned to us.

An Honest Lawyer

AN honest Lawyer, is the *Life-guard* of our *Fortunes;* the best *Collateral security* for an *Estate.*
A trusty *Pilot* to steer one safe through the dangerous and oft-times *Inevitable* Ocean of *Contention.* A true *Priest of Justice,* that neither sacrifices
to *Fraud* nor *Covetousness,* and in this *out-does*
those of a *higher Function,* that he can *make* people
Honest, that are *Sermon Proof.* *H*e is an infallible *Anatomist,* of *Meum* and *Tuum,* that will
presently *search* a Cause to the quick, and find
out the *Peccant humour,* the little *lurking-cheat,*
though mask'd in never so fair *Pretences:* One that
practises *Law,* so as not to forget the *Gospel,* but
always wears a *Conscience* as well as a *Gown;* he
weighs the *Cause* more than the *Gold,* and if *That*
will not bear the *Touch,* in a generous scorn *puts
back* the *Fee.* Though he knows all the *Criticisms*
of his *Faculty,* and the nice *Snapperado's* of *Practice,* yet he never *uses* them, unless in a *Defensive
way* to *Countermine* the plots of *Knavery,* for he
affects not the Devilish skill of *outbaffling Right,*
nor aims at the *shameful* Glory of making *a Bad
Cause good,* but with equal contempt hates the

Wolves study, and the *Dogs eloquence*, and disdains to grow *great* by *Crimes*, or build himself
a *Fortune* on the *spoil* of the *Oppressed*, or the
ruines of *Widows and Orphans*, he has more
Reverence for his *Profession* than to *debauch* it to
unrighteous purposes, and had rather be *dumb*
than suffer his *tongue* to *Pimp* for *Injustice*, or
club his *Parts* to *bolster* up a *Cheat* with the Leger-
demain of *Law-craft;*

He is not fac'd like *Janus*, to take a *Reteyning
Fee* from the *Plaintiff;* and afterwards a *Back-
handed bribe* from the *Defendant*, nor so *double-
tongu'd*, that one may purchase his *Pleading*, and
the other at the same or a larger price, his *silence*.
But when he undertakes a business, he *espouses*
it in earnest, and does not *Follow* a cause but
manage it.   A mollifying letter from the adversaries *Potent Friend*, a noble *Treat*, or the *remora*
of a lusty *Present* to his Wife, have no influence
to make him *slacken* his proceedings, for he is so
zealous for his Clients interest, that you may
sooner *Divorce* the *Sun* from the *Ecliptick*, than
warp him from his integrity, yet still is his Patron
only *usque ad Aras*, (as far as is just) for if once
found he finds the business smell *rank*, *St. Marks
treasure* or the *Mines of Potosi*, are too *small a
Fee* to engage him one *step* further. . . .

He delights to be an *Arbitrator*, not an Incendiary, and has *Beati pacifici* oftner in his mouth
than *Currat Lex*, he never *wheadles* any into end-
less suits for *trifles*, nor animates them to undo
themselves and others for damage *Feasant*, or insignificant *trespases*, *pedibus ambulando*, but (as
Telephus's sword was the best cure for the wounds

it made) advises people to compose their *assaults*
and *slanders* over the same *Ale* that *begot* them;
nor does he in *weightier cases* extort unreasonable
Fees, for whatever the *foul chapp'd rabble* may
suggest, a Lawyers Profession is not *Mercenary;*
the *Money* given him is onely an *Honorary gra-
tuity*, for his *advice* and *trouble*, or a *grateful
acknowledgment*, of our Obligations for his *well
intended* endeavours, and the old Emblem of the
Brambles tearing oft the *sheeps* fleece that run to it
for *shelter* in a *storm*, can have no reflection upon
him, whose *Brain* is as active, and his *Tongue as
voluble* for a penniless *Pauper*, as when *Oyl'd* with
the *aurum potabile* of a *Dozen Guinnies*.

In a word whilst he *lives*, he is the *delight* of
the *Court*, the *Ornament* of the *Bar*, the *Glory* of
his *Profession*, the *Patron* of *Innocency*, the *Upholder* of *right*, the *Scourge* of *oppression*, the
Terrour of *deceit*, and the *Oracle* of his *Country*,
and when *death* calls him to the *Bar* of *Heaven* by
a *Habeas corpus cum Causis* he finds his *Judge*,
his *Advocate*, *nonsuits* the *Devil*, obtains a liberate
from all his infirmities, and continues still *One of
the long robe* in *Glory*.

ANONYMOUS

The Character of the Beaux, . . . Written by a Young
   Gentleman.   London : . . . 1696.   8vo.

Had a Young Gentleman's Nice Affected Beau, the
Beau drawn by ' A Lady ' in *Defence of the Female Sex*,
and Vanbrugh's Lord Foppington in his *Relapse* (1697),
been separately discovered without sign of date or source,
they could have been correctly assigned to the same period,
that of the late Restoration.   Each sketches, and in a
similar way, the fop, as that universal figure was then
becoming the talk of the Town under his new French
label, for the Oxford Dictionary records the first appearance of the term *beau* in 1687.

They could even be approximately assigned to the same
year.   The style of a ' Young Gentleman ' is very similar
to ' A Lady's,' his greater sprightliness in this sketch has
been here preferred.   Vanbrugh's lively portrait is simply
the dramatisation of ' A Lady's ' Beau.   The latter
dines at ' *Locket's*, where his Vanity, not his Stomach, is
to be gratified with something that is *little* and *dear*.'
Lord Foppington declares ' I go to Dinner at *Lacket's* ;
where you are so nicely and delicately serv'd, that, stap
my Vitals, they shall compose you a Dish no bigger than a
Saucer, shall come to Fifty shillings.'

The illustration appeared as the frontispiece in the
three editions of ' A Lady's ' book.   It applies as neatly
to a *Nice Affected Beau*, or, particularly in one detail, to
Vanbrugh's play, for the beau's pocket is in that fashionable
spot, desired by his lordship, ' the Packet becomes no part
of the Body but the Knee.'

A Nice, Affected Beau

ONE, who from Ten till Twelve, receives Visits
in Bed, where he lyes most magnificently with a
long Perriwig neatly laid over the Sheets, extravi-

gantly powder'd, and exactly curl'd; when the
Clock has struck Twelve, that his two hours are
expir'd, he begins to rise, and with much ado,
about Three is drest, which we must allow to be
but a very small time, considering how many little
phidling insignificant things he has to adorn himself withal; as perfuming his Cloaths, using Washes
to make his hands white, beautifying his Face,
putting on two or three little Patches, soaking
his Handkerchief in Rose-water, powdering his
Linnen, which he pretends so stinks of Sope, he's
not able to bear it; and chiefly tying on his Cravat,
which perhaps is done and undone a dozen times,
before it sets with an Air according to his Mind.
Between Three and Four he Dines, and his constant Food is either a *Chicken*, a *Rabbet*, a *Partridge*, or for variety, a little fresh *Fish; Mutton,
Beef, Pork*, or *Veal*, being too strong for his nice
Stomach, and fitter for the grosser and more robust
sort of *Mortals*, as he styles 'em. About Four he
bids his Dog call a Chair, and away he marches to
the *Chocalate-House*, where he affirms himself to
be a Wit; and is frequently chringing into Company, though he knows himself not in the least
acceptable; continually interrupting others more
serious Discourse, to force out his dry Jests, which
are always *Foolish*, if not downright *Nonsense*, and
never move any body but his own *insipid Self*. But
his chiefest aim is, to converse with the *Poets*, and
be of their Society; to be familiar with 'em, and
(if he can) a *Cronie;* that when occasion serves,
he may make use of their Brains for a *Song*, or a
Copy of Verses on such a Ladies Beauty, which
he swears (when conversant with the Ladies) to be

THE COMPLEAT BEAU

his own. By that time he has spent an hour at *Will's*, or the *Chocolate-House*, 'tis almost time for the *Play;* and having put himself in Order, adjusted his *Cravat* and *Wig*, and *daub'd* his Face with *Snuff*, he very soberly enters the House; first in one side Box, then in t'other; next in the *Pit*, and sometimes in the *Galleries*, that the *Vulgar* sort may as well behold and admire the *Magnificence* of his *Apparel*, as those of *Quality:* Before the *Play's* half done, whip he's at t'other House, and being in the *Pit*, between every *Act* leaps upon the Benches, to show his *Shape*, his *Leg*, his *Scarlet Stockings*, his *Meen* and *Air;* then out comes a *Snuff-Box*, as big as an *Alderman's Tobacco-Box*, lin'd with a bawdy Picture, and the Hand's very gracefully lifted to the Nose, to shew the length of its Fingers, its whiteness, its delicacy, and the Diamond Ring; and having play'd a few Monkey Tricks, the Musick ceases, and the Gentleman descends, bowing this way, that way, and t'other way, that the Ladies in the Boxes may take notice of him, and think him a Person of *Quality*, known and respected by every body: Then, while the *Play's* Acting, he turns his Back to the Stage, as disregarding such *Nonsense;* and crying, *Damme*, here's a dam'd Play; then speaking to a *Masque Madam*, says he, *How can your Ladyship sit it?* Why, Sir, *says she?* Methinks 'tis very tolerable; *O ged Madam! no, the Devil take me if I cou'dn't write a more tolerable one* ex Tempore: But if she still persists to commend it, and will needs confute him, as O dear Sir! I'm sure you wrong your Judgment now, this *Scene* is very pretty, and witty; then the *Fop* complies a little, and, with a simple

Grimace, He! He! *Why faith*, Madam, *this is
indifferent, though if such a thing had been* out
or in, 'twou'd ha' been much better; still criticising,
and pretending to amend what he does not understand : When an Hour or two's spent there, he
goes to the *Park*, and, creeping to a Lady, *O
Madam, I'm almost suffocated; stop my Vitals!
the Smoak of* London *is unsufferable: How does
your Ladyship find it?* yet, not permitting her to
Answer; *O* Madam, *renounce me, if I am not
ready to expire; your Ladyship's most humble Servant:* Then the same Stuff to another, always
endeavouring to speak Fine, and Unintelligibly;
and, not being Master of his own Language, inter-
mixes it with Bombast *Latine*, and scraps of
French, that the Ladies may take him for a Man
of Parts, and a true *Linguist:* When he has pretty
well wearied himself with that Diversion, he walks
to some Lady's Lodgings in *Pell-Mell*, or St.
James's-Square; where he spends three or four
Hours at *Ombre*, or *Ticktack*, and so Home again.

A LADY

An Essay in Defence of the Female Sex. In which are
inserted the Characters of

A Pedant,	A Vertuoso,
A Squire,	A Poetaster,
A Beau,	A City-Critick, &c.

In a Letter to a Lady. Written by a Lady. . . .
London, . . . 1696. 8°.

9 characters.

This book has an interest beyond itself. It belongs to
a large group of books and pamphlets which formed part
of the reaction against the Restoration attitude to women.
This movement began in France, and many of the English
works were translations. No French source has been discovered for the present essay,[1] whose authorship is uncertain.

Whoever the writer may be, she can express her
satirical attitude brightly, and with a thoughtful wit. She
uses the characters to amplify points in her argument.
The ' Pedant ' and the ' Country Squire,' for instance,
are given ' to shew that Men may and do often Baffle
and Frustrate the Effects of a liberal Education, as well
by Industry as Negligence.' And she proceeds to discuss
this matter with much good sense.

A Country Squire

THESE are generally sent to School in their
Minority, and were they kept there till they came
to Years of Discretion, might most of 'em stay,
till they cou'd tuck their Beards into their Girdles
before they left carrying a Satchel. In conformity
to Custom, and the Fashion, they are sent early
to serve an Apprenticeship to Letters, and for eight
or nine years are whipt up and down through two

[1] A. H. Upham, *Journal of English and Germanic Philology*,
vol. 12, pp. 262-76. 1913.

or three Counties from School to School; when being arriv'd at Sixteen, or Seventeen Years of Age, and having made the usual *Tour* of Latin and Greek Authors, they are call'd Home to be made Gentlemen. As soon as the young Squire has got out of the House of Bondage, shaken off the awe of Birch, and begins to feel himself at Liberty, he considers that he is now Learned enough, (and 'tis ten to one but his Friends are wise enough to be of his Opinion) and thinks it high time to shake off the barbarous Acquaintance he contracted, with those crabbed, vexatious, obscure Fellows, that gave him so much trouble and smart at School, Companions by no means fit for a Gentleman, that writ only to torment and perplex poor Boys, and exercise the tyranny of Pedants and School-masters. These prudent resolutions taken, his Conversation for some years succeeding is wholly taken up by his Horses, Dogs and Hawks (especially if his Residence be in the Country) and the more sensless Animals that tend 'em. His Groom, his Huntsman, and his Falconer are his Tutors, and his walk is from the Stable to the Dog-kennel, and the reverse of it. His diversion is drudgery, and he is in highest satisfaction when he is most tir'd. He wearies you in the Morning with his Sport, in the Afternoon with the noisie Repetition and Drink, and the whole Day with Fatigue and Confusion. His Entertainment is stale Beer, and the History of his Dogs and Horses, in which he gives you the Pedigree of every one with all the exactness of a Herald; and if you be very much in his good Graces, 'tis odds, but he makes you the Compliment of a Puppy of

one of his favourite Bitches, which you must take
with abundance of Acknowledgments of his Civil-
lity, or else he takes you for a stupid, as well as
an ill bred Fellow. He is very constant at all Clubs
and Meetings of the Country Gentlemen, where
he will suffer nothing to be talk'd or hear'd of but
his Jades, his Curs, and his Kites. Upon these he
rings perpetual Changes, and trespasses as much
upon the patience of the Company in the Tavern,
as upon their Enclosures in the Field, and is least
impertinent, when most drunk. His grand Business is to make an Assignation for a Horse Race,
or a Hunting Match, and nothing discomposes
him so much as a Disappointment. Thus accom-
plish'd, and finish'd for a Gentleman, he enters the
Civil Lists, and holds the Scale of Justice with as
much Blindness as she is said to do. From hence
forward his Worship becomes as formidable to the
Ale-Houses, as he was before Familiar; he sizes an
Ale Pot, and takes the dimensions of Bread with
great Dexterity and Sagacity. He is the terrour
of all the Deer, and Poultry Stealers in the Neighbourhood, and is so implacable a Persecutor of
Poachers, that he keeps a Register of all the Dogs
and Guns in the Hundred, and is the Scare-Beggar
of the Parish. Short-Pots, and unjustifiable Dogs
and Nets, furnish him with sufficient matter for
Presentments, to carry him once a Quarter to the
Sessions; where he says little, Eats and Drinks
much, and after Dinner, Hunts over the last chace,
and so rides Worshipfully Drunk home again. At
home he Exercises his Authority in granting his
Letters Pattents to Petitioners for erecting Shovel
Board, Tables and Ginger Bread Stalls. If he

happen to live near any little Borough or Corporation that sends Burgesses to Parliament, he may become ambitious and sue for the Honour of being made their Representative. Henceforward he grows Popular, bows to, and treats the Mob all round him; and whether there be any in his Discourse or not, there is good Sense in his Kitchin and his Cellar, which is more agreeable and edifying. If he be so happy as to out-tap his Competitour, and Drink his Neighbours into an Opinion of his Sobriety, he is chosen, and up he comes to that Honourable Assembly, where he shews his Wisdom best by his Silence, and serves his Country most in his absence.

A Pedant

For Schollars, though by their acquaintance with Books, and conversing much with Old Authors, they may know perfectly the Sense of the Learned Dead, and be perfect Masters of the Wisdom, be throughly inform'd of the State, and nicely skill'd in the Policies of Ages long since past, yet by their retir'd and unactive Life, their neglect of Business, and constant Conversation with Antiquity, they are such Strangers to, and so ignorant of the Domestick Affairs and manners of their own Country and Times, that they appear like the Ghosts of Old Romans rais'd by Magick. Talk to them of the *Assyrian*, or *Persian* Monarchies, the *Grecian* or *Roman* Common-wealths. They answer like Oracles, they are such finish'd Statesmen, that we shou'd scarce take 'em to have been less than Confidents of *Semiramis*, Tutours to *Cyrus* the great, old Cronies of *Solon* and

Lycurgus, or Privy Councellours at least to the Twelve *Cæsars* successively; but engage them in a Discourse that concerns the present Times, and their Native Country, and they hardly speak the Language of it, and know so little of the affairs of it, that as much might reasonably be expected from an animated *Egyptian* Mummy. They are very much disturbed to see a Fold or a Plait amiss in the Picture of an Old *Roman* Gown, yet take no notice that their own are thred-bare out at the Elbows, or Ragged, and suffer more if *Priscian's* Head be broken then if it were their own. They are excellent Guides, and can direct you to every Ally, and turning in old *Rome;* yet lose their way at home in their own Parish. They are mighty admirers of the Wit and Eloquence of the Ancients; yet had they liv'd in the time of *Cicero*, and *Cæsar* wou'd have treated them with as much supercilious Pride, and disrespect as they do now with Reverence. They are great hunters of ancient Manuscripts, and have in great Veneration any thing, that has scap'd the Teeth of Time and Rats, and if Age have obliterated the Characters, 'tis the more valuable for not being legible. But if by chance they can pick out one Word, they rate it higher then the whole Author in Print, and wou'd give more for one Proverb of *Solomons* under his own Hand, then for all his Wisdom. These Superstitious, bigotted Idolaters of time past, are Children in their understanding all their lives; for they hang so incessantly upon the leading Strings of Authority, that their Judgments like the Limbs of some *Indian* Penitents, become altogether crampt and motionless for want of use.

A Swaggering Coward

[Vanity] is admirably seen in a Writing, reciting Fop Author, is in full lustre in a Beau, but its most unlucky Prospect is in a Swaggering Coward, who is a Fool beyond the Conviction of Smart. His Courage is like an Ague Fit, that leaves him upon a Fright, and returns when he is out of the reach of a Cudgell. He spends much time in the Fencing School, and Fights briskly where there is no danger of Wounds nor Smart. His Hands are instructed, but his Heels do him all the Service. He is a nice observer of Punctilio's, and takes more Affronts than are given him. He draws first, and runs first, and if ever he makes another Man run, it is after him. He is a Pebble that sparkles like a Diamond but wants hardness. He talks perpetually of what he will do, but thinks continually of what he shall suffer. He is often in Quarrels, yet seldom in Rencounters, and is glad of a Challenge, that he may know whom, and when to avoid. He brings up the Rear at an Engagement, and leads the Van in the Retreat. He is a Man of much Passion, but the most predominant is his Fear. He offers affronts readily, but has too much honour to justifie them, and will submit to any terms of satisfaction rather than occasion Blood-shed. He is so full of Courage, that it boils over when there is no occasion, and his *Sword* and *Person* are always at Leisure, and at your Service, till you want them, and then to his great Trouble, he is always indispensably engag'd otherwise. He wears *Red*, and a long *Sword* openly to shew his Valour, and *Mail* privately to shew his Discretion. He threatens terribly, but he is like a Witch, if you draw Blood of him, he has no power to hurt you. No Man shews or boasts more of his Scars with less Reason. He scorns to take a blow in the Face, and a Backpiece is as good to him as a whole sute of Armour. He is at first the Terrour of all the *Young Bullies*, at last their Maygame, and they blood their *Cub Hectors* upon him, as they do young *Beagles* on a *Hare*. Good usage makes him insolent, but he fawns like a *Spaniel* most upon those that beat him. When he is discover'd by all the rest of the World, the Cheat passes still upon himself, and he is pleas'd with the terrible Figure he makes in his Glass, tho' he is ready to shake at his own Shaddow.

A Coffee-House Politician

HE is one whose Brains having been once overheated, retain something of the Fire in 'em ever after. He mistakes his Passion for Zeal, and his Noise and Bustling, for Services. He is always full of Doubts, Fears, and Jealousies, and is never without some notable Discovery of a deep laid Design, or a dangerous Plot found out in a *Meal Tub*, or *Petticoat*. He is a mighty Listner after *Prodigies*, and never hears of a *Whale*, or a *Comet*, but he apprehends some sudden *Revolution* in the State, and looks upon a *Groaning-board*, or a *speaking-head*, as fore-runners of the *Day* of *Judgment*. He is a great Lover of the King, but a bitter Enemy to all about him, and thinks it impossible for him to have any but *Evil Counsellors*, and though he be very zealous for the

Government, yet he never finds any thing in it but *Grievances* and *Miscarriages* to declaim upon. He is a Well-wisher to the *Church*, but he is never to be reconcil'd to the *Bishops* and *Clergy*, and rails most inveterately at the *Act* of *Uniformity*. He hates *Persecution* implacably, and contends furiously for *Moderation*, and can scarce think well of the *Toleration*, because it is an Act of the State. He professes himself of the *Church* of *England*, pretends to like the Worship of it, but he goes to Meetings in spight to the *Parson* of his *Parish*. His *Conscience* is very tender and scrupulous in Matters of Ceremony, but it is as steely and tough as Brawn behind his Counter, and can digest any Sin of Gain. He lodges at home, but he lives at the *Coffee-house*. He converses more with *News Papers*, *Gazettes* and *Votes*, than with his *Shop Books*, and his constant Application to the *Publick* takes him off all Care for his *Private Concern*. He is always settling the *Nation*, yet cou'd never manage his own *Family*. He is a mighty Stickler at all *Elections*, and tho' he has no *Vote*, thinks it impossible any thing shou'd go right unless he be there to Bawl for it. His business is at *Home*, but his thoughts are in *Flanders*, and he is earnestly investing of Towns till the *Sheriff's Officers* beleaguer his Doors. He is busie in forcing of *Counterscarps*, and storming of *Breaches*, while his *Creditors* take his *Shop* by surprize, and make Plunder of his *Goods*. Thus by mending the *State*, He marrs his own *Fortune;* and never leaves talking of the *Laws* of the *Land*, till the Execution of 'em silence him.

ANONYMOUS

Pecuniae Obediunt Omnia Money Does Master all
Things, A Poem Shewing the Power and Influence
of Money over all Arts, Sciences, Trades, Professions,
and ways of Living, in this Sublunary World. . . .
York, . . . 1696. 8vo.

The promise in the title is here fairly fulfilled, for the
volume contains 162 satirical pieces, written in lively
doggerel verse. A good many of these border on the
character-form.

George Wither's complaint of the dishonest bookseller,
made seventy years before, is still heard, and not without
ample reason, 'Good God ! how many dung-botes full
of fruitles Volumnes doe they yearely foyst upon his
Majesties subjectes, by lying Titles, insinuations, and
disparaging of more profitable Books.'

On Joyners and Carpenters

JOYNERS and Carpenters a prey will make
Of you when they a peece of work do take,
If you in Timber-measure have no skill,
Then they strange storyes unto you will tell,
Make you believe more Timber they must have
By far than such a peece of work doth crave,
If they perceive you've Knowledge in the thing,
Then their Contriv'd design about to bring,
They tell you Nails and pins are in their task,
So they can not abate of what they ask,
If you're not willing such a Summe to pay,
They tell you then, they'l work with you by day.
If you agree but either way, O then,
They think themselves for that time, happy Men,

348

For many Idle day-workes then you'l have,
Whether by day or Task, you'l nothing save,
For they're Resolv'd good wages to bring in,
And tho unjustly got they think't no Sin,
Money's the Siren, charmes their Eares and hearts,
Her to acquire, they'l practice all their Arts.

On Book-Sellers

The Book-Seller, for ready Cash, will sell
For as small profit, as another will,
But then you must take special Care and look,
You no new Title, have to an Old Book.
For they new Title-pages often paist,
Unto a Book, which purposely is plac'd,
Setting it forth to be th' Second Edition,
The third, or Fourth, with 'mendments and
    Addition,
But when you come, for to peruse and look,
You will not find one word in all the Book,
Put either in or out, or yet Amended,
For that's a thing which never was intended
By th' Authour, but when e'er a Book doth fail
This is their Trick, to quicken up the Sale,
But when a new Edition comes indeed,
From all the Old Books, which they have, with
    speed
The Title-Pages then, they often tear,
And new ones in their places fixed are,
And have the Confidence to put to sale,
Such Books for new, they know are old and stale,
And so the Buyer, if he don't descry,
Will have a Cheat put on him purposely,
And when an Authours Books do bravely sell,
As those of th' whole duty of Man, do well,

And others, then to gain a Book a Fame
They'l set it forth, under such Authours Name,
Prefixing an Epistle to such Tract,
Declaring to the Reader matter of Fact,
How and by whom, the same was brought to light,
And who hath had the view thereof and Sight,
How worthy the same Book is of the press
And reasons why, it's publisht in such dress,
With bantering stuff, to make the Coppy sell,
Which pollicies they think, do wondrous well. . . .

On Common Swine-herds

THE Common Swine-herds course, is every Morn,
To go about the Town, and wind his horn,
Then People let their Hoggs go out at large,
And th' Swine-herd takes them all into his charge,
And into th' Fields he drives them day by day,
And there attends on them, the time they stay,
And when some signes of Rain or stormes appear,
Unto some ditch or Hedge, he then draws near,
And under Banks does sculke, till Night does come,
Then's Army he draws up, and Marches home,
And thus poor man, he spends his Slavish life,
Some Money to procure, for him and's Wife,
And Family, and tho it be but small,
He gets, it's better far, than none at all;
A little Money brings him some Relief,
But none at all, affords him nought but grief :
So when his Fair is mean, he ne'er complains,
But shapes his Mind according to his Means.

JEAN DE LA BRUYÈRE (1645-1696)

The Characters, or the Manners of the Age. By
    Monsieur De La Bruyère, . . . made English by
    several hands. . . . London, . . . 1699.

[The ' Blockhead ' is extracted from *Of Society and
Conversation*, ' Children ' from the essay *Of Man*.]

' With La Bruyère character became a synonym for
portrait.'

Portraits are scattered freely in his sixteen chapters,
which are a medley of anecdotes, portraits, and general
reflections and maxims bearing, all of them, on the
' manners of the age.' It is art, and not chance, that has
ruled their order. The complete chapters are pleasant
to read ; the thought follows on easily enough from, to
take one grouping, narrative to reflection, and then to a
vivid portrait that symbolises the drift of the essay. A
certain bitterness is felt, but balanced as it is, by shrewd
common-sense, and an underlying sympathy, it is not
otherwise than stimulating.

La Bruyère was well known to Steele and Addison,
and their introduction of this new type of portrait-character
straight from France, with its attractive hint of personal
application suggested by the use of classical names as
pseudonyms, gave sufficient fresh vitality to the English
character to carry it through what still seems to be the
last stage of its development in the periodical essay.

A Vain Blockhead

WHO that keeps much company can promise
himself to avoid meeting certain vain Blockheads,
who are light, familiar and positive. These are
the Speaking Men in all Conversation, and they
compel every one else to hear them. They are
heard in the Antichamber. They enter without

351

Interruption: They continue their Tales without any consideration for such as come in, or go out, or for the rank or quality of the people who make up the Company. They silence him that dares to begin a piece of News, that they may tell it after their own fashion, which to be sure is the best. They had it of *Zamet*, *Raccelay*, or *Conchini*, whom they name familiarly without their Title, tho they never knew 'em, or spoke to 'em in their Lives: They get themselves up sometimes to the best Man in the Company, to gratify him with something new, which no body else knows. They whisper it, and for a world will suffer none but him to partake on't. They hide Names to disguise the Story, and prevent Application. There are some things they must not tell, and some persons whom they cannot name: Their words are engaged to the contrary, 'tis a mystery, a secret of the last importance. Shou'd you ask it, you wou'd demand an impossibility; for whatever you imagine, they are equally ignorant of both persons and actions.

Children

THERE seems to be but one character of Childhood: The Manners at that age is in all much the same, and it must be with a very nice observation, that you can perceive a difference. It augments with Reason, because with it the Passions and Vices increase, which make men so unlike one another, and so contrary to themselves.

Children have in their childhood what old men lose, Imagination and Memory, which are very useful to them in their little sports and amusements; by these helps they repeat what they have heard, and mimick what they see done. By these they work after others, or invent themselves a thousand little things to divert them: Make Feasts, and entertain themselves with good chear, are transported into Inchanted Palaces and Castles, have rich equipages, and a train of followers, lead Armies, give Battel, and rejoyce in the pleasure of Victory, talk of Kings and greatest Princes, are themselves Kings, have Subjects, possess Treasures, which they make of Leaves, Boughs, Shells or Sand; and what they are ignorant of in the following part of their lives. They know at this Age how to be arbiters of their fortune, and masters of their own happiness.

There are no exterior vices, or bodily defects, which are not perceiv'd by Children. They strike 'em at first sight, and they know how to express 'em in agreeable words. Men could not be more happy in their terms; but when they become men, they are loaded in their turn with the same imperfections, and are themselves mock'd.

'Tis the only care of Children to find out their Masters weakness, and the weakness of those to whom they must be subject; when they have found it, they get above 'em, and usurp an Ascendant over them, which they never part with; for what depriv'd them of their Superiority, will keep them from recovering it.

Idleness, Negligence, and Laziness, Vices so natural to Children, are not to be seen in 'em while they are at play: They are then lively, heedful, exact, lovers of rule and order, never pardon one another the least faults: Begin again several times if but one thing is wanting : Certain presages that they may hereafter neglect their duty, but will forget nothing that can promote their pleasure.

To Children, Gardens, Houses, Furniture, Men and Beasts appear great. To Men, the things of the world, and I dare say, for the same reason, because they are little.

ALEXANDER POPE (1688-1744)

Windsor-Forest. . . . By Mr. Pope. . . . London :
    . . . 1713. fol.

This fine sketch is one of those romantic passages of
which there are a fair number in Pope's early work.
Their significance as an element in his genius is discussed
in Professor J. W. Mackail's Leslie Stephen lecture on
Pope (1919), where is also collected a delightful group
of these ' might-have-beens.'

The Happy Man

Happy the Man . . . .
Whom Nature charms, and whom the Muse
    inspires,
Whom humbler Joys of home-felt Quiet please,
Successive Study, Exercise and Ease.
He gathers Health from Herbs the Forest yields,
And of their fragrant Physick spoils the Fields :
With Chymic Art exalts the Min'ral Pow'rs,
And draws the Aromatick Souls of Flow'rs.
Now marks the Course of rolling Orbs on high ;
O'er figur'd Worlds now travels with his Eye.
Of ancient Writ unlocks the learned Store,
Consults the Dead, and lives past Ages o'er.
Or wandring thoughtful in the silent Wood,
Attends the Duties of the Wise and Good,
T' observe a Mean, be to himself a Friend,
To follow Nature, and regard his End.
Or looks on Heav'n with more than mortal Eyes,
Bids his free Soul expatiate in the Skies,
Amidst her Kindred Stars familiar roam,
Survey the Region, and confess her Home !

STEELE AND ADDISON

The Tatler. By Isaac Bickerstaff Esq. 1709-11. fol. [nos. 21, 204, 29, 165, 158].

The Spectator. 1711-12 and 1714. fol. [nos. 77, 108, 354].

The last stage of the history of the ' character ' was begun by Steele and Addison. They wrote the character no longer as an end in itself, and in this sense its story was over. Taking, as he said, what he thought fit from France, Steele adopted La Bruyère's form of the essay, and thus once more ' characters ' were used as illustrations of themes wider than themselves. Steele's main literary interest was in life and manners, and he regarded the character not as a dispassionate sketch of a type, but rather as a means of portraying the qualities of individuals. When, for instance, he draws his ' Gentleman,' his motive is his enthusiasm for an ideal which he wishes to make clear to his middle-class audience in the coffee-houses. He contrasts his Sophronius with those who have not the good sense to approach this ideal, but remain half-developed as ' pretty fellows.' The sketch is drawn with a sympathy that makes the reader feel the ' sweet disposition ' attributed to Sophronius to be the author's own.

The ' character ' of Steele and of Addison refers predominantly to the individual ; at last, to ' draw character ' can be an accurate connotation of the term.

Menalcas is one of Budgell's contributions to the *Spectator*. He was a cousin of Addison's whose rooms he shared towards the end of Queen Anne's reign. His translation of Theophrastus appeared in 1714, and was highly praised by Addison in *The Lover*.

THE TATLER
STEELE

A Gentleman, or Man of Conversation

It is generally thought, That Warmth of Imagination, quick Relish of Pleasure, and a Manner

356

of becoming it, are the most essential Qualities for forming this Sort of Man. But any one that is much in Company will observe, That the Height of good Breeding is shown rather in never giving Offence, than in doing obliging Things. Thus, he that never shocks you, tho' he is seldom entertaining, is more likely to keep your Favour, than he who often entertains, and sometimes displeases you. The most necessary Talent therefore in a Man of Conversation, which is what we ordinarily intend by a Fine Gentleman, is a good Judgment. He that has this in Perfection, is Master of his Companion without letting him see it, and has the same Advantage over Men of any other Qualifications whatsoever, as one that can see would have over a blind Man of Ten times his Strength. This is what makes *Sophronius* the Darling of all who converse with him, and the most Powerful with his Acquaintance of any Man in Town. By the Light of this Faculty, he acts with great Ease and Freedom among the Men of Pleasure, and acquits himself with Skill and Dispatch among the Men of Business. This he performs with so much Success, that, with as much Discretion in Life as any Man ever had, he neither is, nor appears, Cunning. But as he does a good Office, if he ever does it, with Readiness and Alacrity; so he denies what he does not care to engage in, in a Manner that convinces you, that you ought not to have ask'd it. His Judgment is so good and unerring, and that accompanied with so chearful a Spirit, that his Conversation is a continual Feast, at which he helps some, and is help'd by others, in such a Manner, that the Equality of Society is perfectly kept up, and every Man obliges as much as he is oblig'd: For it is the greatest and justest Skill in a Man of Superior Understanding, to know how to be on a Level with his Companions. This sweet Disposition runs through all the Actions of *Sophronius*, and makes his Company desir'd by Women, without being envy'd by Men. *Sophronius* would be as just as he is if there were no Law; and would be as discreet as he is, if there were no such Thing as Calumny.

Tom. Courtly

Tom. Courtly, who is the Pink of Courtesy, is an Instance of how little Moment an undistinguishing Application of Sounds of Honour are to those who understand themselves. *Tom* never fails of paying his Obeisance to every Man he sees, who has Title or Office to make him conspicuous; but his Deference is wholly given to outward Considerations. I who know him, can tell within half an Acre, how much Land one man has more than another by *Tom's* Bow to him. Title is all he knows of Honour, and Civility of Friendship. For this Reason, because he cares for no Man living, he is religiously strict in performing what he calls his Respects to you. To this End he is very learned in Pedigree, and will abate something in the Ceremony of his Approaches to a Man, if he is in any doubt about the bearing of his Coat of Arms. What is the most pleasant of all his Character is, that he acts with a sort of Integrity in these Impertinencies; and tho' he would not do any Man any solid Kindness, he is wonderfully just and careful not to wrong his Quality. But as

Integrity is very scarce in the World, I cannot forbear having a Respect for the Impertinent: It is some Virtue to be bound by any Thing. *Tom.* and I are upon very good Terms for the Respect he has for the House of *Bickerstaff.* Tho' one cannot but laugh at his serious Consideration of Things so little essential, one must have a Value even for a frivolous good Conscience.

A Critick

IT's a particular Observation I have always made, that of all Mortals, a Critick is the silliest; for by inuring himself to examine all Things, whether they are of Consequence or not, he never looks upon any Thing but with a Design of passing Sentence upon it; by which Means, he is never a Companion, but always a Censor. This makes him earnest upon Trifles, and dispute on the most indifferent Occasions with Vehemence. If he offers to speak or write, that Talent which should approve the Work of the other Faculties, prevents their Operation. He comes upon Action in Armour; but without Weapons: He stands in Safety; but can gain no Glory. . . . A thorough Critick is a Sort of Puritan in the polite World. As an Enthusiast in Religion stumbles at the ordinary Occurrences of Life, if he cannot quote Scripture Examples on the Occasion; so the Critick is never safe in his Speech or Writing, without he has among the celebrated Writers an Authority for the Truth of his Sentence.

Addison

A Critick

[Addison, in a later paper, supplements Steele's acute remarks.]

This in the common Acceptation of the Word is one that, without entring into the Sense and Soul of an Author, has a few general Rules, which like Mechanical Instruments he applies to the Works of every Writer; and as they quadrate with them, pronounces the Author perfect or defective. He is Master of a certain Set of Words, as Unity, Style, Fire, Flegm, Easie, Natural, Turn, Sentiment, and the like, which he varies, compounds, divides, and throws together in every Part of his Discourse, without any Thought or Meaning. The Marks you may know him by are, an elevated Eye, and dogmatical Brow, a positive Voice, and a Contempt for every Thing that comes out, whether he has read it or not. He dwells altogether in Generals; he praises or dispraises in the Lump; he shakes his Head very frequently at the Pedantry of Universities, and bursts into Laughter when you mention an Author that is not known at *Will's*. He hath formed his Judgment upon *Homer*, *Horace*, and *Virgil*, not from their own Works, but from those of *Rapin* and *Bossu*. He knows his own Strength so well, that he never dares praise any Thing in which he has not a *French* Author for his Voucher.

Book-Pedants

Tom Folio is a Broker in Learning, employed to get together good Editions, and stock the

Libraries of great Men. There is not a Sale of
Books begins till *Tom Folio* is seen at the Door.
There is not an Auction where his name is not
heard, and that too in the very Nick of Time, in
the Critical Moment, before the last decisive Stroke
of the Hammer. There is not a Subscription goes
forward, in which *Tom* is not privy to the first
rough Draught of the Proposals; nor a Catalogue
printed, that doth not come to him wet from the
Press. He is an universal Scholar, so far as the
Title-Page of all Authors, knows the Manuscripts
in which they were discovered, the Editions
through which they have passed, with the Praises
or Censures which they have received from the
several Members of the Learned World. He has
a greater Esteem for *Aldus* and *Elzevir*, than for
Virgil and *Horace*. If you talk of *Herodotus*,
he breaks out into a Panegyrick upon *Harry
Stephans*. He thinks he gives you an Account
of an Author, when he tells you the subject he
treats of, the Name of the Editor, and the Year
in which it was printed. Or if you draw him
into further Particulars, he cries up the Goodness
of the Paper, extols the Diligence of the Corrector,
and is transported with the Beauty of the Letter.
This he looks upon to be sound Learning and sub-
stantial Criticism. As for those who talk of the
Fineness of Style, and the Justness of Thought,
or describe the Brightness of any particular Passages; nay, tho' they write themselves in the Genius
and Spirit of the Author they admire, *Tom* looks
upon them as Men of superficial Learning, and
flashy Parts. . . .

There is another kind of Pedant, who, with all

Tom Folio's Impertinences, hath greater Superstructures and Embellishments of *Greek* and *Latin*, and is still more insupportable than the other, in the same Degree as he is more learned. Of this Kind very often are Editors, Commentators, Interpreters, Scholiasts, and Criticks; and in short, all Men of deep Learning without common Sense. These Persons set a greater Value on themselves for having found out the Meaning of a Passage in *Greek*, than upon the Author for having written it; nay, will allow the Passage it self not to have any Beauty in it, at the same Time that they would be considered as the greatest Men of the Age for having interpreted it. They will look with Contempt upon the most beautiful Poems that have been composed by any of their Contemporaries; but will lock themselves up in their Studies for a Twelvemonth together, to correct, publish, and expound, such Trifles of Antiquity as a modern Author would be contemn'd for. Men of the strictest Morals, severest Lives, and the gravest Professions, will write Volumes upon an idle Sonnet that is originally in *Greek* or *Latin;* give Editions of the most Immoral Authors, and spin out whole Pages upon the various Readings of a lewd Expression. All that can be said in Excuse for them, is, That their Works sufficiently show they have no Tast of their Authors; and that what they do in this kind, is out of their great Learning, and not out of any Levity or Lasciviousness of Temper.

A Pedant of this Nature is wonderfully well described in Six Lines of *Boileau*, with which I shall conclude his Character.

Un Pêdant enyvré de sa vaine science,
Tout herisse de Grec, tout bouffi d'arrogance,
Et qui de mille Auteurs retenus mot pour mot,
Dans sa tête entassez n'a souvent fait qu'un Sot,
Croit qu'un Livre fait tout, & que sans Aristote
La Raison ne voit goute, & le bon Sens radote.

BUDGELL, STEELE AND ADDISON

Eustace Budgell

Menalcas, the absent Man

MONSIEUR BRUYÈRE has given us the Character of *an absent Man*, with a great deal of Humour, which he has pushed to an agreeable Extravagance; with the Heads of it I shall conclude my present Paper.

'*Menalcas* (says that excellent Author) comes down in a Morning, opens his Door to go out, but shuts it again, because he perceives that he has his Night-cap on; and examining himself further finds that he is but half shaved, that he has stuck his Sword on his right side, that his Stockings are about his Heels, and that his Shirt is over his Breeches. When he is dress'd he goes to Court, comes into the Drawing-room, and walking bolt upright under a branch of Candle-sticks his Wigg is caught up by one of them, and hangs dangling in the Air. All the Courtiers fall a laughing, but *Menalcas* laughs louder than any of them, and looks about for the Person that is the Jest of the Company. Coming down to the Court-gate, he finds a Coach, which taking for his own, he whips into it, and the Coachman drives off, not doubting but he carries his Master. As soon as he stops, *Menalcas* throws himself out of the Coach, crosses the Court, ascends the Stair-case, and runs thro' all the Chambers with the greatest Familiarity, reposes himself on a Couch, and fancies himself at home. The Master of the House at last comes in, *Menalcas* rises to receive him, and desires him to sit down; he talks, muses, and then talks again. The Gentleman of the House is tired and amazed; *Menalcas* is no less so, but is every moment in hopes that his impertinent Guest will at last end his tedious Visit. Night comes on, when *Menalcas* is hardly undeceived.

' When he is playing at Backgammon, he calls for a full Glass of Wine and Water; 'tis his turn to throw, he has the Box in one Hand and his Glass in the other, and being extreamly dry, and unwilling to lose Time, he swallows down both the Dice, and at the same time throws his Wine into the Tables. He writes a Letter and flings the Sand into the Ink-bottle; he writes a second, and mistakes the Superscription : A Noble-man receives one of them, and upon opening it reads as follows. *I would have you, honest Jack, immediately upon the Receipt of this, take in Hay enough to serve me the Winter.* His Farmer receives the other, and is amazed to see in it, *My Lord, I received your Grace's Commands with an intire Submission to——* If he is at an Entertainment, you may see the Pieces of Bread continually multiplying around his Plate : 'Tis true, the rest of the Company want it, as well as their Knives and Forks, which *Menalcas* does not let them keep long. Sometimes in a Morning he puts his whole Family in an hurry, and at last goes out without being able to stay for his Coach or Dinner; and for that Day you may see him in every part of the Town, except the very Place where he had appointed to be upon a Business of Importance. You would often take him for every thing that he is not; for a Fellow quite Stupid, for he hears nothing; for a Fool, for he talks to himself, and has an hundred Grimaces and Motions with his Head, which are altogether involuntary; for a proud Man, for he looks full upon you, and takes no notice of your Saluting him : The Truth on't is, his Eyes are open, but he makes no use of them, and neither sees you, nor any Man, nor any thing else. He came once from his Country-House, and his own Footmen undertook to rob him, and succeeded : They held a Flambeau to his Throat, and bid him deliver his Purse; he did so, and coming home told his Friends he had been robbed; they desire to know the Particulars, Ask my servants, says *Menalcas*, for they were with me.'

Addison

Will Wimble

Will. Wimble is younger Brother to a Baronet, and descended of the ancient Family of the *Wimbles*. He is now between Forty and Fifty; but being bred to no Business and born to no Estate, he generally lives with his elder Brother as Superintendent of his Game. He hunts a Pack of Dogs better than any Man in the Country, and is very famous for finding out a Hare. He is extremely well versed in all the little Handicrafts of an idle Man : He makes a *May*-fly to a Miracle; and furnishes the whole Country with Angle-Rods. As he is a good-natur'd officious Fellow, and very much esteemed upon Account of his Family, he is a welcome Guest at every House, and keeps up a good Correspondence among all the Gentlemen about him. He carries a Tulip-Root in his Pocket from one to another, or exchanges a Puppy between a couple of Friends that live perhaps in the opposite Sides of the County. *Will.* is a particular Favourite of all the young Heirs, whom he frequently obliges with a Net that he has weaved, or a Setting-dog that he has *made* himself: He now and then presents a Pair of Garters of his own knitting to their Mothers or Sisters, and raises a great deal of Mirth among them, by enquiring as often as he meets them *how they wear?* These Gentleman-like Manufactures and obliging little Humours, make *Will.* the Darling of the Country.

Richard Steele

A Devotée

A *Devotée* is one of those who disparage Religion by their indiscreet and unseasonable Introduction of the mention of Virtue on all Occasion: She professes she is what no Body ought to doubt she is, and betrays the Labour she is put to, to be what she ought to be with Chearfullness and Alacrity. She lives in the World, and denies her self none of the Diversions of it, with a constant Declaration, how insipid all things in it are to her. She is never her self but at Church; there she displays her Vertue, and is so fervent in her Devotions, that I have frequently seen her Pray her self out of Breath. While other young Ladies in the House are dancing, or playing at Questions and Commands, she reads aloud in her Closet. She says all Love is ridiculous, except it be coelestial; but she speaks of the Passion of one Mortal to another with too much Bitterness, for one that had no Jealousy mixed with her Contempt of it. If at any Time she sees a Man warm in his Addresses to his Mistress, she will lift up her Eyes to Heaven and cry, What Nonsense is that Fool talking? Will the Bell never ring for Prayers? We have an eminent Lady of this Stamp in our County, who pretends to Amusements very much above the rest of her Sex. She never carrys a white shock Dog with Bells under her Arm, nor a Squirrel, or Dormouse, in her Pocket, but always an abridg'd Piece of Morality to steal out when she is sure of being observed. When she went to the famous Ass-Race (which I must confess was but an odd Diversion to be encouraged by People of Rank and Figure) it was not, like other Ladies, to hear those poor Animals bray, nor to see Fellows run naked, or to hear Country Squires in bob Wigs and white Girdles make love at the Side of a Coach, and cry Madam this is dainty Weather. Thus she described the Diversion; for she went only to pray heartily that no body might be hurt in the Crowd, and to see if the poor Fellows Face, which was distorted with Grinning, might any Way be brought to it self again. She never chats over her Tea, but covers her Face, and is supposed in an Ejaculation before she taste a Sup. This ostentatious Behaviour is such an Offence to true Sanctity, that it disparages it; and makes Virtue not only unamiable but also ridiculous. The sacred Writings are full of Reflexions which abhor this kind of Conduct; and a *Devotée* is so far from promoting

Goodness, that she deters others by her Example.
Folly and Vanity in one of these Ladies, is like
Vice in a Clergyman; it does not only debase him-
self, but makes the inconsiderate Part of the
World think the worse of Religion.

WILLIAM LAW (1686-1761)

A Serious Call To A Devout and Holy Life. . . .
London : . . . 1729. 8vo.

In his *Serious Call* Law uses very effectively for his purpose some of the character-devices of the *Tatler* and *Spectator* for making vivid his ethical conceptions. He declares ' if you are only told in the gross, of the folly and madness of a life devoted to the world, it makes little or no impression upon you ; but if you are shown how such people live every day ; . . . this would be an affecting sight. . . . So that *characters* of this kind . . . are no where more proper than in books of devotion, and practical piety.'

His style is clear, and the choice of detail is frequently Theophrastian in its objectivity and power of observation. A title may be very misleading. The *Holy and Profane State* is an example, for it is one of the most truly amusing of books. The *Serious Call* provides too, if in a less degree, a similarly pleasant surprise.

Flavia. The imprudent use of an estate

IF any one asks *Flavia* to do something in charity, if she likes the person who makes the proposal, or happens to be in a right *temper*, she will toss him *half* a *crown* or a *crown*, and tell him, if he knew what a *long Milliner's bill* she had just received, he would think it a great deal for her to give. A *quarter* of a year after this, she hears a *sermon* upon the *necessity* of charity; she thinks the man preaches well, that it is a very *proper* subject, that people *want* much to be put in mind of it; but she applies nothing to herself, because she remembers that she gave a *crown* some time ago, when she could so ill spare it.

As for *poor* people themselves, she will admit

370

of no complaints from them; she is very positive they are all *cheats* and *lyars*, and will say any thing to get relief, and therefore it must be a sin to encourage them in their evil ways.

You would think *Flavia* had the tenderest conscience in the world, if you was to see, how *scrupulous* and apprehensive she is of the guilt and danger of *giving* amiss.

She buys all books of *wit* and *humour*, and has made an expensive collection of all our *English Poets*. For she says, one cannot have a *true taste* of any of them, without being very conversant with them all.

She will sometimes read a *book* of *Piety*, if it is a short one, if it is much commended for *stile* and *language*, and she can tell where to *borrow* it. *Flavia* is very *idle*, and yet very fond of *fine work*: this makes her often *sit* working in *bed* until *noon*, and be told many a *long story* before she is up; so that I need not tell you, that her morning devotions are not *always* rightly performed.

Flavia would be a *miracle* of Piety, if she was but half so careful of her soul, as she is of her body. The rising of a *pimple* in her face, the sting of a *gnat*, will make her keep her room two or three days, and she thinks they are very *rash* people, that don't take care of things in time. This makes her so over-careful of her *health*, that she never thinks she is well enough; and so *over indulgent*, that she never can be really well. So that it costs her a great deal in *sleeping*-draughts and *waking*-draughts, in *spirits* for the head, in *drops* for the nerves, in *cordials* for the stomach, and in *saffron* for her *tea*.

If you visit *Flavia* on the *Sunday*, you will always meet *good company*, you will know what is doing in the world, you will hear the last *lampoon*, be told who wrote it, and who is meant by every name that is in it. You will hear what *plays* were acted that week, which is the finest song in the *opera*, who was intolerable at the last assembly, and what games are most in fashion. *Flavia* thinks they are *Atheists* that play at *cards* on the *Sunday*, but she will tell you the *nicety* of all the games, what *cards* she held, how she *play'd* them, and the *history* of all that happened at *play*, as soon as she comes from *Church*. If you would know who is *rude* and *ill-natur'd*, who is *vain* and *foppish*, who lives too *high*, and who is in *debt*. If you would know what is the quarrel at a *certain house*, or who and who are in *love*. If you would know how late *Belinda* comes home at night, what *cloaths* she has bought, how she loves *compliments*, and what a long story she told at such a place. If you would know how cross *Lucius* is to his *wife*, what ill-natured things he says to her, when *no body* hears him; if you would know how they hate one another in their *hearts*, tho' they appear so kind in publick; you must visit *Flavia* on the *Sunday*. But still she has so great a regard for the holiness of the *Sunday*, that she has turned a poor old widow out of her house, as a *prophane wretch*, for having been found once *mending her cloaths* on the *Sunday* night.

SAMUEL JOHNSON (1709-1784)

The Rambler. . . . London : . . . 1753. (1750-1752.) fol.

The Idler. . . . London, . . . 1761. 12 mo. [This is the first collected edition ; the paper appeared 1758-60.]

The method of Johnson's characters is closer to that of the Theophrastians of the seventeenth century, than to that of the followers of La Bruyère in his own time. His characters have the effect of set descriptions, and where they are most successful—as in ' Eriphile ' in the *Rambler*, or ' Jack Whirler ' and ' Minim ' in the *Idler* — they are written with the conciseness and point of the early character-sketch, forming a decided contrast to the style of the surrounding passages. There are more characters in the *Idler* than in the *Rambler*, and they are in harmony with the lighter tone of that paper. Their English names, which replace the Latin ones in the *Rambler*, mark this change.

Under the title of ' The Peevish ' are included Johnson's two examples of that quality. ' Those who have grown old in a single State are generally found to be morose, fretful, and captious. . . . Such is the Effect of having lived without the Necessity of consulting any Inclinations but their own.'

Only the end of ' Minim ' is given here, about one-sixth of the complete essay, but it is enough to illustrate the admirably balanced style of the whole, a blend of the wisdom that is a continual delight in Johnson's work and of a pleasantly satiric wit that is more rare.

' Mr. Sober ' is a portrait of Johnson himself, and too personal to be a true ' character,' but it is, on that account, the more precious to Johnson's friends. A passage may be quoted : ' But there is one time at night when he must go home, that his friends may sleep ; and another time in the morning, when all the world agrees to shut out interruption. These are the moments of which poor

373

Sober trembles at the thought. But the misery of these tiresome intervals, he has many means of alleviating . . . his daily amusement is Chemistry. He has a small furnace, which he employs in distillation, and which has long been the solace of his life. . . . [He] sits and counts the drops as they come from his retort, and forgets that, while a drop is falling, a moment flies away.'

The Peevish

THE Irascibility of this Class of Tyrants, is generally exerted upon petty Provocations, such as are incident to Understandings not far extended beyond the Instincts of animal Life. But unhappily he that fixes his Attention on Things always before him, will never have long Cessations of Anger, because every Hour will subject him to new Disturbance. There are many Veterans of Luxury, upon whom every Noon brings a Paroxysm of Violence, Fury, and Execration; who never sit down to their Dinner without finding the Meat so injudiciously bought, or so unskilfully dressed, such Blunders in the seasoning, or such Improprieties in the Sauce, as can scarcely be expiated without Blood; and who, in the Transports of Resentment, make very little Distinctions between Guilt and Innocence, but let fly their Menaces, or growl out their Discontent upon all whom Fortune puts in their Way.

. . . . .

Eriphile has employed her Eloquence for twenty Years upon the Degeneracy of Servants, the Nastiness of her House, the Ruin of her Furniture, the Difficulty of preserving Tapestry from the Moths, and the Carelesness of the Sluts whom she employs in brushing it. It is her Business every Morning to visit all the Rooms, in Hopes of finding a Chair without its Cover, a Window shut or open contrary to her Orders, a Spot on the Hearth, or a Feather on the Floor, that the rest of the Day may be justifiably spent in Taunts of Contempt and Vociferations of Anger. She lives for no other Purpose but to preserve the Neatness of a House and Gardens, and feels neither Inclination to Vice, nor Aspiration after Virtue, while she is engrossed by the great Employment of keeping Gravel from Grass, and Wainscot from Dust. Of three amiable Nieces she has declared herself an irreconcileable Enemy to one, because she broke off a Tulip with her Hoop; to another, because she spilt her Coffee on a Turkey Carpet; and to the third, because she let a wet Dog run into the Parlour. She has broken off her Intercourse of Visits because Company makes a House dirty, and resolves to confine herself more to her own Affairs, and to live no longer in Mire by foolish Lenity and Indulgence.

Jack Whirler

Jack Whirler, whose business keeps him in perpetual motion, and whose motion always eludes his business; who is always to do what he never does, who cannot stand still because he is wanted in another place, and who is wanted in many places because he stays in none.

Jack has more business than he can conveniently transact in one house, he has therefore one habitation near Bow-Church, and another about a mile distant. By this ingenious distribution of himself between two houses, *Jack* has contrived to be found at neither. *Jack's* trade is extensive, and he has many dealers; his conversation is spritely, and he has many companions; his disposition is kind, and he has many friends. *Jack* neither forbears pleasure for business, nor omits business for pleasure, but is equally invisible to his friends and his customers; to him that comes with an invitation to a club, and to him that waits to settle an account.

When you call at his house, his Clerk tells you, that Mr. *Whirler* was just stept out, but will be at home exactly at two; you wait at a Coffee-house till two, and then find that he has been at home, and is gone out again, but left word that he should be at the *Half-moon* Tavern at seven, where he hopes to meet you. At seven you go to the Tavern. At eight in comes Mr. *Whirler* to tell you that he is glad to see you, and only begs leave to run for a few minutes, to a Gentleman that lives near the *Exchange*, from whom he will return before supper can be ready. Away he runs to the *Exchange* to tell those who are waiting for him, that he must beg them to defer the business till to-morrow, because his time is come at the *Half-moon*.

Jack's chearfulness and civility rank him among those whose presence never gives pain, and whom all receive with fondness and caresses. He calls often on his friends, to tell them that he will come again to-morrow; on the morrow he comes again to tell them how an unexpected summons hurries him away. When he enters a house, his first declaration is, that he cannot sit down; and so short are his visits, that he seldom appears to have come for any other reason but to say He must go. . . .

But overwhelmed as he is with business, his chief desire is to have still more. Every new proposal takes possession of his thoughts, he soon ballances probabilities, engages in the project, brings it almost to completion, and then forsakes it for another, which he catches with some alacrity, urges with the same vehemence, and abandons with the same coldness.

Every man may be observed to have a certain strain of lamentation, some peculiar theme of complaint on which he dwells in his moments of dejection. *Jack's* topic of sorrow, is the want of Time. Many an excellent design languishes in empty theory for want of Time. For the omission of any civilities, want of Time is his plea to others; for the neglect of any affairs, want of Time is his excuse to himself. That he wants Time he sincerely believes; for he once pined away many months with a lingering distemper, for want of Time to attend his health.

Thus *Jack Whirler* lives in perpetual fatigue without proportionate advantage, because he does not consider that no man can see all with his own eyes, or do all with his own hands; that whoever is engaged in multiplicity of business must transact much by substitution, and leave something to hazard; and that he who attempts to do all, will waste his life in doing little.

A Critick

MINIM is not so confident of his rules of Judgment as not very eagerly to catch new light from the name of the author. He is commonly so prudent as to spare those whom he cannot resist, unless, as will sometimes happen, he finds the publick combined against them. But a fresh pretender to fame he is strongly inclined to censure, 'till his own honour requires that he commend him. 'Till he knows the success of a composition, he intrenches himself in general terms; there are some new thoughts and beautiful passages, but there is likewise much which he would have advised the author to expunge. He has several favourite epithets, of which he has never settled the meaning, but which are very commodiously applied to books which he has not read, or cannot understand. One is *manly*, another is *dry*, another *stiff*, and another *flimzy;* sometimes he discovers delicacy of style, and sometimes meets with *strange expressions.*

He is never so great, or so happy, as when a youth of promising parts is brought to receive his directions for the prosecution of his studies. He then puts on a very serious air; he advises the pupil to read none but the best Authors, and, when he finds one congenial to his own mind, to study his beauties, but avoid his faults, and, when he sits down to write, to consider how his favourite Author would think at the present time on the present occasion. He exhorts him to catch those moments when he finds his thoughts expanded and his genius exalted, but to take care lest imagination hurry him beyond the bounds of Nature. He holds Diligence the mother of Success, yet enjoins him, with great earnestness, not to read more than he can digest, and not to confuse his mind by pursuing studies of contrary tendencies. He tells him, that every man has his genius, and that

Cicero could never be a Poet. The boy retires illuminated, resolves to follow his genius, and to think how *Milton* would have thought; and *Minim* feasts upon his own beneficence till another day brings another Pupil.

THE WORLD

The World, For the Year One Thousand seven
  Hundred and Fifty Three. By Adam Fitz-
  Adam. The World was all before him, where
  to chuse. Milton. London : . . . fol.

A printed slip pasted on a fly-leaf states that ' R. O.
Cambridge' wrote the paper, No. 76 of *The World*,
which consists mainly of the first two characters printed
here. It was appropriately sold at ' The Globe' in Pater-
noster Row. Price 2d.

' R. O.' tells us that he wishes to set on record this
' modern ' figure. He first warns ' the Visitor of what
he is to guard against ' when his host has a taste for landscape gardening, but that, as the latter's desires to ' improve'
his garden are often associated with a genuine wish to
impart pleasure, he will add an account of a pest, the
' captious Visitor,' by whom the host in turn may be
affected.

Formal gardening, particularly since the Restoration,
had fallen into an extravagance at which many of the
writers of the eighteenth century laughed. Pope complains

> ' The suff'ring eye inverted Nature sees
>   Trees cut to statues, statues thick as trees.'

and he advocates the specific of his time—' let Nature
never be forgot.' Unfortunately, the owners of gardens
who followed the new doctrine soon understood it to
mean that ' gardens must resemble nature ' ; and the
greater the number of varieties of nature they could crowd
into their gardens, the more evident, they believed, was
their devotion to that Goddess. Pope's own five acres
at Twickenham contained ' a shell temple, a large mount,
a vineyard, two small mounts, a bowling-green, a wilderness, a grove, an orangery, a garden-house, and kitchen-
garden.' [Sir Reginald Blomfield's *The Formal Garden
in England* gives an interesting account of this subject.]

R. O. Cambridge
An Improver

Alteration . . . [is] the first great principle of an Improver. When he shews you a plantation, it is constantly prefaced with 'Here stood a wall.' If he directs your eye over an extent of lawn, 'There, says he, we were crouded up with trees.' The lake, you are told, was the spot where stood the old stables or the kitchen-garden; and the mount was formerly a horse-pond. When you have heard this, you are next of all to know how every thing is to be altered still farther: for as the Improver himself never enjoys the present state of things, he labours to disturb the satisfaction you express, by telling you that on the mount is to be a building; that the water is to be altered in shape, size and level, and must have a cascade and a bridge; that the largest trees in the plantation must be cut down to give air and sunshine to shrubs and flowers— In short the description of what is to be, continues through the whole evening of your arrival; and when he has talked you to sleep, and it is evident that you can hear no longer, he compassionately dismisses you to rest, knowing that late hours are incompatible with his designs upon you in the morning. . . . [Nothing will avail you] against an old practised Improver: for the instant you have breakfasted, he proposes your taking a turn or two in the bowling-green for a little fresh air; to which you readily assent; and without imagining there can be any occasion for stepping out of your slippers, you advance with him to the end of the green, where a door in a sunk fence un-expectedly opens to the park. And here, as he assures you *the grass is short*, you are led through all the pleasures of unconnected variety, with this recommendation, that it is but a little way from the Palladian portico to the Gothic tower; from the Lapland to the Chinese house; or from the temple of Venus to the hermitage. By this time you are insensibly enticed to a great distance from the house; when on a sudden he shews you over the park wall a number of labourers mending the highway; and, *since you are got so far*, wishes you to go a little farther, that he may take this oppor-tunity to give a few necessary instructions, and that the road may be mended with the advantage of your opinion and concurrence. In vain do you pull out your watch; in vain remonstrate to him how late it is, or how rude it will be to make the ladies wait dinner: in vain do you try to move him by stroking your chin, and shewing him a most persuasive length of beard, or implore his compassion on your Morocco slippers, pleading that if you had expected so long a walk, you would have put on your strong shoes— He knows that if you had apprehended a walk of half the dis-tance, he never could have moved you from your easy chair; and being thoroughly sensible that it will not be in his power to get you so far again, is resolved to make his advantage of the present opportunity; so leads you to every ditch that is emptying, or brick-kiln that is reeking for him; to his barn that is to be turned into a church, or to his farm that is to be made a ruin for the sake of his prospect; till at length he brings you so late home, that you are obliged to sit down undressed to a spoilt dinner with a family out of humour.

The Captious Visitor

IF the weather be too hot, or too cold for him; if it be windy or showery; if he has slept ill the night before; if he is hungry or sick; if he is tired or sore; if he has lost a bett upon the road; if he has quarrelled with his friend; if he has been rebuked by his wife; or in short, if any thing has offended him, he is sure to take his revenge in full, by finding fault with every thing that was designed for his entertainment. In this disposition of mind, there is nothing safe but the shady gravel walk, with the few plain and necessary resting places, which leads to the undisguised farm, or the navigable river.

HE will be sure to allow you no postulatum. He absolutely denies the existence of hermits, mandarins, and the whole heathen system of divinities. He disputes the antiquity of your ruin, and the genuineness of your hermitage: nay, he will descend to cavil at the bell with which the hermit is supposed to ring himself to prayers. He is so cruel as to controvert your supposition that the new-made water is a river, though he knows it must have cost you an immense sum, and that it covers the richest meadow-ground you are master of. He leads the company to every sunk fence which you chuse should be unobserved. If he suspects a building to be new-fronted, he finds out a private way to the decayed side of it; happy if he can discover it to have been a stable or a pig-stye. His report of your place, after he has left it, is exactly of a piece with his behaviour, while there. He either describes it as a bog that will not bear a horse, or as a sand that cannot produce a blade of grass. If he finds in reality neither bog nor barren sand, his wishes supply his belief, and he labours to persuade himself and others that one of these defects is the characteristic of your soil, but that you hate to be told of it, and always deny it.

ONE cannot but admire his ingenuity in particular cases, where it has been judged impossible to find a fault. If you lead him to a knowl of uncommon verdure varied with the fortunate disposition of old oaks, commanding the most rural scenes, and, at a proper distance, the view of a large city, he shrugs up his shoulders and tells you it wants water. If your principal object be a lake, he will strain a point to report it green and stagnated; or else take the advantage of a thunderstorm to pronounce it white or yellow. If you have a stream, he laments the frequency of floods; if a tide-river, the smell of mud at low-water. He detects your painted cascade, misconstrues your inscriptions, and puns upon your motto's. Within doors he doubts if your pictures are originals, and expresses his apprehensions that your statues will bring the house down.

As I wish most sincerely to reconcile these gentlemen to each other, I shall recommend to the IMPROVER the example of a particular friend of mine. It is said in Milton, that before the angel disclosed to Adam the prospect from the hill in paradise, he

———— *purg'd with euphrasy and rue*
His visual nerve, for he had much to see:

so this gentleman (borrowing the hint from Milton, but preferring a more modern ophthalmic) upon the arrival of his VISITORS, takes care to purge their visual nerves with a sufficient quantity of CHAMPAGNE; after which, he assures me, they never SEE a fault in his IMPROVEMENTS.

ANONYMOUS

One who is never pleased

ARACHNE has accustomed herself to look only on the dark side of every object. If a new poem or play makes its appearance, with a thousand brilliances, and but one or two blemishes, she slightly skims over the passages that should give her pleasure, and dwells upon those only that fill her with dislike. If you shew her a very excellent portrait, she looks at some part of the drapery which has been neglected, or to a hand or finger that has been left unfinished. Her garden is a very beautiful one, and kept with great neatness and elegancy; but if you take a walk with her in it, she talks to you of nothing but blights and storms, of snails and caterpillars, and how impossible it is to keep it from the litter of falling leaves and worm-casts. If you sit down in one of her temples, to enjoy a delightful prospect, she observes to you, that there is too much wood, or too little water; that the day is too sunny, or too gloomy; that it is sultry, or windy; and finishes with a long harangue upon the wretchedness of our climate. When you return with her to the company, in hopes of a little cheerful conversation, she casts a gloom over all, by giving you the history of her own bad health, or of some melancholy accident that has befallen one of her daughter's children. Thus she insensibly sinks her own spirits, and the spirits of all around her, and at last discovers, she knows not why, that her friends are grave.

ANONYMOUS

One who looks on the bright side

MELISSA is the reverse of all this. By constantly habituating herself to look only on the bright side of objects, she preserves a perpetual cheerfulness in herself, which by a kind of happy contagion, she communicates to all about her. If any misfortune has befallen her, she considers it might have been worse, and is thankful to providence for an escape. She rejoices in solitude, as it gives her an opportunity of knowing herself; and in society, because she can communicate the happiness she enjoys. She opposes every man's virtues to his failings, and can find out something to cherish and applaud in the very worst of her acquaintance. She opens every book with a desire to be entertained or instructed, and therefore seldom misses what she looks for. Walk with her, though it be but on a heath or a common, and she will discover numberless beauties, unobserved before, in the hills, the dales, the broom, the brakes, and the variagated flowers of weeds and poppies. She enjoys every change of weather and of season, as bringing with it something of health or convenience. In conversation it is a rule with her never to start a subject that leads to any thing gloomy or disagreeable; you therefore never hear her repeating her own grievances, or those of her neighbours, or (what is worst of all) their faults and imperfections. If any thing of the latter kind be mentioned in her hearing, she has the address to turn it into entertainment, by changing the most odious railing into a pleasant raillery. Thus Melissa, like the bee, gathers honey from every weed; while Arachne, like the spider, sucks poison from the fairest flowers.

Mr. Moore

One who teazes with Advice

ANOTHER . . . *good sort of a man* is he, who upon every occasion, or upon no occasion at all, is teazing you with ADVICE. This gentleman is generally a very grave personage, who happening either to have out-lived his passions, or to have been formed without any, regulates all his actions by the rules of prudence. He visits you in a morning, and is sorry to hear you call those persons your friends who kept you at the King's-arms last night after the clock had struck twelve. He tells you of an acquaintance of his, of a hundred and two years old, who never was up after sun-setting, nor abed after sun-rising. He informs you of those meats which are easiest of digestion, pre-scribes watergruel for your breakfast, and harangues upon the poison of made dishes. He knows who caught a fever by going upon the water, and can tell you of a young lady who had the rheumatism in all her limbs by wearing an India persian in the middle of October. If at a jovial meeting of friends, you happen to have drank a single glass

too much, he talks to you of dropsies and inflama-
tions, and wonders that a man will buy pleasure
in an evening, at the expense of a head-ach in the
morning.   That such a person may really be a *good
sort of a man*, and that he may give his advice out
of pure humanity, I am very ready to allow; but
I cannot help thinking (and I am no advocate for
intemperance) that if it was not now and then for
giving prudence the slip, and for a little harmless
playing the fool, life would be a very insipid thing.

RICHARD CUMBERLAND (1732-1811)

The Observer : Being a Collection of Moral, Literary
and Familiar Essays. . . . London : . . . 1786-90.
5 vols. 8vo.
The first edition, 1785. 1 vol. 8vo.

Richard Cumberland's volume of periodical essays is
one of the last imitations of the ' Spectator.' The
' characters ' it contains reflect another side of his nature
than the one so much better known through his work in
sentimental comedy.

The Damper

THE business of these philosophers in society
is to check the flights and sallies of those volatile
beings, who are subject to be carried away by
imagination and fancy, or, in other words, to act
as a counterpoise against genius; of the vices of
mankind they take little notice, but they are at
great pains to correct their vanity. They have
various receipts for curing this evil; the ordinary
method is by keeping stern silence and an unmoved visage in companies which are disposed to
be chearful. This taciturnity, if well kept up,
never fails in the end to work a cure upon festivity
according to the first principle of Thales : if the
Damper looks morose, every body wonders what
the moody gentleman is displeased with, and each
in his turn suspects himself in the fault; if he
only looks wise, all are expecting when the dumb
oracle will utter, and in the mean time his silence
infects the whole circle; if the Damper seasons his
taciturnity with a shrug of the shoulders, or a

shake of the head, judiciously thrown in, when any talkative fellow raises a laugh, 'tis ten to one if the mortified wit ever opens his mouth again for that evening; if a story is told in his company, and the teller makes a slip in a date, or a name, a true *Damper* may open, provided it is done agreably to the rules of his order, by setting the story-teller right with much gravity, and adjusting the mistake so deliberately, that the spirit of the story shall be sure to evaporate, before the commentator has properly settled his correction of the text. If any lucky wit chances to say what is called *a good thing*, and the table applauds, it is a *Damper's* duty to ask an explanation of the joke, or whether that was all, and what t'other gentleman said, who was the butt of the jest, and other proper questions of the like sort. If one of the company risques a sally for the sake of good-fellowship, which is a little on the wrong side of truth, or not strictly reducible to proof, a *Damper* may with great propriety set him right in the matter of fact, and demonstrate, as clear as two and two make four, that what he has said may be mathematically confuted, and that the merry gentleman is mistaken. A *Damper* is to keep strict watch over the morals of the company, and not to suffer the least indiscretion to escape in the warmth of conviviality; on this occasion he must be ready to call to order, and to answer for his friend to the company, that he has better principles than he affects to have; that he should be sorry such and such an opinion went out against him; and that he is certain he forgot himself, when he said so and so. If any glance is made at private characters, however notorious, a *Damper* steps in with a recommendation of candour, and inveighs most pathetically against the sin of evil-speaking. He is never merry in company, except when any one in it is apparently out of spirits, and with such an one he is always exceedingly pleasant.

A *Damper* is so profest an enemy to flattery, that he never applies it in ever so small a degree even to the most diffident; he never chears a young author for fear of marring his modesty, never sinks truths because they are disagreeable, and if any one is rashly enjoying the transports of public fame on account of some successful production in art or science, the *Damper* kindly tells him what such and such a critic has scoffingly said on the occasion, and, if nothing better offers, lowers his triumphs with a paragraph from a news-paper, which his thoughtless friend might else have overlooked. He is remarkably carefull not to spoil young people by making allowances for spirits or inexperience, or by indulging them in an opinion of their persons or accomplishments. He has many excellent apothegms in his mouth ready to recommend to those, who want them, such as *to be merry and wise;—a grain of truth is better than an ounce of wit;—a fool's bolt is soon shot, but a wise man keeps his within the quiver;—he that was only taught by himself had a fool to his master;*—and many more of the like sort.

WILLIAM WORDSWORTH
(1770-1850)

Oxford Edition. The Poetical Works. . . . Edited by
Thomas Hutchinson, M.A. . . . London, . . .
1904. 8vo.

The external occasion of this piece was the death of
Nelson in October, 1805, and the memory of the poet's
brother John, who was wrecked with his ship in February
of the same year. But very little has a poem to do with
an external cause.

In 1802 the poet had invoked Milton, calling for an
heroic soul in England's need. The answer came to him
in this poem. The ' citizen of Zion ' in Psalm 15, the
' Godly Man ' described by Francis Thynne, Wotton's
' Character of a happy life,' and Crashaw's ' A Man '
are other expressions of ' an ideal man.' Thynne's
' epigram,' included in his *Emblemes and Epigrammes*
(1600) begins.

> ' He is a godlie mann, that doth with tongue and minde
>   and sincere hart, the heavenlie god
>   adore in his true kinde,
> That liberall is to pore, that Justice doth maintaine,
>   and beinge chosen for a Judge,
>   takes noe reward for gayne.'

Character of the Happy Warrior

Who is the Happy Warrior ? Who is he
That every man in arms should wish to be ?
—It is the generous Spirit, who, when brought
Among the tasks of real life, hath wrought
Upon the plan that pleased his boyish thought :   5
Whose high endeavours are an inward light
That makes the path before him always bright :

Who, with a natural instinct to discern
What knowledge can perform, is diligent to
    learn;
Abides by this resolve, and stops not there,   10
But makes his moral being his prime care;
Who, doomed to go in company with Pain,
And Fear, and Bloodshed, miserable train!
Turns his necessity to glorious gain;
In face of these doth exercise a power   15
Which is our human nature's highest dower;
Controls them and subdues, transmutes, bereaves
Of their bad influence, and their good receives:
By objects, which might force the soul to abate
Her feeling, rendered more compassionate;   20
Is placable—because occasions rise
So often that demand such sacrifice;
More skilful in self-knowledge, even more pure,
As tempted more; more able to endure,
As more exposed to suffering and distress;   25
Thence, also, more alive to tenderness.
—'Tis he whose law is reason; who depends
Upon that law as on the best of friends;
Whence, in a state where men are tempted still
To evil for a guard against worse ill,   30
And what in quality or act is best
Doth seldom on a right foundation rest,
He labours good on good to fix, and owes
To virtue every triumph that he knows:
—Who, if he rise to station of command,   35
Rises by open means; and there will stand
On honourable terms, or else retire,
And in himself possess his own desire;
Who comprehends his trust, and to the same
Keeps faithful with a singleness of aim;   40

And therefore does not stoop, nor lie in wait
For wealth, or honours, or for worldly state;
Whom they must follow; on whose head must
    fall,
Like showers of manna, if they come at all:
Whose powers shed round him in the common
    strife,   45
Or mild concerns of ordinary life,
A constant influence, a peculiar grace;
But who, if he be called upon to face
Some awful moment to which Heaven has joined
Great issues, good or bad for human kind,   50
Is happy as a Lover; and attired
With sudden brightness, like a Man inspired;
And, through the heat of conflict, keeps the law
In calmness made, and sees what he foresaw;
Or if an unexpected call succeed,   55
Come when it will, is equal to the need:
—He who, though thus endued as with a sense
And faculty for storm and turbulence,
Is yet a Soul whose master-bias leans
To homefelt pleasures and to gentle scenes;   60
Sweet images! which, wheresoe'er he be,
Are at his heart; and such fidelity
It is his darling passion to approve;
More brave for this, that he hath much to
    love:—
'Tis, finally, the Man, who, lifted high,   65
Conspicuous object in a Nation's eye,
Or left unthought-of in obscurity,—
Who, with a toward or untoward lot,
Prosperous or adverse, to his wish or not—
Plays, in the many games of life, that one   70
Where what he most doth value must be won:

Whom neither shape of danger can dismay,
Nor thought of tender happiness betray;
Who, not content that former worth stand fast,
Looks forward, persevering to the last,   75
From well to better, daily self-surpast:
Who, whether praise of him must walk the earth
For ever, and to noble deeds give birth,
Or he must fall, to sleep without his fame,
And leave a dead unprofitable name—   80
Finds comfort in himself and in his cause;
And, while the mortal mist is gathering, draws
His breath in confidence of Heaven's applause:
This is the happy Warrior; this is He
That every Man in arms should wish to be.   85

S. T. COLERIDGE (1772-1834)

Anima Poetae ... London ... 1895. 8vo.

This embyro-character is one of the many brilliant suggestions which came to Coleridge, but remained inchoate. He is referring to *The Statesmen and Favourites of England since the Reformation.* By David Lloyd, London, 1665-70.

The Worldly-wise Man

AN UNWRITTEN CHARACTER BY COLERIDGE

I WOULD strongly recommend Lloyd's 'State-Worthies' as the manual of every man who would rise in the world. ... N.B.—I have a mind to draw a complete character of a worldly-wise man out of Lloyd. He would be highly-finished, useful, honoured, popular—a man revered by his children, his wife, and so forth. To be sure, he must not expect to be *beloved* by *one* proto-friend; and, if there be truth in reason or Christianity, he will go to hell—but, even so, he will doubtless secure himself a most respectable place in the devil's chimney-corner.

CHARLES LAMB (1775-1834)

The Last Essays of Elia. . . . London : . . . 1833. 8vo.

'The descriptions, in detached sentences, of the "Poor Relation" and the "Convalescent" are Fuller all over.' (Ainger.) It is pleasing to a character-historian, subject to the danger of seeing 'characters' everywhere, when an editor so well known and free from such preoccupations is on his side. Not only here, and in the 'Two Races of Men,' but also in other places, Lamb consciously adopted the character-devices of some of his favourite early writers. It does not lessen his originality that he should clothe his wit in the older fashions. No imitator, though he adopt all Elia's devices, can be mistaken for him, for, as intimately as ever style has been the man, his style was Lamb himself.

Poor Relations

He is known by his knock. Your heart telleth you 'That is Mr. ——.' A rap, between familiarity and respect; that demands, and, at the same time, seems to despair of, entertainment. He entereth smiling, and—embarrassed. He holdeth out his hand to you to shake, and—draweth it back again. He casually looketh in about dinner time—when the table is full. He offereth to go away, seeing you have company—but is induced to stay. He filleth a chair, and your visiter's two children are accommodated at a side table. He never cometh upon open days, when your wife says with some complacency, 'My dear, perhaps Mr. —— will drop in to-day.' He remembereth birth-days—and professeth he is fortunate to have stumbled upon one. He declareth against fish, the turbot being small—yet suffereth himself to be importuned into a slice against his first resolution. He sticketh by the port—yet will be prevailed upon to empty the remainder glass of claret, if a stranger press it upon him. He is a puzzle to the servants, who are fearful of being too obsequious, or not civil enough, to him. The guests think 'they have seen him before.' Every one speculateth upon his condition; and the most part take him to be—a tide-waiter. He calleth you by your Christian name, to imply that his other is the same with your own. He is too familiar by half, yet you wish he had less diffidence. With half the familiarity he might pass for a casual dependent; with more boldness, he would be in no danger of being taken for what he is. He is too humble for a friend, yet he taketh on him more state than befits a client. He is a worse guest than a country tenant, inasmuch as he bringeth up no rent—yet 'tis odds, from his garb and demeanour, that your guests take him for one. He is asked to make one at the whist table; refuseth on the score of poverty, and—resents being left out. When the company break up, he proffereth to go for a coach—and lets the servant go. He recollects your grandfather; and will thrust in some mean, and quite unimportant anecdote of—the family. He knew it when it was not quite so flourishing as 'he is blest in seeing it now.' He reviveth past situations, to institute what he calleth—favourable comparisons. With a reflecting sort of congratulation, he will inquire the price of your furniture; and insults you with a special commendation of your window-curtains. He is of opinion that the

urn is the more elegant shape, but, after all, there
was something more comfortable about the old
tea-kettle—which you must remember. He dare
say you must find a great convenience in having
a carriage of your own, and appealeth to your lady
if it is not so. Inquireth if you have had your
arms done on vellum yet; and did not know till
lately, that such-and-such had been the crest of the
family. His memory is unseasonable; his compliments perverse; his talk a trouble; his stay per-
tinacious; and when he goeth away, you dismiss
his chair into a corner, as precipitately as possible,
and feel fairly rid of two nuisances.

The Convalescent

IF there be a regal solitude, it is a sick bed.
How the patient lords it there! what caprices he
acts without controul! how king-like he sways his
pillow—tumbling, and tossing, and shifting, and
lowering, and thumping, and flatting, and mould-
ing it, to the ever varying requisitions of his
throbbing temples.

He changes *sides* oftener than a politician. Now
he lies full length, then half-length, obliquely,
transversely, head and feet quite across the bed;
and none accuses him of tergiversation. Within
the four curtains he is absolute. They are his
Mare Clausum.

How sickness enlarges the dimensions of a
man's self to himself! he is his own exclusive
object. Supreme selfishness is inculcated upon him
as his only duty. 'Tis the Two Tables of the Law
to him. He has nothing to think of but how to
get well. What passes out of doors, or within

them, so he hear not the jarring of them, affects him not.

A little while ago he was greatly concerned in the event of a law-suit, which was to be the making or the marring of his dearest friend. He was to be seen trudging about upon this man's errand to fifty quarters of the town at once, jogging this witness, refreshing that solicitor. The cause was to come on yesterday. He is absolutely as indifferent to the decision, as if it were a question to be tried at Pekin. Peradventure from some whispering, going on about the house, not intended for his hearing, he picks up enough to make him understand, that things went cross-grained in the Court yesterday, and his friend is ruined. But the word " friend," and the word " ruin," disturb him no more than so much jargon. He is not to think of any thing but how to get better.

What a world of foreign cares are merged in that absorbing consideration!

He has put on the strong armour of sickness, he is wrapped in the callous hide of suffering; he keeps his sympathy, like some curious vintage, under trusty lock and key, for his own use only.

He lies pitying himself, honing [1] and moaning to himself; he yearneth over himself; his bowels are even melted within him, to think what he suffers; he is not ashamed to weep over himself.

He is for ever plotting how to do some good to himself; studying little stratagems and artificial alleviations.

He makes the most of himself; dividing himself, by an allowable fiction, into as many distinct

---

[1] Whining, murmuring. See *O.E.D.*

individuals, as he hath sore and sorrowing members. Sometimes he meditates—as of a thing apart from him—upon his poor aching head, and that dull pain which, dozing or waking, lay in it all the past night like a log, or palpable substance of pain, not to be removed without opening the very scull, as it seemed, to take it thence. Or he pities his long, clammy, attenuated fingers. He compassionates himself all over; and his bed is a very discipline of humanity, and tender heart.

He is his own sympathiser; and instinctively feels that none can so well perform that office for him. He cares for few spectators to his tragedy. Only that punctual face of the old nurse pleases him, that announces his broths, and his cordials. He likes it because it is so unmoved, and because he can pour forth his feverish ejaculations before it as unreservedly as to his bed-post.

To the world's business he is dead. He understands not what the callings and occupations of mortals are; only he has a glimmering conceit of some such thing, when the doctor makes his daily call: and even in the lines of that busy face he reads no multiplicity of patients, but solely conceives of himself as *the sick man*. To what other uneasy couch the good man is hastening, when he slips out of his chamber, folding up his thin douceur so carefully for fear of rustling—is no speculation which he can at present entertain. He thinks only of the regular return of the same phenomenon at the same hour to-morrow. Household rumours touch him not. Some faint murmur, indicative of life going on within the house, soothes him, while he knows not distinctly what it is. He is not to know any thing, not to think of any thing. Servants gliding up or down the distant staircase, treading as upon velvet, gently keep his ear awake, so long as he troubles not himself further than with some feeble guess at their errands. Exacter knowledge would be a burthen to him : he can just endure the pressure of conjecture. He opens his eye faintly at the dull stroke of the muffled knocker, and closes it again without asking 'Who was it?' He is flattered by a general notion that inquiries are making after him, but he cares not to know the name of the inquirer. In the general stillness, and awful hush of the house, he lies in state, and feels his sovereignty.

HEADS OF THE PEOPLE

Heads Of The People : Or, Portraits of the English.
   Drawn by Kenny Meadows.   With Original Essays
   by Distinguished Writers.   London : . . . 1841.   8vo.
   [First series, 1840.]

   These two volumes of essays originated as letterpress to
accompany a set of characteristic English portraits drawn
by Kenny Meadows.   Douglas Jerrold was the editor,
and himself contributed fifteen essays to the first series,
and four to the second.

   It was as M. A. Titmarsh that Thackeray published
several of his own early books which he illustrated himself.

   Many of the essays in these volumes seem too old-
fashioned to be interesting to-day.   Part of Leigh Hunt's
essay on ' the omnibus conductor,' for instance, is a
character, but the type of the conductor who ' won't keep
your promised seat a minute if a last fare presents himself ;
and can't procure a candle any how if you have dropped
a shilling in the straw ' is as obsolete as his vehicle, once
the scene of so much wrangling and jollity.

Douglas Jerrold
The Money-Lender

THE legal Money-Lender is a harpy of the
longest claws : he has no more heart than a drum ;
no more blood than a cricket.   He is notwithstanding, a most respectable solicitor ; as chary of
his reputation as a housewife of a favourite piece
of cracked china ; and resents the slightest insinuation of his infamy with even alarming vigour.
Now and then he is, poor man, grossly libelled by
the press ; whereupon, he becomes one of a society
for the better protection of morals.   Though

steeped from head to sole in rascality—though a moral Ethiop—under the benign protection of the law of libel, he is the purest of the pure; yea, one of the fairest of the sons of men. It is ten to one that he has married prosperously—has caught a rich and inexperienced client—perhaps one of three orphan sisters; and is, thereby, the friend and legal adviser of the unprotected. As such, he absorbs the whole of their substance, enmeshes them in the nets of his craft, and—the process is rapid— they are beggars. That the children of affluence should have nothing to remind them of their past condition—that nothing tangible should remain to them to awaken recollections of happier days, the money-lending lawyer has been known to remove from them every painful memento, even though it were a harp or a piano. He is, nevertheless, a most respectable man; has very handsome chambers, keeps a score of clerks, and lends money from eighty to cent. per cent. His face—we draw from the life—would be inexpressive as a stale muffin, were it not for the two cat-like eyes, and thin, cruel lips, that redeem it from utter blankness. He moves stealthily as an ogre; as though haunted by the memory of a thousand acts that have written him down in the private memoranda of Lucifer. He, the Attorney Money-Lender, is admirably fitted to display the wisdom and philanthropy of the English laws. Had he lived in Spain, he would have made an excelling familiar of the Inquisition; would, with demoniacal complacency, have applied the thumbscrew, the burning pincers, and the molten lead. Born in England, bred an attorney, and adding to his professional cares the anxieties of Money-Lender, he is yet enabled to satisfy his natural and acquired lust of evil, and he therefore *gets up costs*. He has never stood at the bar of a police-office, and yet his hands are dyed with the blood of broken hearts. Under cover of the law, armed with its curious weapons, he lives a life of rapine, hoards wealth, passes for a most respectable man—for he never had a bill protested, and owes no man a shilling—and, when he dies, a tombstone will record his apocryphal virtues for the example of a future generation.

MICHAEL ANGELO TITMARSH
A Fashionable Painter

CARMINE has had the usual education of a painter in this country; he can read and write—that is, has spent years drawing the figure—and has made his foreign tour. It may be that he had original talent once, but he has learned to forget this, as the great bar to his success; and must imitate, in order to live. He is among Artists, what a dentist is among surgeons—a man who is employed to decorate the human head, and who is paid enormously for so doing. You know one of Carmine's beauties at any exhibition, and see the process by which they are manufactured. He lengthens the noses, widens the foreheads, opens the eyes, and gives them the proper languishing leer; diminishes the mouth, and infallibly tips the end of it with a pretty smile of his favourite colour. He is a personable, white-handed, bald-headed, middle-aged man now, with that grave blandness of look which one sees in so many prosperous empty-headed people. He has a collection of little stories and court gossip about Lady This, and my particular friend—Lord So-and-So, which he lets off in succession to every sitter: indeed, a most bland, irreproachable, gentleman-like man. He gives most patronising advice to young Artists, and makes a point of praising all—not certainly too much, but in a gentleman-like, indifferent, simpering way. This should be the maxim with prosperous persons, who have had to make their way, and wish to keep what they have made. They praise everybody, and are called good-natured, benevolent men. Surely no benevolence is so easy; it simply consists in lying, and smiling, and wishing everybody well. You will get to do so quite naturally at last, and at no expense of truth. At first, when a man has feelings of his own—feelings of love or of anger—this perpetual grin and good-humour is hard to maintain. I used to imagine, when I first knew Carmine, that there were some particular springs in his wig (that glossy, oily, curl crop of chestnut hair) that pulled up his features into a smile, and kept the muscles so fixed for the day. I don't think so now, and should say he grinned, even when he was asleep and his teeth were out; the smile does not lie in the manufacture of the wig, but in the construction of the brain. Claude Carmine has the organ of *don't-care-a-damnativeness* wonderfully developed; not that reckless don't-care-a-damnativeness which leads a man to disregard all the world, and himself into the bargain. Claude stops before he comes to himself; but beyond that individual member of the Royal Academy, has not a single sympathy for a single human creature. The account of his friends' deaths, woes, misfortune, or good luck, he receives with equal good-nature; he gives three splendid dinners per annum, Gunter, Dukes, Fortnum and Mason, everything; he dines out the other three hundred and sixty-two days in the year, and was never known to give away a shilling, or to advance, for one half-hour, the forty pounds per quarter wages that he gives to Mr. Scumble, who works the backgrounds, limbs, and draperies of his portraits.

He is not a good painter: how should he be; whose painting as it were never goes beyond a whisper, and who would make a general simpering as he looked at an advancing cannon-ball? but he is not a bad painter, being a keen, respectable man of the world, who has a cool head, and knows what is what. . . . New ladies in white satin, new generals in red, new peers in scarlet and ermine, and stout members of parliament, pointing to ink-stands and sheets of letter-paper, with a Turkey-carpet beneath them, a red curtain above them, a Doric pillar supporting them, and a tremendous storm of thunder and lightning lowering and flash-ing in the back ground, spring up every year, and take their due positions 'upon the line' in the academy, and send their compliments of hundreds to swell Carmine's heap of Consols. If he paints Lady Flummery, for the tenth time, in the character of the tenth muse, what need have we to say any-thing about it? The man is a good workman, and will manufacture a decent article at the best price; but we should no more think of noticing each, than of writing fresh critiques upon every new coat that Nugee or Stultz turned out.

The papers say, in reference to his picture, 'No. 591. "Full-length portrait of her Grace the Duchess of Doldrum. Carmine R.A." Mr. Carmine never fails; this work, like all others by the same Artist, is excellent:'—or, 'No. 591, &c. The lovely Duchess of Doldrum has received from Mr. Carmine's pencil ample justice; the *chiaroscuro* of the picture is perfect; the likeness admirable; the keeping and colouring have the true Titianesque gusto; if we might hint a fault, it has the left ear of the lap-dog a " little " out of drawing? '

LAMAN BLANCHARD (1803-1844)

Sketches from Life ; By the late Laman Blanchard :
    With a Memoir of the Author, by Sir Edward
    Bulwer Lytton, Bart. . . . In three volumes.
    London : . . . 1846. 8vo.

Blanchard's interest in types of human nature, suggested
in the title of these volumes, expressed itself most happily
in the character form. His essays never rise above
amiability, but in the 'characters' their style becomes
more terse and picturesque. The third volume contains
a group of character-essays, which he calls 'Portraits of
Notorious Characters,' and similar descriptions are freely
scattered in the other two volumes. In 1841 he had
contributed an amusing set of twelve *Corporation Characters* to 'Heads of the People,' reprinted separately in
1855.

It is interesting to have Thackeray's reflection on the
kindness of Blanchard's friends in a time of need, for
'M. A. Titmarsh' writes : 'The world, it is pleasant
to think, is always a good and gentle world to the gentle
and good, and reflects the benevolence with which they
regard it.' He goes on to praise Blanchard's 'jolly,
clear laughter,' and his 'wit which was always playing
and frisking about the company.' [*Fraser's Magazine*,
Mar. 1846.]

The Long-Stopper

A VERY dangerous and dread-awakening species
of the Long-stopper is he who drops in soon after
dinner and can't stay a minute. There is always
a chance that the friend who frankly owns he has
come to have out an hour's gossip with you, may
go at the end of three; but of the early departure
of him who can't possibly stop an instant, there's

no hope. If your visiter has a particularly pressing engagement elsewhere, he is sure to stay with you. If he won't take a seat at once, it's all over with you for the evening. If he keeps his hat in his hand, you may ring for your night-cap. He stands, perchance, lolling over the back of a chair for one hour and upwards, filling up a pause every ten minutes with a wilful, lying, hypocritical, 'Well, I must go,' till down he sits, tossing his hat over to the other side of the apartment, with the look, voice, action, and entire manner of a man who is not at all in a hurry, but feels himself quite at home, and is anxious that you should not put yourself out of the way the least in the world on his account. There is something that amounts to the appalling in this specimen of the tribe. He has no superior in the whole race of familiar fender-breakers. Let him once get his foot near your fireside, and he will tantalize you all the night long; not so much by staying, as by hints of the necessity of going, conjuring up a succession of sad hopes, and mocking you with a hundred visionary departures; himself a fixture, part of the furniture of the room all the time. Of all public orators, save us from him who intimates at the outset that he has risen for the purpose of 'making a few brief observations.' We don't mind a long speech much; but spare us a few brief observations, for experience teaches us that there is no end to them. So with the guest with whom time is precious; who has not a moment to stay; who dares not even sit down, because he has an affair of pressing importance on his hands!

The Penny-a-Liner

THE penny-a-liner, like Pope, is 'known by his style.' His fine Roman hand once seen may be sworn to by the most cursory observer. But though in this one respect of identity resembling Pope, he bears not in any other the least likeness to author dead or living. He has no brother, and is like no brother, in literature. Such as he was, he is. He disdains to accommodate his manner to the ever-altering taste of the times. He refuses to bow down to the popular idol, innovation. He has a style, and he sticks to it. He scorns to depart from it, to gratify the thirst for novelty. He even thinks that it improves with use, and that his pet-phrases acquire a finer point and additional emphasis upon every fresh application. Thus, in relating the last fashionable occurrence, how a noble family has been plunged into consternation and sorrow by the elopement of Lady Prudentia a month after marriage, he informs you, as though the phrase itself carried conviction to the heart, that the 'feelings of the injured husband may be more easily conceived than described.' If he requires that phrase twice in the same narrative, he consents to vary it by saying that 'they may be imagined but cannot be depicted.' In reporting an incident illustrative of the fatal effects of taking prussic acid, he states that the 'vital spark is extinct,' and that not the smallest hopes are entertained of the unfortunate gentleman's recovery. A lady's bag is barbarously stolen from her arm by 'a monster in the human form.' A thunderstorm is described as having 'visited' the metropolis, and the memory of the oldest inhabitant furnishes no parallel to the ravages of the 'electric fluid.' A new actress 'surpasses the most sanguine expectations' of the public, and exhibits talents 'that have seldom been equalled, never excelled.' A new book is not simply published, it 'emanates from the press.' On the demise of a person of eminence, it is confidently averred that he had a hand 'open as day to melting charity,' and that 'take him for all in all, we ne'er shall look upon his like again.' Two objects not immediately connected are sure to be 'far as the poles asunder'; although they are very easily brought together and reconciled in the reader's mind by the convenience of the phrase 'as it were,' which is an especial favourite, and constantly in request. He is a great admirer of amplitude of title, for palpable reasons; as when he reports, that 'Yesterday the Right Honourable Lord John Russell, M.P., his Majesty's Secretary of State for the Home Department, dined with,' &c. He is wonderfully expert in the measurement of hailstones, and in the calculation of the number of panes of glass which they demolish in their descent. He is acquainted with the exact circumference of every gooseberry that emulates the plenitude of a pumpkin; and can at all times detect a phenomenon in every private family, by simply reckoning up the united ages of its various members. But in the discharge of these useful duties, for the edification and amusement of the public, he employs, in the general course of things, but one set of phrases. If a fire can be rendered more picturesque by designating it the 'devouring element,' the devouring element rages in the

description to the end of the chapter. Once a hit
always a hit; a good thing remains good for ever;
a happy epithet is felicitous to the last. The only
variation of style that he can be prevailed upon
to attempt, he introduces in his quotations. To
these he often gives an entirely new aspect, and
occasionally, by accident, he improves upon the
originals. Of this, the following may stand as a
specimen:

> ' 'Tis not in mortals to *deserve* success;
> But we'll do more, Sempronius, we'll *com-
> mand* it.'

The Theatrical Lessee

THE theatrical lessee is a practical logician.
Being destitute of money, he enters into contracts,
binding himself to pay some fifty thousand pounds
per annum: being equally destitute of morals, he
undertakes to provide rational entertainment for a
'discerning public.' Peculiarly innocent of all
idea of the uses and objects of the stage, he
resolves upon taking the drama under his special
protection. In short, having nothing to lose, he
determines to risk all he is worth; being *Dogberry*,
he becomes constable of the watch, as the 'most
desartless man.' He regards Shakespeare as an
author properly honoured in having his statue
erected *outside* the theatre: he confesses that if
'Hamlet' were now to be offered him, an entirely
new play, he would not produce it; unless, perhaps, the author undertook to appear as the Ghost.
As an indifferently bad actor, even Shakespeare
would have a claim upon him. He evinces his

understanding of the scope and principle of the drama, when he observes, ' We don't want *literature*, we want *pieces*.' He objects to all productions that have much ' talk ' in them; they only tend to encourage the high-priced actors. First-rate performers he looks upon as necessary evils, and he engages them, one at a time, at short intervals : third-rates are his favourites, because they show by their acting that the ' regular drama sends people to sleep ; ' they *prove* that Shakespeare ' don't draw! ' That is the only point which he conscientiously struggles to establish: that the public despises excellence : and upon the truth of his proposition *his* chance of being tolerated depends. . . .

The Picture-Hunter

THERE are people who can hardly set foot out of doors in a large city without ' picking up ' a picture. Ferret is one of this fortunate set of prize-finders. Pictures are to him the sole realities of life. The only tangible things he knows of are panel and canvas, except gilt frames. To his eye the whole world presents but two colours, oil colour and water colour. The earth, as he walks upon it, seems to have a coat of varnish over it; and society, from the point whence he surveys it, is only a great work of art : a large, bold composition, in which, however, the lights are too much concentrated, and the shadows too abrupt and deep. The finest compliment he can pay to nature is to think she looks gloriously artificial; and when he sees the fiery flush of a sunset, he feels that it almost comes up to Turner. He nothing cares about the

common salt sea and mere salt sea wonders; he is
for poetry's

> '. . . painted ship
> Upon a painted ocean;'

floating on real water, as he says exultingly, like
Stanfield's! He never paused to look on a noble
scene, from hill, valley, or river, without considering how it would 'come,' when properly
reduced by the artist. No, never did he linger
over a rich and varied landscape, except to determine in his mind how it would look framed, in
an exhibition; perhaps, what it would sell for at
an auction, or how it would exchange for a Ben-
jamin West that he didn't want.

When he went to Niagara, and first stood within
view of the great fall, he said musingly, 'Ah!
I should like to have *that* in my back drawing-
room!' Were he the spectator of a scene in New-
gate, the view would excite a similar feeling; ' it
would hang extremely well opposite the window,'
between the two Websters. When he takes a
country stroll, he tells you that he went down the
lane, passed the bit of Gainsborough, till he came
to a Hofland, between the trees; and were he to
direct a stranger to the next town, he would desire
him to leave the Nasmyth on his left hand, turn
off by the Collins at the cottage, and keep on till
he saw a David Roberts before him. . . .

Patrons of art cannot dream *chefs d'œuvre* upon
their walls, and talk old masters into their galleries.
Unless they steal, or buy them, they must infallibly 'pick them up.' This is what my friend
Ferret does; this is what he came into the world
to do, and he has done nothing else. . . .

What a life has he led, and what contradictions compose his destiny! Seeking for beauty inexpressible, he has passed years amidst the squalid and reeking dens of towns and cities. For pearl, he has gone to swine. With an eye beholding, in the intensity of its inquiry, nothing less bright than the hues of Rubens, he has pried unweariedly into the innermost recesses of old brokers' shops; with a sense appreciating the seraphic forms of Guido, he has tumbled over, unloathingly, the treasures of a temple sacred to marine stores. He has, indeed, sought sunshine in the shady places.

No auction that happens to have a picture in it ever escapes his notice. He knows the contents of every public gallery, nay, every private collection in the kingdom. He is a living catalogue of the 'gems' in every dealer's hands. Mention a picture-cleaner, and he will particularise the fine specimens at that moment in his keeping. He can tell you who had the Giorgione that was for sale in Tottenham-court Road, and who bought the doubtful Titian in the Minories. . . .

It would be ludicrous, if it were not so *very* absurd, to hear him tell the truth about his prices and purchases. His boast is, that he has not, for ten years, expended five pounds upon a painting. His maxim being, that all fine pictures sell either for very large or for very small sums, he has watched the market at the latter turn; and then, profiting by his dexterous system of exchanges in other instances, he is enabled fairly to estimate his expenditure upon every separate gem. . . . 'That's good, the Wouvermans; that and the Ruysdael I got for nothing: that is, I gave a big West for them.   Here: you wouldn't think, now, that this Hobbema cost me but eleven and sixpence, with discount for ready money!   But come this way: there's a true Correggio! for which I swapped, receiving fifteen pounds to buy a frame, two villanous things, one called "Game," and the other "Fruit," which had been thrown into a lot I bought at an auction!'

My friend Ferret thus walks and talks amidst his treasures; while of mankind he knows nothing whatever, save of the few who buy and sell pictures.   To him, the ideal is actual; the forms of things are the substances.   If the soul, as some wise philosophers have suspected, ever returns to the earth it has once quitted, Ferret's will assuredly be found somewhere, looking complacently out of a gold frame, sixteen inches by eleven.

G. W. E. RUSSELL (1853-1919)

Social Silhouettes . . . London, . . . 1906.   8vo.

These interesting studies of social types, connected chiefly with the University, the professions and Parliament, suggest a new means of expression for the conception of Theophrastus whose objective view of his subject is here happily combined with the ease and fluidity of the essay. For the distinctive quality of these essays is their power of objective portraiture in the gently satiric manner of a true follower of Theophrastus.   Many regular characters could be detached from the forty-six chapters, but it would be found that the context from which they had been taken was equally Theophrastian in spirit.

The Plutocrat

THE Plutocrat is essentially a Londoner.   If he is not in London, he is at Paris or at Brighton; but he does not care much for the country.   Of course he has a country house, for that is a necessary element in his scheme of life; but he does not inhabit it very often, and, when he does, he contrives to make it look and seem exactly like a London house on a larger scale.   Bridge rages from morn till midnight; the telephone-bell tinkles without intermission, and telegrams fall like autumn leaves.   If he builds his house for himself, it reproduces the worst monstrosities of Park Lane. If he buys an old house, he commits the most shameless atrocities in the way of reconstruction, and decoration.   He stuffs the gallery of an Elizabethan manor with furniture of the French Empire, or repairs the breaches of an Edwardian ruin with Italian marble and gilds the roof of the Baron's

418

Hall. Whether his house be ancient or modern, he lives and moves and has his being by the aid of electricity—electric light, electric bells, electric baths, and electric lifts. The house is very hot, and smells overpoweringly of exotic flowers. From the drawing-room you can step into a winter-garden full of sham rockwork and tin ivy. From the walls of the dining-room Gainsboroughs and Hoppners, bought at fabulous prices from decayed gentility, look down with astonished eyes upon their new surroundings. The gardens are on an enormous scale, and the glasshouses cover acres; and the Plutocrat rejoicingly tells you the precise number of gardeners which is required to keep the place in order. The stables are beautifully ornate, with maple-wood fittings and blue tiles; the harness-room glitters like a silversmith's shop; and the Stud Groom's cottage is a villa. The curious observer will note that there are a good many more harness-horses than hacks or hunters; for the Plutocrat is not much at home on a horse, and prefers the security and dignity of a carriage. The lamented Mr. G. A. Sala declared that a Plutocrat for whom he laboured used to begin a conversation by saying, 'I have just returned from my drive. How did you get here? I suppose *you* walked.' . . .

But, when all is said and done, the Plutocrat does not really care for any kind of sport. In nine cases out of ten he is an alien or a cockney, or both, and sport is only a way of gaining admission to the social life of the county in which he fixes his abode. What he really enjoys is motoring. For him the motor must have been invented; in it he finds the realization of all his ideals. It combines every element of life which he most enjoys— luxury, ostentation, insolence, and the sense that he is envied and admired. As he does not drive the car, there is no demand on his skill or courage. It poisons the air with dust and stench. It occasionally kills an old woman or mutilates a child, but the pace is too good to admit of enquiries. It brings the glare and noise and swagger of London into the 'sweet, sincere surroundings of country life'; and, by practically annihilating distance, it makes the Kentish castle or the manor-house in the New Forest a suburb of Park Lane or Piccadilly. And this the Plutocrat calls 'sport.' He presumes to bracket it with hunting among his amusements in 'Who's Who'; and in the vivacious columns of the 'Motorist' he gains the acceptable but ill-deserved praise of 'a keen all-round sportsman,' though there is no single sport, in the sense in which that term used to be understood by English gentlemen, in which he can hold his own.

But perhaps it is when he turns his attention to politics that the Plutocrat is most offensive. He regards a seat in Parliament exactly as he regards a Sir Joshua, a tiara, a cabinet, or a villa. It exists, he wants it, and it can be bought. Such is his simple philosophy, and no one can say that it is wholly inconsistent with experience. The method is changed, but the principle remains the same as in the good old days of Shoreham and Retford and St. Albans. The Plutocrat no longer buys his votes at so much a head—the voters are too many and the results are too uncertain. But he pursues his end by subscriptions and entertainments, patronage and custom. '*I ply the gyme*,' said such an one in a burst of candour, and his notion of 'plying the gyme' was to make the constituency feel that, as long as he was member, there would be money circulating in the neighbourhood, and that every one had a chance. When the Plutocrat is pitted against a poor man the contest is too unequal to be amusing, but when Plutocrat meets Plutocrat then comes the tug of war. I remember a small tradesman in a country town saying with smug complacency: 'Both the candidates are wealthy men. The Liberal candidate is Mr. Cashington of the Stock Exchange, and the Unionist is Baron Shekelheim of South Africa. We are looking forward to a very interesting contest.' There was great significance in that epithet 'interesting.'

JOHN GALSWORTHY

A Commentary . . . London Grant Richards 1908 8vo.
[Second edition]. Duckworth & Co. 1910. 8vo.

One of the factors in Mr. Galsworthy's genius is the
Theophrastian. Like the Greek philosopher he can
crystallise his apprehension of life into human types. But
working on the large canvas of the novel, his scope is
wider, and the pictures that result are more than sketches in
outline, for they can give us the whole man—who is always
more than a type—moving in the intricate net of circumstances which constrains him. It remains true that the
interest in type, in that element which is constant in human
nature and liable to reappear on any occasion, is outstanding in Mr. Galsworthy's conception of the novel.
He makes this clear himself in his preface to the *Forsyte
Saga* (1922), for instance, ' Human nature, under its
changing pretensions and clothes, is and ever will be very
much of a Forsyte. . . .' In the course of his novels he
is fond of pointing out how typical the individual often is.

Mr. Galsworthy seems to have an idealised conception
of society lying behind and influencing his choice and
presentation of character. Some of the men whom he
portrays succeed in realising this, though many fail. He
creates them as individuals, but they wear their individuality
with a difference, for to Mr. Galsworthy their significance
depends upon their relation to his ideal world, and in
expressing his sense of this, he tends to class them according
as they are with him, or still on the other side.

In *A Commentary* we have a set of essays in which a
view of society is presented through a study of certain
individuals, at moments of their lives chosen to illustrate
a typical aspect. Mr. Galsworthy's humour is merciful,
and this has enabled him to give us balanced views of
what his penetrating insight has discovered.

Four or five of the nineteen essays are close to the

character-form, particularly 'The Careful Man,' 'Money,'
' Facts,' perhaps the terrible picture of the ' House of
Silence,' ' The Mother,' and ' Comfort.'

Facts

EACH morning a noise of poured-out water
revived him from that state in which his thoughts
were occasionally irregular. Raising his face, with
its regular nose above a regular moustache just
going grey, he asked the time. Each morning he
received the same answer, and would greet it with
a yawn. Without this opening to his day he would
not have known for certain that it had begun.
Assured of the fact, he would leap from his bed
into his bath, and sponge himself with cold, clear
water. 'Straight out of bed—never lose heat! '
Such was his saying; and he would maintain it
against every other theory of the morning tub. It
was his own discovery—a fact on which, as on all
facts, he set much store; and every morning he
kept his mind fixed on its value. Then, in that
underclothing, of which he said, ' Never wear any
other—lets the skin act! ' he would take his stand
in a chosen light before a glass, dipping in boiling
water a razor on which was written the day's name,
and without vanity inspect his face to see that it
preserved its shade of faintly mottled red against
the encroachments of the Town. Then, with a
slanting edge—'Always shave slanting'—he would
remove such hairs as seemed to him unnecessary.
If he caught himself thinking, he would go to a
bottle on the washstand and pour out a little bitter
water, which he would drink; then, seizing a pair
of Indian clubs, he would wave them. ' I believe
in Indian clubs! ' he often said. Tying his tie at

the angle he had tied it for nearly thirty years, and placing lavender water—the only scent he ever used—about his handkerchief, he would open his wife's door, and say, ' How are you, my dear? ' Without waiting for an answer he would shut it, and go down.

His correspondence was set out on his writing-table, and as he was not a stupid man he soon disposed of it; then, with his daily paper—which he had long selected out of every other—he would stand before the hearth, reading, and believing that the news he read was of a definite importance. He took care that this reading should not stimulate his thoughts. He wanted facts, and the fact that the day's facts were swallowed by the morrow's did not disturb him, for the more facts he read the better he was pleased.

After his breakfast—eaten opposite his wife, and ended with some marmalade—he would go forth at ten o'clock, and walk the two miles to the Temple. He believed in walking, wet or fine, for, as he said: ' It keeps your liver acting! '

On his way he would think of many things, such as : Whether to lay down Gruaud La Rose, 1900, or Château Margaux, 1899 ? And, though alive to its importance, he would soon decide this question, since indecision was repugnant to his nature. He walked by way of the Green Park and Thames Embankment, expanding his chest quietly, and feeling inward satisfaction. To the crossing-sweeper nearest Big Ben he gave on every day, save Saturdays, a nod, and on Saturdays sixpence; and, because he thus assisted him, he believed the man to be worthy of assistance. He passed all other crossing-sweepers without being conscious of their presence; and if they had asked for pennies would have put them down as lazy persons making an illicit living. They did not ask, however, accepting his attitude towards them as correct, from the vigour of its regularity. He walked always at the same pace, neither fast nor slow, his head erect, looking before him with an air of : I am getting there; this is salubrious!

And on getting there he looked at his watch— not because he did not know what it would tell him, but to satisfy his craving for the ascertainment of a fact. It took, he knew, thirty-two minutes between door and door.

Up the stone staircase he would pause half-way and glance through the window at a certain tree. A magpie had once built there. It had been gone now fifteen years, but the peculiar fact remained. Meeting his clerk in the dark narrow passage beyond the oaken door, he would address the young man thus: 'Mornin', Dyson. Anything fresh?' and pass on into his light and airy room, with its faint scent of Law Reports. Here, in an old Norfolk jacket, a meerschaum pipe, rarely alight, between his teeth, he would remain seated before papers of all sorts, working hard, and placing facts in order, ready for the conclusions of his chief, a man of genius, but devoid of regularity.

At one o'clock he would go out and walk some little way to lunch. When tempted to go elsewhere he would say, 'No, no! Come with me; better grub at Sim's!' He knew this for a fact —no novelty of any kind could alter it. Cigar in mouth, he would then walk for twenty minutes in the Temple Gardens, his hands behind his back, alone or with some friend, and his good-humoured laugh would frequently be heard—the laugh of a fat man; for though by careful weighing he kept his body thin, he could not weigh his soul, and having thus no facts to go by, could never check its bulk.

From two to four he would continue the arrangement of his facts, and on the rising of the Courts place them before his chief. Strong in his power of seeing them as facts with no disturbing relevance to other things, he would show a shade of patronage to that disorderly distinguished man. Then, washing with Pears' soap, and saying to his clerk, 'Evenin', Dyson; nothing that won't keep,' he would take his umbrella and walk west. And again he would reflect on many things, such as: Whether to use the iron or cleek for the approach to that last hole? and would soon decide on one or on the other.

Passing the portals of his Club, of which he used to say, 'I've belonged here twenty years; that shows you!' he would hang his hat upon a certain peg and go into the card-room, where, for small stakes that never varied, he played the game of Bridge till seven o'clock. Then in a hansom cab he would go home, resting body and brain, and looking straight before him at the backs of cabs in front. Entering his drawing-room he would go over to his wife, kiss her, and remark: 'Well, old girl, what have you been doing?' and at once relate what he himself had done, finishing thus: 'Time to dress for dinner! I've got a twist!' In a white tie and swallow tail if they were dining out, a black tie and tail-less coat if they were dining in —for these were the proved facts of suitability— he would go to his wife's room, take up one of her toilet bottles, examine the stamp on it, and tell her his programme for the morrow.

His habits in dining out were marked by regularity. A sweet or ice he never touched for fear of gout, of which he had felt twinges. He drank brandy with his coffee, not for fear of sleeplessness, which he had never had, but because he found it adjusted preceding facts more nicely than liqueurs; after champagne he would consume a glass or two of port. Some men drank claret, believing that it did less harm, but he would say : ' Port after champagne—proved it a dozen times.' For, though it was really not important to his body which he drank, it concerned his soul to make the choice, and place importance on it. When the ladies had withdrawn, he would talk on the facts of Politics and Guns, of Stocks and Women; and, chiefly in the form of stories—facts about facts. To any one who linked these facts to an idea he would remark at once : ' Exactly ! ' and, staring slightly, restore order with another fact. At last he would go home, and in the cab would touch his wife to see that she was there.

On Sundays he played golf—a game in which, armed with a fact, he hit a little fact long distances until he lodged it in a hole, when he would pick it out again and place it on a little fact and hit it off once more. And this was good for him. Returning in the train with other players of the game, he would sit silently reviewing the details

of the business, and a particularly good and pleasant look would come upon his face, with its blue
eyes, red cheeks, and fair moustache just going
grey. And suddenly he would begin speaking to
his neighbour, and tell him how at certain moments
he had hit the little fact with an unwonted force,
or an unusual gentleness.

Two days before the 12th of August he would
take his guns and wife to Scotland, where he rented
annually a piece of ground inhabited by grouse.

On arriving he would have a bath, then go out
with his keeper and a ferret to 'get his eye in';
and his first remark was always this: 'Well,
M'Nab, and how are you? Afraid I'm a bit above
myself!' And his old keeper would answer thus:
'Aye, I'm no saying but ye'll be as well for a day
on the hill.'

Each evening on returning from the moors he
would cause the dead facts to be turned out of the
pony's paniers and laid in rows before him, and,
touching them with the end of a stick so as to
make sure, he would count them up; and the more
there were of them the better he was pleased.
Then, when they were removed and hung, he
would enter their numbers in a book. And as
these numbers grew, he compared them day by
day and week by week with the numbers of each
former year; thus, according to whether they were
more or less, he could tell at any moment how
much he was enjoying life.

On his return to London he would say: 'First-
class year—five hundred brace.' Or, shake his
head and murmur: 'Two hundred and thirty brace
—a wretched year!'

Any particularly fine creature that he shot he would have stuffed, so that the fact might be remarked for ever.

Once, or perhaps twice, each year, *malaise* would come on him, a feeling that his life was not quite all he wished, a desire for something that he could not shape in words, a conviction that there were facts which he was missing. At these times he was almost irritable, and would say : ' Mistake for a man to marry, depend on it—narrows his life.' And suddenly one day he would know what he wanted, and, under pretext perhaps of two days' sport, would go to Paris. The fact accomplished, of irregularity, that he would not have committed in England for the world—was of advantage to his soul, and he would return, more regular than ever.

For he was a man who must be doing, who respected only the thing done. He had no use for schemes of life, theories, dreams, or fancies. Ideas were ' six a penny ' he would say. And the fact that facts without ideas were ' six a ha'penny ' was perhaps the only fact that he did not appreciate. He was made, in fact, for laying trains of little facts, in almost perfect order, in almost all directions. Forced by his nature to start laying without considering where they led to, he neither knew nor cared when or what they would blow up; and when in fact they blew up something unexpected, or led into a *cul de sac*, he would start at once laying them again in the first direction that seemed open. Thus actively employed, he kept from brooding, thinking, and nonsense of all kinds, so busy that he had no time to look ahead and see where he was going;

and since, if he had got there he would not have known it, this was just as well.

Beyond everything, he believed in freedom; he never saw the things that his way of acting prevented him from doing, and so believed his life to be the freest in the world.

Nothing occasioned him a more unfeigned surprise than to tell him his ways were typical of the country where he lived. He answered with a stare, knowing well enough that no such likeness could be shown him as a fact. It was not his habit to be conscious; he was neither conscious of himself nor of his country, and this enabled him to be the man he was.

When he met himself about the town (which hourly happened) he had no knowledge that it was himself; on the contrary he looked on himself as specially designed, finding most other people 'rather funny.'

An attempt to designate him as belonging to a type or class he mistrusted as some kind of Socialism. And yet he ate with himself in restaurants and private houses, travelled with himself in trains, read the speeches of himself in Parliament, and the accounts of how he had been surrounded by persons of Dutch origin, or on some frontier punished a tribe whose manners were not quite his own. He played golf with himself, and shot with his very images. Nor was he confined to his own class; but frequently drove himself home in cabs, watched himself drilling in the barrack squares, or, walking up and down in blue, protected his own house at night from burglars. If he required to send a message from his Club, he sent himself; he sold himself his waistcoats, and even laid the pavements of the streets that he trod daily in his pilgrimage. From his neighbourhood Imagination stretched its wings and flitted further on. Patron of precedent, pattern of order, upholder of the Law, where he dwelt an orderly disorder reigned. He was for ever doing things, and out of everything he did there sprang up two more things that wanted to be done, and these things he would do—in time! Believing no real harm of others or himself, he kept young and green! Oh very green and young! . . .

And in old age, past doing things, seated in the Club smoking-room, he will recount behind his comely grey moustache that day's shooting and that day's run; the marriage of that fine girl; the death of that dear old chap; the details of that first-rate joke, or that bad dinner; and dwelling with love on these isolated facts, his old blue eyes will twinkle. Presently, when it is late and he is left alone, he will put his old tired feet up on the sofa, remove the cigar from his old lips, and, holding it a foot from off his eyes, look closely at the ash; finding this fact a little yellow, he will frown.

INDEX OF CHARACTERS

CHANGES AND CORRECTIONS

[The item corrected is enclosed within brackets which the page number follows.]

Mote (moat) 2 ; too (to) 12 ; side, (:) 15 ; soule (sonle) 20 ; chamber-fellowes (—,) 34 ; worst ; (; from 6th ed., ' worst ' in 1st) 41 ; Meere [in title] (Mere) 76 ; Latine (—,) 61 ; negatives : (—.) 76 ; learned (lerne) 79 ; its owne sake (it—) 101 ; on horse-backe (an —) 102 ; sounded (founded) 102 ; horse-rases (— races) 107 ; cake-bread (cakebread) 113 ; hang (hangs) 119 ; sprawles (spawles) 123 ; debtors (debttors) 125 ; reflexion (replexion) 135 ; Wardrob, (Wardrop,) 135 ; paggled (pagged) 142 ; statue (statute) 159 ; bush : (: in 1633, 8. ' bush,' here) 160 ; gun-powder (— power) 161 ; applauded, (, in 1633. ' applauded ' here) 165 ; body, for sixe (body for sixe) 165 ; combustion (cum-bustion) 166 ; Tactikes (Tractikes) 167 ; Fire. (—,) 169 ; touchy (teachy) 171 ; abused again into a reconcilement ; and you can (omitted here by error, added from 1629 ed.) 172 ; Shee is a Nonconformist (shee) 173 ; Women (Woemen, cf. p. 229. One example retained p. 242) 175 ; speake out (speake, out) 177 ; Lawier (Lawer) 177 ; handfull (hanfull) 177 ; Argument (argumne) 180 ; buzze, mixt (buzze-mixt) 180 ; legends of Popery (legends Popery) 181 ; and setled (end —) 183 ; any thing, of another mans : (any thing : of another mans,' in 1629. any thing, of another mans : in 1633) 184 ; Thersites, (, 1638. ' Thersites ' 1629, 1633) 185 ; 'tis (ti's) 187 ; acquaintance (acquainance) 188 ; cryes (*cryes*) 192 ; knives (knifes) 205 ; invented ; (invented) 205 ; petty-officers (—,) 207 ; sometimes (somtimes) 208 ; guiltlesse off (— of) 209 ; beareth (beare) 213 ; sound (—,) 217 ; αὐτòς (ἄυτος in 1631, 1635) 218 ; neither (nether) 220 ; colde meat (colde, meat) 222 ; sweet-hearts, (swee-thearts) 222 ; landry (—e) 223 ; Curates (Curats) 223 ; convey (convay) 223 ; fro (froe) 225 ; brook. (brook) 228 ; either (other) 228 ; Fisher-woemen (— women) 229 ; ordinarily (—.) 229 ; a drinking-house, (an —) 230 ; same shop (sameshop) 240 ; This Generall Warre (this —) 242 ; What the Epigram (what —) 244 ; fifteen (fiften) 244 ; Monday (*M*onday) 246 ; book lets (books —) 246 ; scriveners (scrivoners) 246 ; City ; when (City, when) 247 ; Padington (Padingion) 248 ; quintessences (quintences) 255 ; oppertunity (opertunity) 261 ; Horse-race (Hors-race) 261 ; won't (wo'nt) 262 ; scurrilous (scurrulous) 264 ; Pourlieus (Pourliens) 266 ; infinitie (infinite) 267 ; Seneca (Senica) 267 ; barer (bearer) 278 ; à la mode (a —) 278 ; many look (— looks)

278 ; Ladies delight (— delights) 279 ; arrogantly (arogantly) 281 ; Gaps in the (Gaps the) 302 ; Howlet. (Howlet) 316 ; Cavalry (Cavalray) 318 ; Anchor (Anhor) 319 ; blazing (blazeing) 319 ; Ancestors. (—,) 319 ; Mimick (Minick) 320 ; acquaintance (acquainance) 322 ; Scene, (Scene) 322 ; prettiness (prettyness) 322 ; pawn'd (pawm'd) 322 ; working. (working,) 322 ; One Another. (One Another) 324 ; too (two) 333 ; trifles (triffles) 333; oppression, (oppression) 334 ; struck (struct) 336 ; stinks (stink) 336 ; at Sixteen (a Sixteen) 341 ; Repetition (Repetion) 341 ; Letters Pattents (Letters, —) 342 ; Persian (Perssian) 343 ; Grecian (—s) 343 ; Statesmen (Statemen) 343 ; hardly (heardly) 344 ; Quarrels (Quarels) 345 ; by day (by day.) 348 ; Old Book. (Old Book,) 349 ; fixed are, (fixed are) 349 ; draws (drawns) 350 ; Candle-sticks, (, inserted) 364 ; insipid (insiped) 367 ; amiable (aimiable) 375 ; invisible (ininvisible) 376 ; its appearance (it's —)385 ; disagreeable (disagreable) 391 ; p. xiv, *In Afrum* from *All Ovids Elegies* ; p. xv, *Groningen* (Gronigen) ; ll. 11-12 from Harl. MS. 1836 ; sooner (souner) ; Turk (—e) devis'd (—ed) ; Christendom, (—e) ; it : (it).

The device on the title-page was first used in 1549 (see R. B. McKerrow's *Printers' and Publishers' Devices* ... p. 112) : it is here taken from one of its clearest reproductions, in *The Recantations . . . by W. Tedder and A. Tyrrell*, 1588. It was used in 'The Character of a Prince' in 1689, Prudentia (Love and Lyve) on the tablet.

PRINTED IN GREAT BRITAIN BY ROBERT MACLEHOSE AND CO. LTD.
THE UNIVERSITY PRESS, GLASGOW